FUNDAMENTALS

OF

MATHEMATICS

FUNDAMENTALS OF MATHEMATICS

JOSEPH MARANO   **KENNETH KAUFMAN**

Department of Mathematics
Nassau Community College
Garden City, New York

Prentice-Hall, Inc., Englewood Cliffs, New Jersey

Library of Congress Cataloging in Publication Data

MARANO, JOSEPH
    Fundamentals of mathematics.

    1. Mathematics—1961– I. Kaufman,
Kenneth, joint author. II. Title.
QA39.2.M34   512'.1   72-10393
ISBN 0-13-341081-1

To Marie, Mollie, and Harry

Printed in the United States of America

10 9 8 7 6 5 4 3 2 1

PRENTICE-HALL INTERNATIONAL, INC., *London*
PRENTICE-HALL OF AUSTRALIA, PTY. LTD., *Sydney*
PRENTICE-HALL OF CANADA, LTD., *Toronto*
PRENTICE-HALL OF INDIA PRIVATE LIMITED, *New Delhi*
PRENTICE-HALL OF JAPAN, INC., *Tokyo*

CONTENTS

III ALGEBRAIC EXPRESSIONS
INVOLVING EXPONENTS   84

IV LINEAR EQUATIONS AND
INEQUALITIES IN ONE VARIABLE   134

V EQUATIONS AND INEQUALITIES
INVOLVING ABSOLUTE VALUES   175

VI GRAPHING THE SOLUTION SETS
OF LINEAR EQUATIONS AND INEQUALITIES
IN TWO VARIABLES   188

VII SYSTEMS OF
LINEAR EQUATIONS   221

VIII QUADRATIC
EQUATIONS   257

PREFACE

This textbook is intended for those students who have had little background in mathematics in high school, and for those students who have been away from mathematics for some time. It is designed for an introductory mathematics course that develops skills and the use of concepts. This book can be used in a terminal course, as well as in a preparatory course for those who must take further courses to meet a graduation requirement. It has been used at Nassau Community College in its preliminary form in a preparatory course for those who will take further courses (Logic and Set Theory; Introduction to Statistics) to meet their graduation requirement. For this course the emphasis was placed on chapters I, II, IV, IX, and X. This book has also been used in its preliminary form in Fordham University School of General Studies in a two-semester terminal sequence, where all ten chapters are covered. For those using the book in a one-semester terminal course we feel the emphasis should be placed on chapters I, II, IX and X. In any case chapters IX and X may be covered immediately after chapter I, if desired, for the basis of these chapters is solely the concept of sets.

We have tried to avoid a "too wordy" exposition, for this normally gives rise to tremendous confusion and difficulty in getting the main ideas on the part of the students. On the other hand the concepts are adequately explained, and further clarified by the use of *numerous illustrative examples*. In addition, formal and rigorous definitions and theory have been eliminated. From our many years of experience with students on this level, we are able to conclude that this type of writing in mathematics is most easily read and understood.

Another outstanding feature of the book is the use of its *many good problem sets*. We feel that it is extremely important that the problems after each section not be just a rehashing of the ideas and concepts of the preceding five or so pages, but that the problems should constantly involve concepts and techniques of earlier sections and chapters. This continuity in the problems is of great help to the students in the learning of the concepts. Besides the many problem sets there is a review test at the end of each chapter. Also included in the text are the answers to all exercises.

We would like to extend a special thanks to Marie Marano for her aid in the preparation of the manuscript.

Kenneth L. Kaufman
Joseph A. Marano

I ELEMENTARY SET THEORY

1.1 INTRODUCTION

The set is one of the basic and important concepts of mathematics. The concept of sets was introduced by the mathematicians George Boole and George Cantor at the end of the nineteenth century. The concept and language of sets are now used virtually throughout mathematics. It is important for you to know some simple set definitions and symbols to understand what will follow.

1.2 WHAT IS A SET?

SET

A set is a *collection of objects*. The objects in a set are called its *elements* or *members*. A set should be *well defined* so that we know what elements belong to the set and what elements do not. The order in which the elements are listed in a set does not affect their membership, and we do not list the same element more than once. Let us now consider some examples of sets.

Examples of Sets

1. The set of vowels in the English alphabet.
2. The set of whole numbers.

3. The set of former Presidents of the United States.
4. The set consisting of the whole numbers 1, 3, 5.
5. The set of days of the week.
6. The set of all living people over the age of 500 years.
7. The set consisting of this book, yourself, and your mathematics teacher this semester.

Exercise Set 1.2

1. List the names of the elements in the following sets:
    (a) The set of all days of the week beginning with the letter S.
    (b) The set of all whole numbers between 10 and 50 that end in 3.
    (c) The set of months of the year that begin with the letter J.
    (d) The set of vowels in the English alphabet.
    (e) The set of Presidents of the United States since 1952 including the present President.
    (f) The set of letters in the word "intersection."
    (g) The set of whole numbers between 7 and 36 that are divisible by 5.

2. Describe the set whose elements are given:
    (a) a, b, c, d
    (b) Tuesday, Thursday
    (c) 2, 12, 22, 32, 42
    (d) April, August
    (e) forward, guard, center

1.3 SET NOTATION

Let us now describe the different symbols that we will use in the study of sets. Capital letters such as A, B, C, will be used to name complete sets.

In writing down the set we separate the names of the elements by commas and then enclose them in braces { }.

Example of Set Notation

The set A consists of the whole numbers 2, 5, 7.

$$\text{This may be written } A = \{2, 5, 7\}$$

We introduce the symbol "ϵ", the Greek letter epsilon, which will be read, "is an element of." The symbol $\notin$ then will be read, "is not an element of." Thus considering the set $A = \{2, 5, 7\}, 9 \notin A$

means 9 is *not* an element of *A* and 2 ∈ *A* means 2 is an element of *A*.

ROSTER METHOD OF SET DESCRIPTION

When a set is described by listing the elements within the braces, we call such a set description the *roster method*.

Example 1

Let *A* be the set of days of the week. Write the set *A* using the roster method.

$$A = \{\text{Sun., Mon., Tues., Wed., Thurs., Fri., Sat.}\}$$

Example 2

Let *B* be the set consisting of the whole numbers between 1 and 10. Write the set *B* using the roster method.

$$B = \{2, 3, 4, 5, 6, 7, 8, 9\}$$

Example 3

Using the roster method write the set *P* of all positive whole numbers.

The set of positive whole numbers consists of the numbers 1, 2, 3, 4, etc. Thus it would be impossible to list the names of all the positive whole numbers within the braces. Yet we can use the roster method in the following way:

$$P = \{1, 2, 3, \ldots\}, \quad \text{where} \ldots \text{means etc.}$$

Note

It is important to realize that the etc. here implies *continuing in the same pattern as that which precedes the* ... . Thus if we were to continue in the same pattern with which we began in the set *P*, we would be able to reach any positive whole number that we desired.

Suppose we consider the set of all living people born before January 1, 1970. You can immediately see that it would be rather difficult, to say the least, to describe this set using the roster method. How could we even begin a pattern to include any living person born before January 1, 1970?

RULE METHOD OF SET DESCRIPTION

However there is another way in which a set can be described. Instead of listing the elements, we place within the braces the *condition which must be satisfied for an element to belong to this set.* This method of set description is known as the *rule method,* for we are actually writing within the braces a *rule* which tells you just what elements belong to the set.

The set considered above, of all living people born before January 1, 1970, can be described by the rule method in the following way:

$$A = \{x | x \text{ is a living person, born before Jan. 1, 1970}\}$$

Notation

The vertical bar is read, "such that." The entire expression for the set A would then read, "A is the set of *all elements* x, such that x is a living person, born before January 1, 1970."

Example 4

Describe the set P of positive whole numbers using the rule method.

$$P = \{x | x \text{ is a positive whole number}\}$$

This is read, "P is the set of *all elements* x, such that x is a positive whole number."

Example 5

Describe the set A of days of the week using the rule method.

$$A = \{x | x \text{ is a day of the week}\}$$

This is read, "A is the set of *all elements* x, such that x is a day of the week."

Example 6

Using the rule method write the set consisting of the whole numbers between 3 and 8.

$$A = \{x | x \text{ is a whole number between 3 and 8}\}$$

How would you read this?

Exercise Set 1.3

1. Use the *roster* method to write the following sets:
   (a) The set of letters in the name of your school.
   (b) The set of living Presidents of the United States.
   (c) The set of positive whole numbers less than 5.
   (d) The set of positive whole numbers greater than 3.
   (e) The set of positive whole numbers divisible by 5.

2. Use the *rule* method to write the following sets:
   (a) The set of numbers 1, 2, 3, 4, 5.
   (b) The set of positive whole numbers greater than 10.
   (c) The set of states Kentucky, Kansas.
   (d) The set of numbers 11, 22, 33, 44, 55, 66, 77, 88, 99.
   (e) The set of numbers 10, 20, 30, 40, ...

3. Express each of the following sets in a different way:
   (a) {George Washington}
   (b) $\{x|x$ is the name of a state in the United States starting with the letter S$\}$
   (c) $\{2, 4, 6, 8, 10, \ldots\}$
   (d) $\{x|x$ is a playing position on a baseball team$\}$
   (e) {clubs, hearts, diamonds, spades}

4. Determine which of the following statements are true and which are false:
   (a) $3 \in \{1, 3, 5, 7\}$
   (b) $4 \notin \{1, 2, 3, 5, 7\}$
   (c) $4 \in \{x|x$ is a positive whole number divisible by 3$\}$
   (d) March $\notin \{x|x$ is a month of the year having exactly 30 days$\}$
   (e) Canada $\notin \{x|x$ is a country in North America$\}$

1.4 SETS OF REAL NUMBERS

Since we will be using many sets of numbers throughout the remainder of this book, we will now define some of these sets.

POSITIVE INTEGERS

The *positive integers* are the positive whole numbers 1, 2, 3, 4, ... We will use the letter P to denote this set. In set notation this can be written:

$$P = \{1, 2, 3, \ldots\} \qquad \text{(Roster method)}$$

or

$$P = \{x|x \text{ is a positive integer}\} \qquad \text{(Rule method)}$$

Note

The set of positive integers is also called the set of *counting numbers* and the set of *natural numbers*.

SET NOTATION FOR THE NEGATIVE INTEGERS

The set of *negative integers* N can thus be written:

$$N = \{-1, -2, -3, \ldots\}$$

or

$$N = \{x \mid x \text{ is a negative integer}\}$$

THE SET OF INTEGERS

The set of *integers* I is the set consisting of the positive integers, the negative integers, and zero. In set notation this can be written:

$$I = \{0, +1, -1, +2, -2, +3, -3, \ldots\}$$

or

$$I = \{x \mid x \text{ is an integer}\}$$

THE SETS OF EVEN AND ODD INTEGERS

The integers may also be broken down into *even integers* and *odd integers*. The set of even integers can be written as:

$$E = \{0, +2, -2, +4, -4, +6, -6, \ldots\}$$

and the set of odd integers as:

$$O = \{+1, -1, +3, -3, +5, -5, \ldots\}$$

Note

Zero is an even integer, since the even integers are defined as the integral multiples of 2. That is, if you multiply each integer by 2 you will produce the even integers. Now $0 \cdot 2 = 0$ (the $\cdot$ here represents multiplication), and thus as was stated 0 is even. To produce the odd integers you need only add or subtract one from each even integer.

In arithmetic as well as in everyday usage, we have all encountered numbers other than integers, such as $\frac{1}{2}, \frac{1}{4}, \frac{3}{8}, 1\frac{1}{2}, 3\frac{1}{4}$, 0.5, 0.25, 0.12. This leads us to the definition of a rational number.

RATIONAL NUMBER

A *rational number* is any number which *can be expressed* as a quotient in the form $\frac{a}{b}$, where a and b are integers, but b *cannot be 0*.

Note

Every rational number is a quotient of two integers. However division by 0 is not defined. For example, a quotient of the form $\frac{5}{0}$ is meaningless. This will be explained further in Chapter II, where we will define division of real numbers.

Examples of Rational Numbers

Let us now consider the following examples of rational numbers:

1. $\frac{1}{2}, \frac{-2}{5}, \frac{17}{8}, \frac{11}{-4}$
2. $1\frac{1}{2}$, since it can be expressed as $\frac{3}{2}$
3. $-2\frac{1}{4}$, since it can be expressed as $\frac{-9}{4}$
4. 0.12, since it can be written as $\frac{12}{100}$
5. -0.25, since it can be written $\frac{-25}{100}$
6. *Every integer* is a rational number, for we can express any integer a as $\frac{a}{1}$. For example 3 can be written $\frac{3}{1}$, -5 can be written $\frac{-5}{1}$, 0 can be written $\frac{0}{1}$.

Note

0 can be represented not only by $\frac{0}{1}$ but also by $\frac{0}{3}, \frac{0}{4}, \frac{0}{159}$, in fact, by $\frac{0}{b}$ where b is any integer except 0.

If we use the letter Q for the set of rational numbers, suppose we attempt to write this set using the roster method. You may decide to write:

$$Q = \{1, \tfrac{1}{2}, \tfrac{1}{3}, \tfrac{1}{4}, \dots \}$$

But you would realize immediately that this pattern *only includes a select group* of rational numbers. How are the rational numbers $\frac{7}{8}, \frac{5}{9}, \frac{7}{13}$, 3, and 4 for example included in this pattern? They are not. If you continue to try other patterns, you will see that it is rather difficult to obtain a pattern that would include all the rationals. The problem could simply be avoided by using the rule method instead of the roster method. Thus the set Q of rational numbers can be written:

$$Q = \{x \mid x \text{ is a rational number}\}$$

or, using the definition of the rational numbers, we could write

$$Q = \{x \mid x = \tfrac{a}{b}, \qquad a \text{ and } b \text{ are integers}, \qquad b \neq 0\}$$

Let us now consider some of these rational numbers in *decimal form.* For example $\tfrac{1}{2}$ = 0.5, $\tfrac{1}{4}$ = 0.25, $\tfrac{3}{8}$ = 0.375, $\tfrac{5}{16}$ = 0.3125. As you may recall from arithmetic, the decimal representation of $\tfrac{5}{16}$ for example is obtained by dividing 16 "into" 5. Note that these decimal representations all *terminate* after a certain digit. If at this time you are thinking that all decimal representations of rational numbers will terminate after a certain digit, you need only consider the rational number $\tfrac{1}{3}$.

Examples of Nonterminating, Repeating Decimals

1. $\tfrac{1}{3}$ can be written 0.333 . . . where, upon dividing 3 "into" 1, the remainder will always be 1, thus producing a *nonterminating* decimal in which the digit 3 keeps on repeating.

2. Consider the decimal representation for $\tfrac{37}{33}$. Upon dividing 33 "into" 37, we obtain:

$$
\begin{array}{r}
1.1212\ldots \\
\hline
33)\overline{37.0000\ldots} \\
33 \\
\hline
40 \\
33 \\
\hline
70 \\
66 \\
\hline
40 \rightarrow \text{repetition starts here} \\
33 \\
\hline
70 \\
66 \\
\hline
4
\end{array}
$$

Thus $\tfrac{37}{33}$ = 1.121212 . . . where the digits 12 repeat in groups of 2.

3. Let us now reconsider the rational numbers $\tfrac{1}{2}, \tfrac{1}{4}, \tfrac{3}{8}, \tfrac{5}{16}$. They too can be written as *nonterminating repeating* decimals simply by introducing the digit 0 at the end of each decimal representation and letting this digit *repeat indefinitely.* Thus

$$\tfrac{1}{2} = 0.5000\ldots$$
$$\tfrac{1}{4} = 0.25000\ldots$$
$$\tfrac{3}{8} = 0.375000\ldots$$
$$\tfrac{5}{16} = 0.3125000\ldots$$

Note

Thus we can see that *all decimals can be considered nonterminating decimals.*

It can be shown that *every* rational number can be written as a *nonterminating repeating* decimal. Although this will not be proven here, you can easily illustrate this for any given rational number $\frac{a}{b}$, $b \neq 0$, by performing the indicated division.

Example 4

Write the rational number $\frac{3}{7}$ in decimal form.

If you perform the indicated division, you will obtain the result $\frac{3}{7} = 0.\underline{428571}\underline{428571}\ldots$ which repeats in groups of 6.

It can also be shown that every nonterminating repeating decimal can be written as a rational number in the form $\frac{a}{b}$, where a and b are integers, $b \neq 0$. Let us illustrate this with the following examples. If you encounter difficulty in understanding these illustrations, you will better understand them after completing Chapter IV.

Example 5

Suppose we have a number x with decimal representation $0.3333\ldots$. We know that $x = \frac{1}{3}$ but let us now see how this result would be obtained.

Step (1) $x = 0.3333\ldots$

(2) Since repetition begins after the tenth's place, we multiply the number x by 10.
$$10x = 3.333\ldots$$

(3) Subtracting step (1) from step (2) would now give
$$10x = 3.333\ldots$$
$$\underline{x = 0.333\ldots}$$
$$9x = 3.000\ldots$$
Thus we see that 9 times the number x is 3.

(4) Therefore $x = \frac{3}{9}$ or $\frac{1}{3}$.

Example 6

Suppose x has decimal representation 1.1212 .... As we have seen in example 2, this is the representation for $\frac{37}{33}$. Let us see how this can be obtained.

Step (1) $x = 1.121212\ldots$

(2) Since repetition begins after the hundredth's place, we multiply the number x by 100.
$100x = 112.1212\ldots$

(3) Subtracting step (1) from step (2) would give

$$100x = 112.1212\ldots$$
$$\underline{x = 1.1212\ldots}$$
$$99x = 111.000\ldots$$

(4) Thus $x = \frac{111}{99}$, or reducing to lowest terms gives $\frac{37}{33}$.

The question is, do all nonterminating decimals repeat? This question can be answered by considering the following decimals.

Examples of Nonterminating Nonrepeating Decimals

7. $0.101001000100001000001\ldots$ where the number of zeros between successive 1's keeps increasing by one. Thus this decimal does not repeat.

8. $3.212112111211112111112\ldots$

Why don't you try writing some other nonterminating nonrepeating decimals?

Since these nonterminating decimals do not repeat, they cannot be rational numbers, for as was shown previously if they were rational then they would repeat. Therefore they cannot be expressed in the form $\frac{a}{b}$, where a and b are integers, $b \neq 0$. Such nonterminating nonrepeating decimals are called *irrational numbers*.

THE SET OF IRRATIONAL NUMBERS

The set of *irrational numbers*, denoted by Q', read "Q prime," is the set whose elements are all numbers with decimal representations that are *nonterminating* and *nonrepeating*. In set notation this can be written:

$$Q' = \{x \mid x \text{ is an irrational number}\}$$

Some other elements of Q' are $\sqrt{2}, \sqrt{3}, -\sqrt{5}$. Although it cannot be exhibited that the decimal representations of these numbers will never repeat, there are mathematical proofs that these numbers cannot be expressed in the form $\frac{a}{b}$ where a and b are integers, $b \neq 0$ and thus are irrational.

Note

$\sqrt{2}$ and $\sqrt{3}$ carried out to 15 decimal places would be:

$\sqrt{2} = 1.414213562373095 \ldots$

$\sqrt{3} = 1.732050807568877 \ldots$

THE SET OF REAL NUMBERS

The rational numbers together with the irrational numbers make up our *real number system,* also known as the *set of real numbers,* which will be denoted by R. This set can be written:

$$R = \{x \mid x \text{ is a real number}\}$$

SUMMARY

We can summarize the relationships between the sets of numbers mentioned in this section with the following diagram:

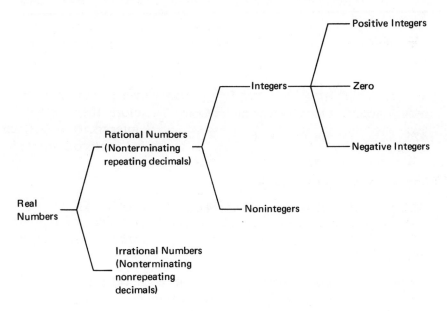

Exercise Set 1.4

In exercises 1-10 let $P = \{x \mid x$ is a positive integer$\}$, $I = \{x \mid x$ is an integer$\}$, $Q = \{x \mid x$ is a rational number$\}$, $Q' = \{x \mid x$ is an irrational number$\}$, and $R = \{x \mid x$ is a real number$\}$. Determine whether the given statements are true or false.

1. $\frac{1}{2} \epsilon I$

2. $-3 \epsilon P$

3. $-2 \epsilon R$

4. $0.83 \epsilon Q$

5. $2.232323 \ldots \epsilon Q'$

6. $0 \epsilon Q$

7. $-7 \epsilon I$

8. $\frac{-3}{2} \epsilon Q$

9. $\sqrt{5} \epsilon R$

10. $\frac{3}{0} \epsilon Q$

In exercises 11-16 write the given set in another way.

11. $\{x \mid x$ is an even integer greater than 8 but less than 20$\}$

12. $\{7, 9, 11, 13\}$

13. $\{-1, -2, -3, -4, -5\}$

14. $\{x \mid x$ is a nonnegative integer$\}$

15. $\{3, 9, 15, 21, 27, 33, 39\}$

16. $\{x \mid x = 2 \cdot n, n$ is any integer$\}$

In exercises 17-18 write the given decimal in the form $\frac{a}{b}$, where a and b are integers, $b \neq 0$.

17. $11.4444 \ldots$

18. $0.232323 \ldots$

In exercises 19-23 determine whether the given statement is true or false.

19. $\frac{5}{11}$ in decimal form is a repeating decimal.

20. All rational numbers are integers.

21. 0 is an integer and a rational number.

22. All real numbers are integers.

23. A nonrepeating, nonterminating decimal is a rational number.

1.5   EQUAL AND EQUIVALENT SETS

Suppose we consider the set $A = \{2, 4, 6\}$ and the set $B = \{x \mid x$ is an even integer between 1 and 7$\}$. Although these sets are represented differently, you can see that they have exactly the same elements 2, 4, 6. Any two such sets that have exactly the same elements are said to be *equal*.

EQUAL SETS

Set *A* is said to be *equal* to set *B*, written *A* = *B*, if and only if both sets have exactly the same elements.

The following are some examples of equal sets:

Example 1

Set $A = \{1, 3, 5, 7\}$ and set $B = \{5, 3, 7, 1\}$.

Note

Sets *A* and *B* have exactly the same elements even though these elements do not appear in the same order in the two sets.

Example 2

Set $A = \{x \mid x$ is a letter of the alphabet in the name Willie Mays$\}$

and

set $B = \{W, i, l, e, M, a, y, s\}$.

Note

Recall that we could have listed the letters i and l a second time without affecting their membership, however they would have only been counted once. Therefore it was not necessary to list them a second time.

Suppose we now consider the sets $A = \{1, 3, 5\}$ and $B = \{a, b, c\}$. These sets are certainly not equal, but they do have something in common, that is, they both have three elements. Suppose however we were not able to count. We would still be able to establish that both sets have the same number of elements. This can be done simply by *pairing* each element of *A* with a *single* element of *B*, and each element of *B* with a *single* element of *A*, and seeing that no elements are left over in either set. This can be shown by the following scheme:

$$A = \{1, 3, 5\}$$
$$\uparrow \quad \uparrow \quad \uparrow$$
$$B = \{a, b, c,\}$$

Such pairing is known as a one-to-one correspondence.

ONE-TO-ONE CORRESPONDENCE

A *one-to-one correspondence between two sets A* and *B* is a pairing of the elements of these sets in such a way that each element of set *A* is paired with a *single* element of *B*, and each element of *B* is paired with a *single* element of *A*.

EQUIVALENT SETS

Two sets *A* and *B* are said to be *equivalent,* written $A \sim B$, if and only if they can be put into one-to-one correspondence.

Example 3

$A = \{1, 3, 5, 7, 9\}$ and $B = \{2, 4, 6, 8, 10\}$.

Sets *A* and *B* are equivalent ($A \sim B$) as can be seen by the pairing:

$$A = \{1, 3, 5, 7, 9\}$$
$$\uparrow \quad \uparrow \quad \uparrow \quad \uparrow \quad \uparrow$$
$$B = \{2, 4, 6, 8, 10\}$$

Note

The above pairing in example 3 is *by no means unique.* That is, a one-to-one correspondence can be set up in more than one way. Another pairing for example 3 might be

$$A = \{1, 3, 5, 7, 9\}$$
$$B = \{2, 4, 6, 8, 10\}$$

Can you see other pairings for these two sets?

Example 4

Let $A = \{x \mid x \text{ is a day of the week}\}$ and $B = \{2, 3, 7, 9, 10, 12, 13\}$.

If *A* is rewritten using the roster method, we can then exhibit a one-to-one correspondence to show that $A \sim B$.

A = {Sun., Mon., Tues., Wed., Thurs., Fri., Sat.}

B = {2,   3,   7,   9,   10,   12, 13}

Example 5

Let A = {1, 3, 5, 7, 9} and B = {2, 3, 4, 5, 6, 8}.

Here set A is *not* equivalent to set B, for in attempting to pair each element of A with a single element of B there will always be an element of B left over. One such attempt is made in the following diagram:

A = {1, 3, 5, 7, 9}

B = {2, 3, 4, 5, 6, ⑧ }

Example 6

Let A = {a, b, c, d, e, f} and B = {2, 4, 6, 8}.

A = {a, b, c, d, ⓔ , ⓕ }

B = {2, 4, 6, 8}

Here A is *not* equivalent to B. Why?

Example 7

Let A = {1, 2, 4, 7}, B = {4, 7, 1, 2}, and C = {1, 5, 7, 9}.

Set $A = B$, $A \sim B$, $A \sim C$, $B \sim C$. Note that sets A and B have exactly the same elements but the elements are not listed in the same order.

Note

All equal sets must be equivalent, but equivalent sets are not necessarily equal. In example 7 above, $A \sim C$ but they are not equal.

FINITE SET

A set is said to be *finite* if and only if it can be put into one-to-one correspondence with the set {1, 2, 3, . . . , n}, where n is some *positive integer.*

Examples of Finite Sets

8. $A = \{a, b\}$. This set can be put into one-to-one correspondence with the set $\{1, 2\}$. Here n is 2.
9. $B = \{x \mid x$ is a playing position on a baseball team$\}$. This set can be put into one-to-one correspondence with the set $\{1, 2, 3, 4, 5, 6, 7, 8, 9\}$. Here n is 9.
10. $C = \{x \mid x$ is a positive integer between 7 and 11$\}$. This set can be put into one-to-one correspondence with the set $\{1, 2, 3\}$. Here n is 3.
11. $D = \{x \mid x$ is a state of the U.S.A.$\}$. This set can be put into one-to-one correspondence with the set $\{1, 2, 3, \ldots, 50\}$. Here n is 50.

Note

Thus essentially a finite set is one in which the elements can be counted, with the counting coming to an end.

A well defined set may have no elements in it. Such a set is called an *empty* or *null set*. However, since we really can't distinguish between one null set and another, we refer to every null set as *the null set*.

THE NULL SET

The *null set* is any set that has no elements.

NOTATION

We use the symbol "$\emptyset$" to represent the null set. Note that there are no braces around this symbol. Let us now consider some examples of the null set.

Examples of the Null Set

12. $A = \{x \mid x$ is a living person over the age of 500 years$\}$
13. $B = \{x \mid x$ is an odd integer between 3 and 5$\}$
14. $C = \{x \mid x$ is a person in the U.S. over 15 ft. tall$\}$
15. $D = \{x \mid x$ is a positive integer less than zero$\}$

Note

The null set will be defined to be *a finite set*.

You may have already noticed that there are sets which cannot be put into one-to-one correspondence with the set $\{1, 2, 3, \ldots, n\}$, where n is a positive integer; for example, the set $P = \{1, 2, 3, \ldots\}$ and the set $Q = \{x \mid x$ is a rational number$\}$. Notice that the elements in these sets cannot be counted, with the counting coming to an end.

INFINITE SET

Any set which is *not finite* is said to be *infinite*.

Let us now consider some other examples of infinite sets.

Examples of Infinite Sets

16. The set $E = \{0, +2, -2, +4, -4, +6, -6, \ldots\}$.
17. The set $I = \{x \mid x$ is an integer$\}$.
18. The set $R = \{x \mid x$ is a real number$\}$.

What would you say about the set of all children born in the United States on February 12, 1945? Is this set finite or infinite? Although this set has quite a large number of elements, it is still possible, with enough time and resources, to count the elements of this set, with the counting coming to an end, and thus the set is finite.

Note

You may have noticed by this time that two finite sets are equivalent, if and only if they have the *same number of elements,* and that *no infinite set can be equivalent to a finite set.*

Exercise Set 1.5

In exercises 1-10 state whether the given set is finite or infinite.

1. The set of positive integers less than 100.

2. The set of all positive integers greater than 5.

3. The set of even integers greater than 2 that end in 5.

4. The set of all cities in the United States.

5. The set of odd numbers greater than 3 but less than 50.

6. The set of all integers less than 7.

7. The set of all living signers of the Declaration of Independence.

8. The set of all students in your school who are taking mathematics.

9. The set of all rational numbers between 1 and 2.

10. The set of all integers between 1 and 2.

  In exercises 11-15 determine whether or not the given pair of sets can be put into one-to-one correspondence.

11. The set of all playing positions on a baseball team and the set of fingers on two hands.

12. The set of legs on a normal dog and the set of even integers between 3 and 11.

13. The set $N = \{x \mid x$ is a negative integer$\}$ and $\{x \mid x$ is an integer from 1 to 1,000,000$\}$.

14. The set of all cards in a regular deck of playing cards and the set of states of the United States.

15. $A = \{-7, -6, \ldots, -1, 0, 1, 2, \ldots, 7\}$ and $B = \{1, 2, 3, \ldots, 14\}$.

  In exercises 16-23 let $A = \{1, 2, 3, 4, 5, 6, 7, 8, 9\}, B = \{1, 3, 5, 7, 9\}$, $C = \{2, 6, 10, 14, 18\}, D = \{x \mid x = 2 \cdot n, n \in B\}, E = \{x \mid x = 2 \cdot n, n \in A\}$. Determine whether the given statements are true or false.

16. $B = C$

17. $B \sim C$

18. $A = E$

19. $A \sim E$

20. $C = D$

21. $D = E$

22. $C \sim D$

23. $D \sim E$

1.6 SUBSETS

SUBSET

The set A is a *subset* of the set B if every element of A is also an element of B. Symbolically this is written $A \subseteq B$, which is read, "A is a subset of B."

Example 1

Given set $B = \{1, 3, 5, 7, 9\}$ and set $A = \{1, 7, 9\}$, then A is a subset of B, since all the elements of A are also elements of B.

Example 2

Let $A = \{3, 7, 8, 10\}$ and $B = \{7, 3, 10, 8\}$.

In this case A is a subset of B, and also B is a subset of A, for every element of A is also an element of B, and every element of B is also an element of A. You should also note that the two sets are equal.

In light of example 2 we can now redefine equality of sets.

EQUAL SETS

Two sets A and B are *equal* if and only if A is a subset of B $(A \subseteq B)$ *and* B is a subset of A $(B \subseteq A)$.

PROPER SUBSET

Furthermore, a set A is a *proper subset* of a set B if it is a subset of B and if there are *elements of B which are not elements of A*. Symbolically this is expressed $A \subset B$.

In example 1, A is a proper subset of B, for A is a subset of B and there are elements of B that are not elements of A, namely 3 and 5. In example 2, A is not a proper subset of B, for there are no elements of B that are not elements of A. *In other words if A is a subset of B it is also a proper subset unless the two sets are equal.*

Example 3

If $A = \{1, 3, 4, 5\}$, $B = \{1, 4\}$, $C = \{5, 4, 1, 3\}$, and $D = \{1, 2, 3, 4, 5, 6\}$, list all the subset relations among these four sets.

$$\left.\begin{array}{l} A \subseteq C \\ C \subseteq A \end{array}\right\} \quad A = C \qquad\qquad \begin{array}{l} C \subset D \\ B \subset A \\ B \subset C \end{array}$$
$$\begin{array}{l} A \subset D \\ B \subset D \end{array}$$

Since every element of a set A belongs to A, every set A is a subset of itself $(A \subseteq A)$.

Note

By definition we will say that the null set $\emptyset$ is *a subset of every set.*

Example 4

List all the subsets of the following set:

$$A = \{a, b, c\}$$

(1) ∅   (3) {b}   (5) {a, b}   (7) {b, c}
(2) {a}   (4) {c}   (6) {a, c}   (8) {a, b, c}

    Which of these subsets are *not* proper? {a, b, c} is not a proper subset of A. Why?

    In order to proceed in the next section we need the definition of a universal set.

UNIVERSAL SET

A universal set, denoted by U, is a set containing at least all of the elements of the sets under discussion in a particular problem. Thus, *every set* in a particular problem is a *subset* of the universal set for that problem.

Example 5

$A = \{1, 3, 5\}$, $B = \{3, 5, 7, 9\}$, $C = \{1, 4, 6\}$. Then $U = \{1, 2, 3, 4, 5, 6, 7, 8, 9, 10\}$ may be used as the universal set, for all the elements of the sets A, B, and C belong to U.

Note

There are other possible choices for U in example 5. The set P of positive integers and the set Q of rational numbers are two other possible choices.

Example 6

If $A = \{x \mid x$ is a furniture salesman} and
   $B = \{y \mid y$ is a salesman who made over \$10,000 last year}, then the set

   $U = \{w \mid w$ is a salesman} may be used as the universal set for this discussion, for all of the elements of the sets A and B belong to U.

Exercise Set 1.6

In exercises 1-10 let $A = \{1, 3, 5, 7\}$, $B = \{2, 4, 6, 8\}$, $C = \{1, 7\}$, $D = \{7, 5, 1, 3\}$, and $E = \{a, b\}$. Determine whether the given statements are true or false.

1. $A \subset B$

2. $A = B$

3. $C \subseteq B$

4. $C \subset A$

5. $A = D$

6. $A \subset D$

7. $B \backsim D$

8. $A \backsim D$

9. $E = C$

10. $D \subseteq A$

In exercises 11-13 write a universal set that would contain all of the given sets as subsets.

11. $A = \{a, b, c, d, e\}$ $B = \{a, e, i, o, u\}$ $C = \{w, x, y, z\}$

12. $A = \{-7, -5, -3, -1\}$ $B = \{0\}$ $C = \{2, 4, 6, 8\}$

13. $A = \{\text{Chevrolet, Pontiac}\}$ $B = \{\text{Pontiac, Buick, Oldsmobile}\}$
    $C = \{\text{Chevrolet, Buick, Cadillac}\}$

14. List all the subsets of the set $A = \{1, 3\}$. Which of the subsets are proper?

15. List all the subsets of the set $B = \{a, b, c, d\}$. Which of the subsets are proper?

16. Let $U = \{x \mid x \text{ is a positive integer}\}$
    $A = \{x \mid x \text{ is a positive even integer}\}$
    $B = \{x \mid x \text{ is an integer between 1 and 10}\}$
    $C = \{x \mid x \text{ is a positive integer less than 9}\}$
    $D = \{2, 4, 6, 8\}$.
    List all subset relations among these five sets.

1.7 OPERATIONS ON SETS

Different relationships between sets are of interest. We shall now explore several of these relationships.

INTERSECTION OF TWO SETS

The *intersection* of two sets A and B is the *set* consisting of all the elements which belong to both A *and* B. Symbolically this is written $A \cap B$. Using the rule method we can write

$$A \cap B = \{x \mid x \in A \text{ and } x \in B\}$$

Example 1

Let $A = \{1, 3, 5, 7, 9\}$ and $B = \{2, 4, 5, 9\}$. Find $A \cap B$.

Since 5 and 9 belong to both A and B, and there are no other common elements, $A \cap B = \{5, 9\}$.

Example 2

If $A = \{$Smith, Brown, Jones$\}$ and $B = \{$Jones, Perry$\}$, find $A \cap B$.

Since Jones belongs to both A and B, and there are no other common elements, $A \cap B = \{$Jones$\}$.

Example 3

If $A = \{1, 3, 5, 7\}$ and $B = \{2, 4, 6\}$, then

$$A \cap B = \emptyset$$

That is, $A \cap B$ has no elements.

Example 4

Let $A = \{x \mid x$ is a positive integer between 2 and 8$\}$ and $B = \{1, 5, 7, 9\}$.

$$A \cap B = \{5, 7\}$$

UNION OF TWO SETS

The *union* of two sets A and B is the set consisting of all the elements belonging to *A or to B or to both.* Symbolically this is written $A \cup B$. Using the rule method

$$A \cup B = \{x \mid x \in A \text{ or } x \in B\}$$

where "*or*" here means the element belongs to *A or to B or to both.*

Example 5

If $A = \{1, 2, 4, 5\}$ and $B = \{1, 2, 4, 7, 8\}$, then

$$A \cup B = \{1, 2, 4, 5, 7, 8\}$$

7 is an element of the union because it belongs to set B, 4 is an element of the union because it belongs to both, 5 is an element of the union because it belongs to A, and so forth.

Example 6

A = {Smith, Brown, Jones}, B = {Jones, Perry}

$A \cup B$ = {Smith, Brown, Jones, Perry}

Smith and Brown are elements of the union because they belong to set A, Perry is an element of the union because he belongs to set B, and Jones is an element of the union because he belongs to both sets.

COMPLEMENT OF A SET

The *complement of a set A* is the *set* of all elements that belong to the universal set, but are *not* elements of A. Symbolically the complement of A is written A'. This definition may be written:
$$A' = \{x \mid x \in U \text{ but } x \notin A\}$$

Example 7

If A = {1, 3, 5} and U = {1, 2, 3, 4, 5, 6}, then
$$A' = \{2, 4, 6\}$$

since the elements 2, 4, and 6 are elements of the universal set but they do *not* belong to the set A.

Example 8

A = {$x \mid x$ is a positive odd integer between 0 and 10}
U = {1, 2, 3, 4, 5, 6, 7, 8, 9, 10}

Then A' = {2, 4, 6, 8, 10}, since A = {1, 3, 5, 7, 9}.

Example 9

If A = {2, 5, 7}, B = {3, 5, 6, 8, 10}, C = {1, 3, 5, 7}, D = {1, 9}, and U = {1, 2, 3, 4, 5, 6, 7, 8, 9, 10}, find

(a) $A \cap B$ (c) $B \cap C$ (e) $A \cup D$
(b) $A \cup B$ (d) $A \cap D$ (f) C'

(a) $A \cap B$ = {5}   (d) $A \cap D$ = $\emptyset$
(b) $A \cup B$ = {2, 3, 5, 6, 7, 8, 10}   (e) $A \cup D$ = {1, 2, 5, 7, 9}
(c) $B \cap C$ = {3, 5}   (f) C' = {2, 4, 6, 8, 9, 10}

Let's now try a complex problem.

Example 10

Given $U = \{1, 2, 3, 4, 5, 6, 7, 8, 9, 10\}$, $A = \{1, 3, 4, 7, 9\}$, $B = \{2, 4, 6, 8\}$, and $C = \{1, 3, 5, 7\}$. List the elements of the following sets:

(a) A' (d) B' (g) $A \cap B'$

(b) $A \cap B$ (e) C' (h) $A \cup (C \cap B')$

(c) $A \cup B$ (f) $B \cap C$ (i) $C' \cap (A \cup B)$

                                               (j) $(A \cap C)'$

(a) $A' = \{2, 5, 6, 8, 10\}$

(b) $A \cap B = \{4\}$

(c) $A \cup B = \{1, 2, 3, 4, 6, 7, 8, 9\}$

(d) $B' = \{1, 3, 5, 7, 9, 10\}$

(e) $C' = \{2, 4, 6, 8, 9, 10\}$

(f) $B \cap C = \emptyset$ because there are no elements belonging to both B and C

(g) $A \cap B' = \{1, 3, 7, 9\}$. To find $A \cap B'$ we find the elements of B' and then intersect B' with the set A.

(h) $A \cup (C \cap B') = \{1, 3, 4, 5, 7, 9\}$. We find the set $C \cap B'$, which is $\{1, 3, 5, 7\}$ and then take the union of this set and the set A, obtaining the above result.

(i) $C' \cap (A \cup B) = \{2, 4, 6, 8, 9\}$. We have already found $A \cup B = \{1, 2, 3, 4, 6, 7, 8, 9\}$ and $C' = \{2, 4, 6, 8, 9, 10\}$ and now we intersect these two sets and obtain the result for $C' \cap (A \cup B)$.

(j) $(A \cap C)' = \{2, 4, 5, 6, 8, 9, 10\}$. This result is obtained by first finding $A \cap C$, which is $\{1, 3, 7\}$, and then taking the complement of this result.

Example 11

Let $U = \{x \mid x$ is a salesman$\}$

     $A = \{y \mid y$ is a camera salesman$\}$ and

     $B = \{w \mid w$ is a salesman who made over \$10,000 last year$\}$.

Now consider each of the following sets.

(a) A' is the set of salesmen who do not sell cameras.

(b) $A \cap B$ is the set of camera salesmen who made over \$10,000 last year.

(c) $A \cup B$ is the set of all salesmen who sell cameras or made over \$10,000 last year.

(d) B' is the set of all salesmen who made $10,000 or under last year.

(e) $A' \cap B'$ is the set of all salesmen who do not sell cameras and who made $10,000 or less last year.

You may use a diagram to help you in example 11 above. Any geometric figure may be used symbolically to represent the containment of sets A and B (that is, to represent the universal set). A large rectangular region will be used here to represent the universal set. $A \subset U$, $B \subset U$, with A and B represented by circular regions drawn inside the rectangle. The circular regions A and B overlap (intersect) as in Figure 1.1 to indicate that there are camera salesmen who made over $10,000.

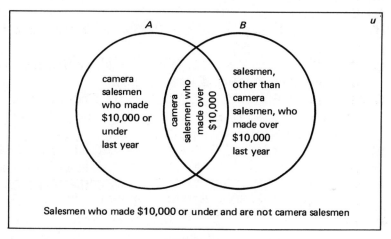

FIGURE 1.1

Exercise Set 1.7

In exercises 1-10 let $U = \{1, 2, 3, 4, 5, 6, 7, 8, 9, 10\}$, $A = \{2, 4, 6, 8, 10\}$, $B = \{1, 2, 3, 4, 5\}$, $C = \{1, 3, 5, 7, 9\}$, and $D = \{4, 6, 7, 9\}$. List the elements in the given sets.

1. $A \cap B$ 6. $A \cup (C \cap D)$

2. $C \cup D$ 7. $A \cap (B \cup D)$

3. $A' \cap C$ 8. $A \cap D'$

4. $A' \cap C'$ 9. $(A' \cup B)'$

5. $(A \cap B)'$ 10. $B \cap (C \cup D)'$

In exercises 11-13 let $U = \{1, 2, 3, 4, 5, 6\}$, $A = \{1, 2, 3\}$, $B = \{2, 3, 4\}$, and $C = \{5, 6\}$.

11. $(A \cap B) \cup C =$

12. $(A \cap B)' \cup C' =$

13. $[(B' \cap C) \cap (A' \cup C)']' =$

In exercises 14-22 supply the answer from the sets $A, A', \emptyset, U$, where A is any set.

14. $A \cap \emptyset =$ **17.** $(A')' =$ **20.** $A \cap A' =$

15. $A' \cup A =$ **18.** $A \cup U =$ **21.** $A \cap (A')' =$

16. $U \cup \emptyset =$ **19.** $A \cap U =$ **22.** $A' \cup \emptyset =$

In exercises 23-28 let $U = \{x \mid x$ is an automobile $\}$
$A = \{y \mid y$ is a Volkswagen $\}$.
$B = \{w \mid w$ is an automobile with an exterior color of white $\}$
$C = \{z \mid z$ is an automobile with automatic transmission $\}$.

Describe the given sets.

23. A' **25.** $A \cup C$ **27.** $(C \cap B)'$

24. $A \cap B$ **26.** $A \cap B'$ **28.** $A \cap C$

In exercises 29-32 let $U = \{x \mid x$ is an animal $\}$, $A = \{x \mid x$ is a dog $\}$, $B = \{x \mid x$ is an animal with a long tail $\}$.

29. The set of dogs with long tails would be represented by which of the following sets?

(a) $A \cup B$ (b) $A' \cup B$ (c) $A' \cap B$ (d) $A \cap B'$ (e) $A \cap B$

30. The set of animals which do not have long tails and are not dogs would be represented by which of the following sets?

(a) $A \cup B$ (b) $A' \cap B'$ (c) $A \cap B$ (d) $(A \cap B)'$ (e) $A' \cup B'$

31. The set of dogs that do not have long tails would be represented by which of the following sets?

(a) $A \cap B'$ (b) $A' \cup B$ (c) $A' \cap B$ (d) $A \cup B'$ (e) $A' \cup B'$

32. The set of animals that are either dogs or have long tails would be represented by which of the following sets?

(a) $A \cap B$ (b) $A' \cap B'$ (c) $A \cup B$ (d) $A' \cup B'$ (e) $A' \cup B$

1.8 DIAGRAMS OF SET OPERATIONS

Diagrams of set operations will help us visualize the intersection, union, and complement of sets. We will use a rectangular region to indicate the universal set, and circular regions drawn inside the rectangle to indicate other sets. In Figures 1.2 and 1.3 the shaded region represents the intersection of A and B.

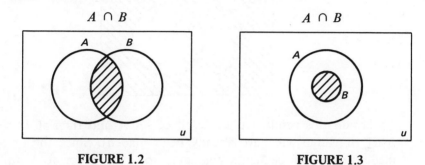

$A \cap B$ $A \cap B$

FIGURE 1.2   **FIGURE 1.3**

The shaded region in Figures 1.4 and 1.5 represents the union of A and B. The complement of A is shaded in Figure 1.6.

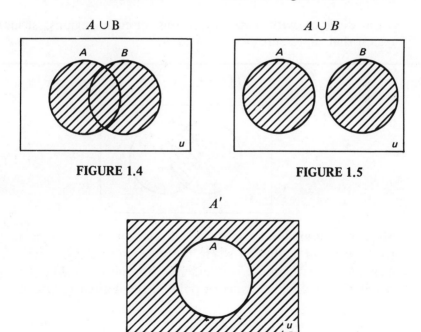

$A \cup B$ $A \cup B$

FIGURE 1.4   **FIGURE 1.5**

A'

FIGURE 1.6

Example 1

In a diagram with two intersecting circular regions, shade the region that represents $A \cup B'$.

$$A \cup B'$$

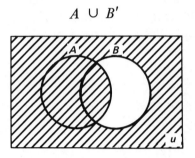

To obtain this result, we shade all of set A and then all of set B' (part of which will have already been shaded). Since the union is made up of all elements belonging to A or B' or to both, the entire shaded region represents $A \cup B'$.

Example 2

In a diagram with two intersecting circular regions, shade the region that represents $(A \cup B') \cap B$.

$$(A \cup B') \cap B$$

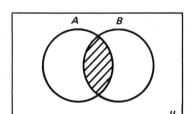

Since the desired set consists of all elements that belong to both $(A \cup B')$ and B, if you shade the region $(A \cup B')$, arrived at in example 1, with one color and B with another color, the region where the two colors overlap would be the desired intersection.

Let us now shade a diagram with three circular regions representing three different sets.

The shaded region in Figure 1.7 represents $B' \cap C$. If you shade B' with one color and C with another color, then the intersection would be the region where the two colors overlapped. Why don't you try it on a piece of paper?

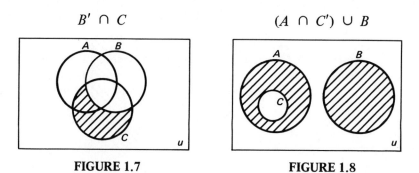

$B' \cap C$	$(A \cap C') \cup B$
FIGURE 1.7	**FIGURE 1.8**

The shaded region in Figure 1.8 above represents $(A \cap C')$ $\cup$ B. If you shade A with one color and C' with another color, then $(A \cap C')$ should be the region where the two colors overlap. Now that we have shaded $(A \cap C')$, shade the set B. Being that we want the union of $(A \cap C')$ and B, leave the coloring for $(A \cap C')$ and B so as to obtain the union. When you try some of our exercises you will find that a little practice on your part will make shading of diagrams quite simple.

Exercise Set 1.8

In exercises 1-3 let A, B, and C be subsets of U. Construct a diagram described by given conditions.

1. Sets A and C do not intersect. A and B have elements in common but they are not subsets of each other. B and C have elements in common but they are not subsets of each other. There are elements that do not belong to either A, B, or C.

2. Sets A and B do not intersect. B is a subset of C or C is a subset of B. There are elements that belong to B but do not belong to C. There are elements that do not belong to either A, B, or C.

3. Set C is a proper subset of A. A and B have elements in common but they are not subsets of each other. B and C have elements in common but they are not subsets of each other. There are elements that do not belong to either A, B, or C.

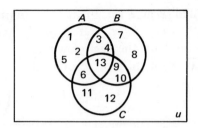

Exercises 4-7 refer to the following information. If the elements of sets A, B, and C are those shown in the diagram above, state the elements of the given sets. *Note*: there are no elements in U which do not belong to either A, B, or C.

4. $(A \cap B) \cup C =$
   (a) $\{3, 4, 6, 9, 10, 11, 12, 13\}$ (d) $\{6, 9, 10, 13\}$
   (b) $\{3, 4, 6, 9, 10, 13\}$ (e) $\{6, 9, 10, 11, 12\}$
   (c) $\{13\}$

5. $(A \cup B)' =$
   (a) $\emptyset$ (d) $\{11, 12\}$
   (b) $\{6, 9, 10, 11, 12, 13\}$ (e) none of these
   (c) $\{3, 4, 11, 12, 13\}$

6. $(A' \cup B) =$
   (a) $\{1, 2, 3, 4, 5, 6, 7, 8, 9, 10, 13\}$ (d) $\{3, 4, 6, 7, 8, 9, 10, 11, 12, 13\}$
   (b) $\{7, 8, 9, 10\}$ (e) $\{3, 4, 7, 8, 9, 10, 11, 12, 13\}$
   (c) $\{3, 4, 7, 8, 9, 10, 13\}$

7. $B \cap (C \cup A)' =$
   (a) $\{7, 8\}$ (d) $\{1, 2, 3, 4, 5, 6, 9, 10, 11, 12, 13\}$
   (b) $\{1, 2, 5, 6, 11, 12\}$ (e) $\{7, 8, 9, 10\}$
   (c) $\{3, 4, 7, 8, 9, 10, 13\}$

In exercises 8-15 shade the region that represents the given set.

8. $B \cap A'$ **9.** $(A \cap B') \cup B$

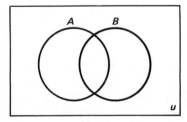   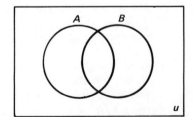

10. $(A \cap B') \cup (B \cap A')$ **11.** $A' \cup (B \cap A)$

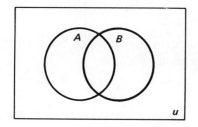   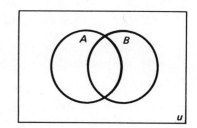

12. $(A \cup B) \cap C$ **13.** $(C \cup A') \cap B$

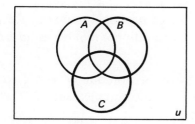   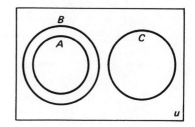

14. $(A \cap B') \cup C'$ **15.** $(A' \cap B) \cup C$

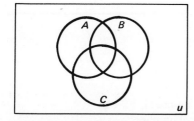   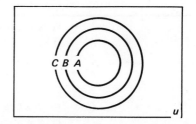

1.9 REVIEWING THE SUBSETS OF THE SET OF REAL NUMBERS

Suppose we now review the relationships between some of the subsets of the set R of real numbers. As you read the following list, try to describe the given sets.

(1) $P = \{1, 2, 3, 4, \ldots\}$
(2) $I = \{0, +1, -1, +2, -2, \ldots\}$
(3) $E = \{0, +2, -2, +4, -4, +6, -6, \ldots\}$

(4) $O = \{+1, -1, +3, -3, +5, -5, \ldots\}$
(5) $Q = \{x \mid x = \frac{a}{b}, a$ and b are integers, $b \neq 0\}$
(6) $R = \{x \mid x$ is a real number$\}$

Suppose we now consider some relationships between the above sets. As you read these, try to justify them.

(1) Sets P, I, E, O, Q are all proper subsets of R.
(2) Sets P, E, and O are proper subsets of I.
(3) P, E, O, and I are proper subsets of Q.
(4) $E \cup O = I$
(5) $E \cap O = \emptyset$
(6) $P \cap I = P$
(7) If we let R be the universal set for this discussion, then $Q \cup Q' = R$, where Q' is the set of irrational numbers. Recall that every real number that is not a rational number is an irrational number.

Thus it can now be seen why the notation Q' was used for the set of irrational numbers, for Q' is the complement of Q when the set R is taken as the universal set.

Exercise Set 1.9

In exercises 1-9 let

$$\begin{aligned}
U = R &= \{x \mid x \text{ is a real number}\} \\
I &= \{x \mid x \text{ is an integer}\} \\
P &= \{x \mid x \text{ is a positive integer}\} \\
N &= \{x \mid x \text{ is a negative integer}\} \\
Z &= \{0\} \\
Q &= \{x \mid x \text{ is a rational number}\} \\
Q' &= \{x \mid x \text{ is an irrational number}\}.
\end{aligned}$$

1. $N \cup Q =$
   (a) N (b) I (c) U (d) Q (e) $\emptyset$

2. $I \cup R =$
   (a) I (b) R (c) $\emptyset$ (d) Q (e) P

3. $Q' \cap N =$
   (a) Q' (b) N (c) $\emptyset$ (d) $Q \cup P$ (e) U

4. $P \cap I' =$
   (a) N (b) $N \cup Z$ (c) U (d) I (e) $\emptyset$

1.9 REVIEWING THE SUBSETS OF THE SET OF REAL NUMBERS

5. $N \cap Q$ =
   (a) Q (b) N (c) $\emptyset$ (d) P (e) Q'

6. $(R \cup Q)'$ =
   (a) $\emptyset$ (b) U (c) Q' (d) $R \cup Q'$ (e) I

7. $P' \cap I$ =
   (a) $\emptyset$ (b) N (c) Q (d) $N \cup Z$ (e) Z

8. $I' \cap Q$ =
   (a) Q (b) I' (c) Q' (d) U (e) none of these

9. $(I \cap Q)'$ =
   (a) I (b) Q (c) Q' (d) I' (e) none of these

REVIEW TEST FOR CHAPTER I

Note: This review test as well as all subsequent tests should be tried under examination conditions. The review test for Chapter I should be completed within 75 minutes.

Answer questions 1-8 true or false.

1. The union of the set of positive integers and the set of negative integers is the set of all integers.

2. All equivalent sets are equal.

3. If $A \cap B = \{0\}$, then A and B have no elements in common.

4. If A is a proper subset of B, then every element of B must also be an element of A.

   For questions 5-8 let A = $\{x \mid x$ is a positive integer$\}$
   B = $\{2, 4, 6, 8, 10, \ldots\}$
   C = $\{3, 5, 7, 9, 11, \ldots\}$
   D = $\{1, 3, 5, 7, 9\}$.

5. $A = B \cup C$

6. $A \subseteq B$

7. $D \subseteq C$

8. $B \cap C = \emptyset$

For questions 9-25 select the letter corresponding to the correct answer.

9. The set of all integers less than 5 is:
    (a) a finite set   (b) an infinite set

10. $B' \cap U =$
    (a) B (b) U (c) $\emptyset$ (d) B' (e) none of these

11. If $x \in (A \cup B)'$, then
    (a) $x \in A'$ and $x \in B'$ (c) $x \in A \cup B$ (e) $x \in A$ but $x \notin B$
    (b) $x \in A'$ but $x \notin B'$ (d) $x \in A$ and $x \in B$

12. $A \cup \emptyset =$
    (a) A (b) A' (c) $\emptyset$ (d) U (e) none of these

13. If A is a subset of B and B is a subset of A, then:
    (a) $A \cap B = \emptyset$ (c) either $A = \emptyset$ or $B = \emptyset$ (e) $A \cup B = U$
    (b) $A \cup B = \emptyset$ (d) $A = B$

14. $A' \cap (A')' =$
    (a) A' (b) A (c) $\emptyset$ (d) U (e) none of these

15. Which of the following is not a rational number?
    (a) $\frac{0}{4}$ (b) $\frac{\sqrt{3}}{2}$ (c) $\frac{-1}{2}$ (d) $\frac{16}{7}$ (e) 0.2531

16. If A and B are nonempty sets such that $A = B$, then which one of the following statements is false?
    (a) $A \cup B = A$ (c) $A \cap B' = \emptyset$ (e) $A \cap B = \emptyset$
    (b) $A' \cap B' = B'$ (d) $A \cap A' = \emptyset$

For questions 17-21 let $U = \{1, 2, 3, \ldots, 10\}$, $A = \{1, 2, 3, 4, 5, 6, 7\}$, $B = \{5, 6, 7, 8, 9, 10\}$, and $C = \{1, 2, 9, 10\}$.

17. $A \cap B =$
    (a) $\{5, 6, 7\}$ (b) B (c) $\emptyset$ (d) $\{7\}$ (e) none of these

18. $B' \cap C =$
    (a) $\{9, 10\}$ (b) $\{1, 2\}$ (c) U (d) $\emptyset$ (e) none of these

19. $(A \cup C)' =$
    (a) $\{8, 9, 10\}$ (b) U (c) $\{8\}$ (d) $\emptyset$ (e) none of these

20. $(A \cap B)' \cup C =$
    (a) C (b) $A \cup B$ (c) $(A \cup B)'$ (d) $A \cup C$ (e) none of these

21. $(A \cup B)' \cap C' =$
    (a) U (b) $\emptyset$ (c) A' (d) C' (e) none of these

22. The shaded region in the figure on the right describes which set?

(a) $A \cup B'$
(b) $(A \cup B) \cup B'$
(c) $A' \cap B$
(d) A'
(e) B

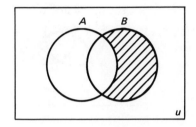

23. The shaded region in the figure on the right describes which set?

(a) $A' \cup B'$
(b) $A \cup B'$
(c) $A \cap B'$
(d) $A' \cap B'$
(e) $A' \cup B$

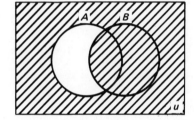

24. The shaded region in the given diagram is correctly described by which of the sets to the left of the diagram?

(a) $A \cup (B \cap C)$
(b) $(A \cup B) \cap C$
(c) $A \cap (B \cap C)$
(d) $(A \cap B) \cup C$
(e) $(A \cup C) \cap B$

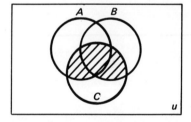

25. Which of the following diagrams describes $(A \cup C)' \cap B$?

a.

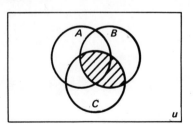

b.

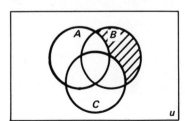

c.

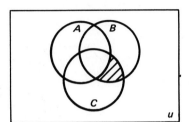

d.

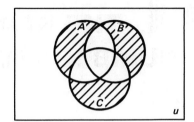

II THE REAL NUMBER LINE

2.1 DEFINING THE REAL NUMBER LINE

We would like to consider now the set R of real numbers and its association with any straight line.

A straight line can be considered as a *set of points*. Suppose we now draw a straight line L, with arrows at each end to indicate that the line continues unending in either direction, as follows:

Now suppose we choose any point O on this line, and with this point we *pair* the number 0 from the set R of real numbers. To indicate this pairing we will place the number 0 right below the point O on the line as follows:

This point O is referred to as the origin. Now let us choose any other point P_1 (read "P sub 1") to the *right* of O and pair this point with the number 1, placing the number 1 right below the point P_1. Then upon measuring the distance between O and P_1, we will have established a *standard unit of measure* or a *unit length* (see Figure 2.1).

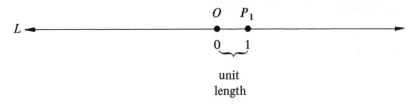

unit
length

FIGURE 2.1

If we now mark off another unit of measure to the right of the point P_1, we can pair the point P_2 so obtained with the number 2. Continuing this process, we will have paired 0 as well as each positive integer with a single point on the line L (see Figure 2.2).

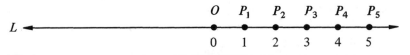

FIGURE 2.2

As you may have realized by this time, if we mark off one unit of measure to the *left* of the origin we can pair the point P_{-1} so obtained with the number -1. One unit to the left of P_{-1} gives us the point P_{-2}, which we pair with the number -2, and so forth. Continuing in this way *to the left* of the origin, we will have paired each negative integer with a single point on the line L. (See Figure 2.3.)

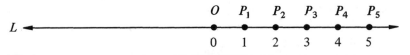

FIGURE 2.3

In summing up what we have done, we have established a one-to-one correspondence between the set of integers I and the set of points on the line chosen by the process outlined above. This set of points is a subset of the set of *all* points on the line.

Suppose we now attempt to pair each rational number with a single point on the line L. Let us consider the numbers $\frac{1}{2}$, $\frac{7}{4}$, $\frac{12}{5}$, and $\frac{22}{7}$, for example.

Example 1

To locate the point corresponding to the number $\frac{1}{2}$ we would subdivide the unit line segment from "0 to 1" into two equal parts, and the point of subdivision would be the point desired.

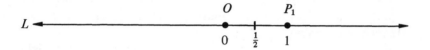

Example 2

To locate the point corresponding to the number $\frac{7}{4}$ or $1\frac{3}{4}$ we would subdivide the unit line segment from "0 to 1" into four equal parts. The first subdivision point would correspond to $\frac{1}{4}$. Then count off seven such subdivisions to the right of the origin to obtain the desired point.

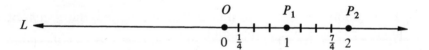

Example 3

To locate the point corresponding to $\frac{12}{5}$ or $2\frac{2}{5}$ we would subdivide the unit line segment from "0 to 1" into five equal parts. The first subdivision point would correspond to $\frac{1}{5}$. Then count off twelve such subdivisions to the right of the origin to obtain the "point $\frac{12}{5}$."

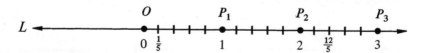

Why don't you try to locate the point corresponding to $\frac{22}{7}$? In a similar manner we can pair each positive rational number $\frac{a}{b}$, $b \neq 0$ with a single point on the line L. That is, we divide the unit line segment from "0 to 1" into b equal parts. The first subdivision point would correspond to $\frac{1}{b}$. Then count off a such subdivisions to the right of the origin.

If we carry out the same procedure to the *left* of the origin, we can pair each negative rational number with a single point on the line L. Thus we have now established a one-to-one correspondence between the set of rational numbers Q, of which the integers is a subset, and a subset of points on the line L.

It can also be shown that to each irrational number there corresponds a unique point on the line L, not already chosen to correspond to any rational number, and to each point on L not paired with a rational number, there corresponds a unique irrational number.

THE REAL NUMBER LINE

Thus a one-to-one correspondence can be established between *the set of all real numbers R* and the *set of all points on the line L.* This line L as well as any other line whose points are put into one-to-one correspondence with the set R of real numbers is called the *real number line.*

GRAPH OF A NUMBER

Each point on the real number line is called the *graph* of the number to which it corresponds.

THE COORDINATE OF A POINT

Each real number is called the *coordinate* of the point to which it corresponds.

Example 4

Suppose the number 5 is paired with the point P on the real number line as shown:

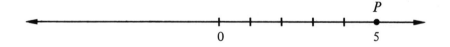

Then 5 is the coordinate of the point P and P is the graph of the number 5.

Exercise Set 2.1

In each of the exercises 1-9 draw a real number line and locate the graph of the given number.

1. 6   **4.** $\frac{9}{4}$ **7.** 1.25

2. -4   **5.** $-3\frac{5}{8}$ **8.** -2.333 . . .

3. $\frac{1}{3}$ **6.** $-\frac{13}{6}$ **9.** 2.125

10. Write at least two rational numbers between $\frac{1}{3}$ and $\frac{1}{2}$ and locate the graphs of these numbers on a real number line.

2.2 ORDER ON THE REAL NUMBER LINE

Suppose we let c and d be any real numbers. We can now define the following relationships between c and d:

(1) We say that c *is less than* d, written $c < d$ if and only if the graph of c lies to the *left* of the graph of d.
(2) We say that $c = d$, if and only if the graph of c coincides with the graph of d.
(3) We say that c *is greater than* d, written $c > d$, if and only if the graph of c lies to the right of the graph of d.

Examples

1. $3 < 6$ These relationships can be seen by consider-
2. $4 > 1$ ing the following diagram:
3. $0 > -3$
4. $-5 < -2$
5. $-1 < 1$

$$-7\ -6\ -5\ -4\ -3\ -2\ -1\ \ 0\ \ 1\ \ 2\ \ 3\ \ 4\ \ 5\ \ 6\ \ 7$$

Example 6

$\frac{1}{2} > \frac{1}{3}$ This can be seen by writing $\frac{1}{2}$ as $\frac{3}{6}$ and $\frac{1}{3}$ as $\frac{2}{6}$ and con-
             sidering the following diagram:

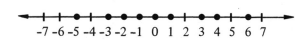

$$0\qquad \tfrac{1}{3}\ \tfrac{1}{2}\qquad\quad 1$$

Example 7

$-\frac{7}{5} < -\frac{9}{10}$ This can be seen by writing $-\frac{7}{5}$ as $-\frac{14}{10}$ and considering the following diagram:

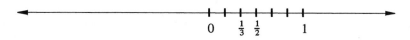

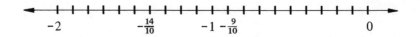

NEGATIVE AND POSITIVE INTEGERS

In light of our new definitions we can now rewrite the set of *negative integers* as:

$$N = \{x \mid x \in I, x < 0 \}$$

and the set of *positive integers* as

$$P = \{x \mid x \in I, x > 0\}$$

Recall that I is the set of integers.

Suppose we now consider the set $A = \{x \mid x \in R, x > 2\}$, in other words the set of *real numbers* that are greater than 2. The graph of this set on the real number line can be represented as follows:

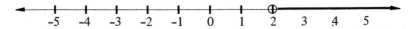

Note that the number 2 is *not* included in this set, which is indicated by the circle around the point corresponding to the number 2.

If we wish to consider the set B, which has all the elements of A, but also has the number 2 in it as well, then we would write:

$$B = \{x \mid x \in R, x \geqslant 2\}$$

where the symbol "$\geqslant$" is read, "is greater than or is equal to." The graph of the set B on the real number line would be:

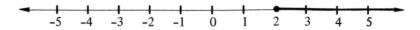

Note here that the graph of 2 is included.

Let us now consider some further examples of graphs of subsets of R.

Example 8

Draw the graph of the set $A = \{x \mid x \ \epsilon \ R, x < -1\}$.

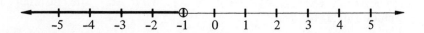

Example 9

Draw the graph of the set $B = \{x \mid x \ \epsilon \ R, 2 \leqslant x \leqslant 5\}$.

This is read, "B is the set of all real numbers x, such that x is greater than or equal to 2 *and* less than or equal to 5."

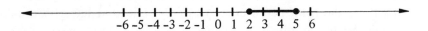

Example 10

Draw the graph of the set

$$C = \{x \mid x \ \epsilon \ R, x \leqslant 0 \text{ or } x > 3 \}$$

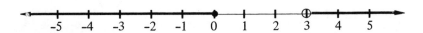

Example 11

Let $D = \{x \mid x \ \epsilon \ I, -3 \leqslant x < 2\}$. Draw the graph of D.

Note that this set has only the *integers* that are greater than or equal to -3 and less than 2. What would these integers be?

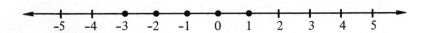

Example 12

Let $A = \{x \mid x \ \epsilon \ R, x > 1\}$ and
$\quad\quad B = \{x \mid x \ \epsilon \ R, x \leqslant 5\}$.

Draw the graph of $A \cap B$ and write the result in set notation.

If you draw the graph of A in one color and the graph of B in another color, the portion of the line where the two colors overlap would be the graph of $A \cap B$.

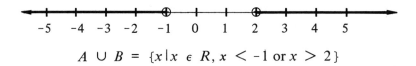

$A \cap B = \{x \mid x \in R, 1 < x \leqslant 5\}$. Why isn't the number 1 included in $A \cap B$?

Example 13

Let $A = \{x \mid x \in R, x < -1\}$ and
$\quad B = \{x \mid x \in R, x > 2\}$.

Draw the graph of $A \cup B$ and write the result in set notation.

If you draw the graph of A in one color, and then the graph of B in another, the *total* of all portions of the line that have been colored would be the graph of $A \cup B$.

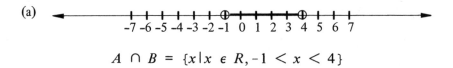

$$A \cup B = \{x \mid x \in R, x < -1 \text{ or } x > 2\}$$

Example 14

Let $A = \{x \mid x \in R, -3 \leqslant x < 4\}$ and
$\quad B = \{x \mid x \in R, -1 < x \leqslant 6\}$.

Draw the graphs of $A \cap B$ and $A \cup B$ and write the results in set notation.

If you use two colors once again and the procedure outlined in examples 12 and 13 above, you will obtain the following results:

(a)

$$A \cap B = \{x \mid x \in R, -1 < x < 4\}$$

(b)

$$A \cup B = \{x \mid x \in R, -3 \leqslant x \leqslant 6\}$$

Exercise Set 2.2

In exercises 1-10 insert the correct symbol from among $<$, $>$, $=$.

1. 10 _____ -15

2. -12 _____ -8

3. $\frac{1}{3}$ _____ $\frac{1}{2}$

4. $\frac{1}{2}$ _____ 0.5

5. $\frac{1}{3}$ _____ 0.333

6. $\frac{22}{7}$ _____ 3.14

7. $-1\frac{1}{4}$ _____ -1.25

8. $-\frac{2}{3}$ _____ $-0.666\ldots$

9. 3.001 _____ 3.01

10. $-\frac{7}{8}$ _____ -0.88

In exercises 11-20 graph the given set, where possible. Where not possible, state why.

11. $\{2, 4, 6, 8, 10\}$

12. $\{-3, -2.5, -\frac{3}{4}, 0, 1.5\}$

13. $\{x \mid x \in I, 2 < x \leqslant 6\}$

14. $\{x \mid x \in I, -5 < x < -4\}$

15. $\{x \mid x \in R, x < -5 \text{ or } x > -4\}$

16. $\{x \mid x \in R, x \geqslant 0\}$

17. $\{x \mid x \in I, -5 \leqslant x \leqslant 5\}$

18. $\{x \mid x \in R, 0 < x \leqslant 7\}$

19. $\{x \mid x \in R, x < -2 \text{ and } x > 0\}$

20. $\{x \mid x \in R, x < 4 \text{ or } x < -2\}$

21. Let $A = \{x \mid x \in I, -3 < x \leqslant 2\}$ and $B = \{x \mid x \in I, x \geqslant 0\}$. Draw the graph of $A \cap B$ and write the result in set notation.

22. Let $A = \{x \mid x \in R, -3 < x \leqslant 2\}$ and $B = \{x \mid x \in R, x \geqslant 0\}$. Draw the graph of $A \cap B$ and write the result in set notation.

23. Let $A = \{x \mid x \in R, x \leqslant -3\}$ and $B = \{x \mid x \in R, x \geqslant -1\}$. Find $A \cap B$.

24. Let $A = \{x \mid x \in I, -1 \leqslant x < 2\}$ and $B = \{x \mid x \in I, 0 < x < 5\}$. Draw the graph of $A \cup B$ and write the result in set notation.

25. Let $A = \{x \mid x \in R, -1 \leqslant x < 2\}$ and $B = \{x \mid x \in R, 0 < x < 5\}$. Draw the graph of $A \cup B$ and write the result in set notation.

26. Let $A = \{x \mid x \in R, x < -2\}$ and $B = \{x \mid x \in R, x \geqslant -4\}$. Find $A \cup B$ and draw the graph of the result.

27. Let $A = \{x \mid x \in R,\ x > 3 \text{ or } x < -7\}$ and $B = \{x \mid x \in R,\ -10 < x < -5\}$.
    (a) Draw the graph of $A \cap B$ and write the result in set notation.
    (b) Draw the graph of $A \cup B$ and write the result in set notation.

28. Let $A = \{x \mid x \in R,\ -4 < x \leqslant -2\}$ and $B = \{x \mid x \in R,\ -2 < x < 2\}$.
    (a) Find $A \cap B$.
    (b) Find $A \cup B$.

In exercises 29-33 using set notation, describe each of the given sets.

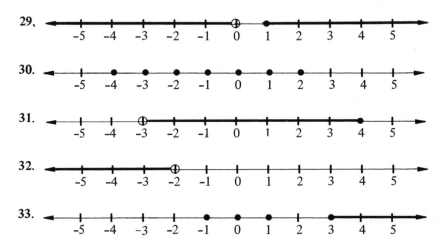

29.

30.

31.

32.

33.

2.3 PROPERTIES OF ADDITION AND MULTIPLICATION OF REAL NUMBERS

Before we actually perform the arithmetic operations on the real numbers, we should first examine some very important properties which are associated with the set R of real numbers together with the operations multiplication and addition.

CLOSURE OF A SET UNDER ADDITION

A set A is said to be *closed* under the operation of *addition* if and only if whenever we add any two elements of A the sum is also an element of A.

CLOSURE OF A SET UNDER MULTIPLICATION

Similarly a set A is said to be *closed* under the operation of *multiplication*, if and only if whenever we multiply any two elements of A, the product is also an element of A.

Since whenever we add any two real numbers the sum is also a real number, and whenever we multiply any two real numbers the product is also a real number, we can say that the set R of real numbers is closed under the operations of addition and multiplication.

PROPERTY I
CLOSURE

If a and b are any elements of R, then $(a + b) \in R$ and $(a \cdot b) \in R$ (where + represents addition and $\cdot$ represents multiplication).

Suppose we now consider the following sets with the given operations.

Example 1

Let $A = \{1, 2, 3\}$. This set is neither closed under the operation of addition, nor is it closed under multiplication, for if we add *any* two elements of A the sum is *not necessarily* a member of A, and if we multiply *any* two elements of A the product is *not necessarily* an element of A.

$$(1 + 3) \notin A, \qquad (2 \cdot 3) \notin A$$

Example 2

The set I of integers is closed under addition and multiplication. Why?

Example 3

Let $A = \{x \mid x \text{ is an odd integer}, x > 0\}$.

This set is closed under multiplication, for if we multiply any two positive odd numbers the product is a positive odd number.

However, this set is *not* closed under addition, for we need only see that $3 + 5 = 8$, for example. That is the sum of any two positive odd numbers is not necessarily a positive odd number. (In fact the sum of two positive odd integers will always be an even integer.)

PROPERTY II
COMMUTATIVE LAWS

If a and b are any real numbers, then

$a + b = b + a$ (Commutative law of addition)

$a \cdot b = b \cdot a$ (Commutative law of multiplication)

Example 4

$2 + 3 = 3 + 2,$ $42 \cdot 6 = 6 \cdot 42$

PROPERTY III
ASSOCIATIVE LAWS

If $a, b, c \in R$, then

$a + (b + c) = (a + b) + c$ (Associative law of addition)

$a \cdot (b \cdot c) = (a \cdot b) \cdot c$ (Associative law of multiplication)

That is, if we add a to the sum of b and c, we will obtain the same result as when we add the sum of a and b to c.

If we multiply a by the product of b and c, we will obtain the same result as when we multiply the product of a and b by c.

Example 5

$$3 + (4 + 7) = 3 + 11 = 14$$
$$(3 + 4) + 7 = 7 + 7 = 14$$

Example 6

$$6 \cdot (3 \cdot 8) = 6 \cdot 24 = 144$$
$$(6 \cdot 3) \cdot 8 = 18 \cdot 8 = 144$$

ASSOCIATIVE LAWS REWRITTEN

From the commutative and associative laws we can see that the three numbers a, b, and c can be added in any order, and thus the associative law for addition can simply be written as:

$$a + (b + c) = (a + b) + c = a + b + c$$

By a similar process, we can show that:

$$a \cdot (b \cdot c) = (a \cdot b) \cdot c = a \cdot b \cdot c$$

PROPERTY IV
DISTRIBUTIVE LAW

If $a, b, c, \in R$, then

$$a \cdot (b + c) = (a \cdot b) + (a \cdot c)$$

or

$$(b + c) \cdot a = (b \cdot a) + (c \cdot a)$$

That is, if we multiply a by the sum of b and c, we would obtain the same result as when we multiply *both b and c* by a and add the resulting products.

Example 7

$$3 \cdot (4 + 5) = 3 \cdot 9 = 27$$
$$(3 \cdot 4) + (3 \cdot 5) = 12 + 15 = 27$$

Example 8

Using the distributive law, write the sum $3 + 12$ as a product.

Writing 3 as $3 \cdot 1$ and 12 as $3 \cdot 4$, we have

$$3 + 12 = (3 \cdot 1) + (3 \cdot 4) = 3 \cdot (1 + 4)$$

PROPERTY V
ADDITIVE IDENTITY

There exists a *unique* real number 0, such that $a + 0 = 0 + a = a$, for *any* real number a.

That is, if 0 is added to any real number the sum is that real number. 0 is called the *additive identity* element of the set R of real numbers.

Note

Uniqueness here simply means that 0 is the only real number displaying the above property.

PROPERTY VI
ADDITIVE INVERSE

For each real number a there exists another real number $-a$, known as the *additive inverse* of a, such that $a + (-a) = (-a) + a = 0$.

In other words, the additive inverse of a real number a is that real number which when added to a gives the additive identity, 0.

Note

There is *one and only one* additive inverse for any given real number.

The additive inverse of 4 is -4, since $4 + (-4) = (-4) + 4 = 0$. At the same time we can see that 4 must be the additive inverse of -4 since the number that must be added to -4 to give 0 is $+4$. However, from the statement of Property VI (additive inverse property) the additive inverse of -4 is $-(-4)$, since the additive inverse of *any* real number a is $-a$. But we know that there is *one and only one* additive inverse for any real number. Therefore we must have that

$$-(-4) = +4$$

Example 9

What is the additive inverse of $-\frac{2}{5}$?

You could say that the additive inverse of $-\frac{2}{5}$ is $+\frac{2}{5}$ or you could say that the additive inverse of $-\frac{2}{5}$ is $-(-\frac{2}{5})$. Both answers would be correct, but knowing that the additive inverse is unique it must be the case that

$$-(-\tfrac{2}{5}) = +\tfrac{2}{5}$$

Note

In general $-(-a) = +a$ for any real number a.

PROPERTY VII
MULTIPLICATIVE IDENTITY

There exists a *unique* real number 1, such that $a \cdot 1 = 1 \cdot a = a$ for any real number a.

That is, if any real number is multiplied by 1, the product is that real number. The number 1 is called the *multiplicative identity* element of the set R of real numbers.

PROPERTY VIII
MULTIPLICATIVE INVERSE

For each real number a, except $a = 0$, there exists another real number $\frac{1}{a}$, known as the *multiplicative inverse* of a, such that

$$a \cdot \left(\tfrac{1}{a}\right) = \left(\tfrac{1}{a}\right) \cdot a = 1$$

In other words, the multiplicative inverse of a real number a, $a \neq 0$, is that number which when multiplied by a, produces the multiplicative identity, 1.

Note I

$$a \cdot 0 = 0 \cdot a = 0 \text{ } for \text{ } any \text{ } real \text{ } number \text{ } a.$$

This can be proven by showing that $a \cdot 0$ is the additive identity element of R, for upon showing this, and knowing that 0 is the *unique* additive identity element of R, we must have that $a \cdot 0 = 0 \cdot a = 0$. Our line of reasoning would be as follows:

(1) Since $1 + 0 = 1$ (0 is the additive identity of R), we can write $a \cdot 1$ as $a \cdot (1 + 0)$. That is,

$$a \cdot 1 = a \cdot (1 + 0)$$

(2) But by the distributive law

$$a \cdot (1 + 0) = (a \cdot 1) + (a \cdot 0)$$

(3) Therefore from steps (1) and (2) we have

$$a \cdot 1 = (a \cdot 1) + (a \cdot 0)$$

(4) But $a \cdot 1 = a$ (1 is the multiplicative identity of R).
(5) Thus we now have

$$a = a + (a \cdot 0)$$

We have now shown what we set out to do, that $a \cdot 0$ must be the additive identity element of R, and therefore $a \cdot 0 = 0$. Since $0 \cdot a = a \cdot 0$ by the commutative law we have now completed our proof.

Note II

From Note I we can now see that *0 has no multiplicative inverse*, for $0 \cdot a = 0$ for any real number a and $0 \neq 1$. That is, there is no real number a, which when multiplied by 0 produces the multiplicative identity element.

Note III

There is *one and only one* multiplicative inverse for any real number $a, a \neq 0$.

The multiplicative inverse of 3 is $\frac{1}{3}$, since $3 \cdot (\frac{1}{3}) = (\frac{1}{3}) \cdot 3 = 1$. At the same time we can see that the multiplicative inverse of $\frac{1}{3}$ is 3. However, from the statement of Property VIII, the multiplicative inverse of $\frac{1}{3}$ is $\frac{1}{\frac{1}{3}}$, since the multiplicative inverse of any real number $a, a \neq 0$ is $\frac{1}{a}$. But we know that the multiplicative inverse of any nonzero real number is unique. Therefore we must have

$$\frac{1}{\frac{1}{3}} = 3$$

Example 10

What is the multiplicative inverse of $\frac{1}{5}$?

You could say the multiplicative inverse of $\frac{1}{5}$ is 5 or you could say the multiplicative inverse of $\frac{1}{5}$ is $\frac{1}{\frac{1}{5}}$. Both answers would be correct, but knowing that the multiplicative inverse is *unique*, it must be the case that

$$\frac{1}{\frac{1}{5}} = 5$$

Note

In general $\frac{1}{\frac{1}{a}} = a$ for any real number $a, a \neq 0$.

Notation

In order to simplify our notation, in our further work we will omit the "$\cdot$" for multiplication and simply write ab for $a \cdot b$. We will also often use the notation $(a)b$ or $a(b)$ or $(a)(b)$ to represent the product $a \cdot b$. For three numbers we may write $a(bc)$, $(ab)c$, or abc to represent the product $a \cdot b \cdot c$.

The associative laws and distributive law can be extended to include the cases where more than three real numbers are involved.

EXTENSION OF ASSOCIATIVE LAWS

If a, b, c, and d are any real numbers, then

$$a + b + c + d = a + (b + c + d)$$
$$= (a + b + c) + d, \quad \text{etc.}$$

and

$$abcd = (abc)d$$
$$= a(bcd), \quad \text{etc.}$$

EXTENSION OF DISTRIBUTIVE LAW

If a, b, c, and d are any real numbers, then

$$a(b + c + d) = ab + ac + ad$$

Example 11

$$3(4 + 6 + 2) = 3(12) = 36$$
$$3(4) + 3(6) + 3(2) = 12 + 18 + 6 = 36$$

Example 12

Using the distributive law, write the sum $5 + 20 + 35$ as a product.

Writing 5 as $5(1)$, 20 as $5(4)$, and 35 as $5(7)$, we have

$$5(1) + 5(4) + 5(7) = 5(1 + 4 + 7)$$

Exercise Set 2.3

Determine whether or not the given sets in exercises 1-6 are closed under the stated operation.

1. $\{x \mid x \text{ is an even integer}, x > 0\}$; addition

2. $\{x \mid x \text{ is an even integer}, x > 0\}$; multiplication

3. $\{0, 1\}$; addition

4. $\{0, 1\}$; multiplication

5. $\{2, 4, 8, 16, 32, 64, \ldots\}$; addition

6. $\{2, 4, 8, 16, 32, 64, \ldots\}$; multiplication

In exercises 7-15 write the *additive* inverse of the given number.

7. 91

8. $+37$

9. 11

10. $-\frac{1}{2}$

11. $-5\frac{3}{8}$

12. $-(-6)$

13. $-(-3.715)$

14. $\sqrt{2}$

15. $(3 + 9)$

In exercises 16-27 write the *multiplicative* inverse of the given number if an inverse exists.

16. 7   **20.** 0.4   **24.** -1

17. -7 **21.** $\frac{0}{3}$ **25.** $\frac{1}{7}$

18. $\sqrt{3}$ **22.** $\frac{1}{\frac{3}{4}}$ **26.** $\frac{1}{-7}$

19. $\frac{3}{5}$ **23.** 1   **27.** $3\frac{1}{2}$

In exercises 28-42 state the property of the real numbers which is illustrated.

28. $3 \cdot 4$ is a real number.

29. $-6 + 0 = -6$

30. $5 + (-3) = -3 + 5$

31. $(22 + 8) + 21 = 22 + (8 + 21)$

32. $-\frac{1}{2} + \frac{1}{2} = 0$

33. $(0.321)(1) = 0.321$

34. $\frac{1}{2}(4 + 6) = (\frac{1}{2})4 + (\frac{1}{2})6$

35. $-3[2 + (-7 + 8)] = (-3)2 + (-3)(-7 + 8)$

36. $(\frac{1}{7})7 = 7(\frac{1}{7})$

37. $(3 + 7)1 = 3 + 7$

38. $(\frac{1}{8})(\frac{1}{\frac{1}{8}}) = 1$

39. $a(b + c) = (b + c)a$

40. $-(-a) + (-a) = 0$

41. $[2 + (3 + a)] + (5 + b) = 2 + [(3 + a) + (5 + b)]$

42. $ab + a(c + d) = ab + ac + ad$

In exercises 43-47 determine whether the given statement is true or false.

43. $5(2 + 3) = (2 + 3)5$ is an illustration of the distributive law.

44. $a(b + c) = ab + c$ is an illustration of the distributive law.

45. $6 + 1 = 3(2 + \frac{1}{3})$

46. $(\frac{1}{0})0 = 1$

47. The additive inverse of $-[-(-5)]$ is 5.

2.4 ADDITION ON THE REAL NUMBER LINE

In order to illustrate addition on the real number line we must first define *direction* on the real number line.

DIRECTION ON THE REAL NUMBER LINE

Any movement to the *right* on the real number line will be defined as movement in the *positive* direction; to the *left* as movement in the *negative* direction.

Let us now illustrate the addition of integers on the real number line. Suppose we wish to add the numbers 2 and –5. Starting at the *origin* we would move 2 units in the positive direction. From *this point* we would now move 5 units in the negative direction. This movement would *terminate* 3 units to the left of the origin. Thus the sum of 2 and –5 would be –3. That is,

$$2 + (-5) = -3 \qquad \text{(See Figure 2.4.)}$$

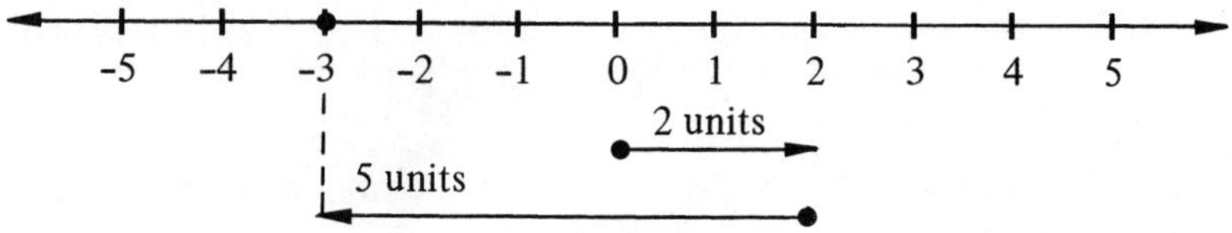

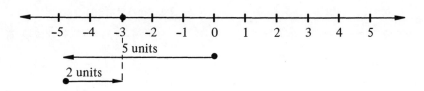

FIGURE 2.4

We could have obtained the same result by first moving 5 units to the left of the origin and then 2 units to the right (see Figure 2.5). This is an illustration of the commutative law of addition.

FIGURE 2.5

Example 1

Add on the real number line: $-3 + (-4)$

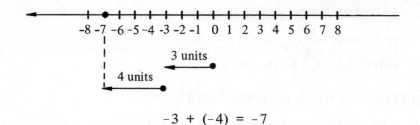

$$-3 + (-4) = -7$$

Example 2

Add on the real number line: $-4 + 6$.

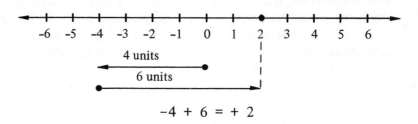

$$-4 + 6 = +2$$

Exercise Set 2.4

In exercises 1-15 use the real number line to find the given sum.

1. $3 + 5$

2. $6 + (-6)$

3. $(-3) + 5$

4. $7 + (-4)$

5. $6 + (-8)$

6. $-13 + 8$

7. $-2 + (-2)$

8. $(-4) + (-1)$

9. $(-5) + 9 + (-9)$

10. $2 + 7 + (-10)$

11. $(-2) + 8 + (-3)$

12. $(-3) + (-1) + (-4)$

13. $(-5) + (8) + (-7) + 3$

14. $(-4) + (-4) + 8 + (-3)$

15. $4 + (-2) + 7 + 0 + (-7)$

2.5 RULES FOR ADDITION AND SUBTRACTION
OF REAL NUMBERS

In order to state a set of rules for the addition of real numbers we will have to consider what is meant by the *magnitude* or *absolute value* of a real number.

ABSOLUTE VALUE OF A REAL NUMBER

The *magnitude* or *absolute value* of a real number a, written $|a|$, is defined as follows:

$$|a| = a \quad \text{if} \quad a \geqslant 0$$

$$|a| = -a \quad \text{if} \quad a < 0$$

Examples

1. $|5| = 5$

2. $|-3| = -(-3) = 3$

3. $|0| = 0$

4. $|-(-6)| = 6$, since $-(-6) = +6$

5. $|-0.23| = -(-0.23) = 0.23$

6. $|-\frac{1}{3}| = -(-\frac{1}{3}) = \frac{1}{3}$

Note

In essence the absolute value of a number is the distance of its graph from the origin. We've seen this illustrated on the real number line, where to reach the number +6 from the origin we *move 6 units* in the positive direction, whereas to reach the number −6 from the origin we again *move 6 units*, but this time in the negative direction. Thus the graphs of +6 and −6 are the same distance from the origin, and therefore 6 and −6 have the same absolute value, namely 6.

With our definition of absolute value, let us now state a set of *rules for the addition of real numbers*.

RULE I$_a$ (READ "ONE SUB a," THE a REFERRING TO ADDITION)

$a + 0 = a$, for any real number a. (*Recall*: 0 is the additive identity element of the set R.)

RULE II$_a$ (LIKE SIGNS)

If a and b are any two *nonzero* real numbers having the *same sign*, then the sum of a and b is obtained by adding their absolute values and placing their *common sign* in front of this sum.

RULE III$_a$

$a + (-a) = 0$, for any real number a. (*Recall*: $-a$ is the additive inverse of a.)

RULE IV$_a$ (UNLIKE SIGNS)

If a and b are any two nonzero real numbers, with unequal absolute values and *unlike signs*, then the sum of a and b is obtained by subtracting the smaller of the *absolute* values from the larger, and using the sign of the number with the larger of the two absolute values.

Example 7

$$-5 + 0 = -5 \qquad \text{(Additive identity)}$$

Example 8

Add: $-4 + (-6)$.

Using Rule II$_a$:

Step (1) $|-4| = 4$ and $|-6| = 6$
     (2) $4 + 6 = 10$
     (3) The common sign is $-$.

Thus $-4 + (-6) = -10$.

Example 9

$$-\tfrac{1}{5} + \tfrac{1}{5} = 0 \qquad \text{(Additive inverse)}$$

Example 10

Add: $-11 + 8$.

Using Rule IV$_a$:

Step (1) $|-11| = 11$ and $|8| = 8$
     (2) $11 - 8 = 3$
     (3) The sign of the number with the larger absolute value is $-$.

Thus $-11 + 8 = -3$.

Example 11

Add: $7 + (-4)$.

$$7 + (-4) = 3 \qquad \text{(Adding unlike signs)}$$

Example 12

Add: $8 + (-3) + (-7)$.

$$8 + (-3) + (-7) = [8 + (-3)] + (-7) \qquad \text{(Associative law)}$$
$$= 5 + (-7) \qquad \text{(Adding unlike signs)}$$
$$= -2 \qquad \text{(Adding unlike signs)}$$

or

$$8 + (-3) + (-7) = 8 + [(-3) + (-7)] \qquad \text{(Associative law)}$$
$$= 8 + (-10) \qquad \text{(Adding like signs)}$$
$$= -2 \qquad \text{(Adding unlike signs)}$$

Example 13

Add: $-11 + 17 + (-8) + 21$.

$$-11 + 17 + (-8) + 21 = -11 + (-8) + 17 + 21 \qquad \text{(Commutative law)}$$
$$= [-11 + (-8)] + 17 + 21 \qquad \text{(Associative law)}$$
$$= -19 + 38 \qquad \text{(Adding like signs)}$$
$$= 19 \qquad \text{(Adding unlike signs)}$$

Why don't you try this example by grouping the numbers differently?

SUBTRACTION OF TWO REAL NUMBERS

When it is said "subtract 3 from 5," this may be written $5 - 3 = 2$. We will define the difference $a - b$ of any two real numbers a and b in the following way:

$$a - b = a + (-b)$$

Thus in the example above, by $5 - 3$ we mean $5 + (-3)$, which by Rule IV$_a$ is equal to 2. Let us now consider some further examples of subtraction.

Example 14

Subtract 8 from 13.

This may be written $13 - 8 = 13 + (-8) \qquad$ (Definition of subtraction)
$$= 5 \qquad \text{(Adding unlike signs)}$$

Example 15

Subtract 9 from 4.

This may be written 4 – 9 = 4 + (–9)   (Definition of
                                              subtraction)
                      = – 5   (Adding unlike signs)

Example 16

Take the difference: –6 – 11.

–6 – 11 = –6 + (–11)   (Definition of subtraction)

      = –17   (Adding like signs)

Example 17

Take the difference: 7 – (–3).

7 – (–3) = 7 + [–(–3)]   (Definition of
                              subtraction)
        = 7 + 3   (Recall –(–3) = +3)
        = 10   (Adding like signs)

Example 18

Perform the indicated operations: 5 – 8 – 3.

5 – 8 – 3 = 5 + (–8) + (–3)   (Definition of
                                      subtraction)
         = 5 + [(–8) + (–3)]   (Associative law)
         = 5 + (–11)   (Adding like signs)
         = –6   (Adding unlike signs)

Example 19

Perform the indicated operations: 11 – 5 + 3 – 9.

11 – 5 + 3 – 9 = 11 + (–5) + 3 + (–9)   (Why?)
             = [11 + (–5)] + [3 + (–9)]   (Why?)
             = 6 + (–6)   (Why?)
             = 0   (Why?)

Note I

We need not define a separate set of rules for subtraction, for *subtraction is defined in terms of addition.*

Note II

To this point we have confined our examples to the addition and subtraction of integers. However, you should note that the rules for addition *hold for all real numbers*. We will consider the process for adding and subtracting fractions of the form $\frac{a}{b}$, where a and b are integers, $b \neq 0$ (rational numbers), after we have considered multiplication.

Exercise Set 2.5

In exercises 1-6 find the absolute value of the given number.

1. 8   **3.** 0   **5.** -0.37

2. $\frac{3}{2}$ **4.** -5 **6.** $-(-0.25)$

In exercises 7-11 state a reason for each given step.

Example: $7 + (-3) + 4$

(a) $7 + (-3) + 4 = [7 + (-3)] + 4$ (Associative law)
(b) $= 4 + 4$ (Adding unlike signs)
(c) $= 8$ (Adding like signs)

7. (a) $7 + (-3) + 4 = 7 + 4 + (-3)$ (?   )
   (b) $= [7 + 4] + (-3)$ (?   )
   (c) $= 11 + (-3)$ (?   )
   (d) $= 8$ (?   )

8. (a) $8 - 5 - 3 = 8 + (-5) + (-3)$ (?   )
   (b) $= 8 + [(-5) + (-3)]$ (?   )
   (c) $= 8 + (-8)$ (?   )
   (d) $= 0$ (?   )

9. (a) $12 + (-5) + 11 + (-15) = 12 + 11 + (-5) + (-15)$
   (b) $= [12 + 11] + [(-5) + (-15)]$ (?   )
   (c) $= 23 + (-20)$ (?   )
   (d) $= 3$ (?   )

10. (a) $-13 + 22 - 5 - 9 = (-13) + 22 + (-5) + (-9)$ (?   )
    (b) $= 22 + (-13) + (-5) + (-9)$ (?   )
    (c) $= 22 + [(-13) + (-5) + (-9)]$ (?   )
    (d) $= 22 + [-27]$ (?   )
    (e) $= -5$ (?   )

11. (a) $7 - |-11| + 8 - 3 + |-8| = 7 - 11 + 8 - 3 + 8$ (?)

   (b) $= [7 - 11] + [8 - 3 + 8]$ (?)

   (c) $= [7 + (-11)] + [8 + (-3) + 8]$

                                                                  (?)

   (d) $= -4 + [8 + (-3) + 8]$ (?)

   (e) $= [(-4) + 8] + [(-3) + 8]$

                                                                  (?)

   (f) $= 4 + 5$ (?)

   (g) $= 9$ (?)

In exercises 12-42 perform the indicated operations.

12. $16 + 3$

13. $-6 + 12$

14. $4 + (-7)$

15. $-7 + (-8)$

16. $-9 - 3$

17. $7.3 + (-7.3)$

–18. $5 - (-3)$

19. $-5 - (-3)$

20. $|5| - |-3|$

21. $-3 + |-5|$

22. $18 + |-7|$

23. $|5| + |0|$

24. $17 + 0 + 23$

25. $16 - 9 + 5$

26. $12 + (-5) + (-8)$

27. $-18 + 27 - 9$

28. $-7 - 12 - 3$

29. $3 + 4 - (-5)$

30. $8 - (-3) - 6$

31. $-5 + |-8| + |3|$

32. $|-13| - |-11| - |9|$

33. $-6 - (-6) - [-(-6)]$

34. $23 + 2 - 29 + 13$

35. $17 - 3 + 11 - 28$

36. $37 - 18 - (-8) - (-4)$

37. $-7.91 - 5 - (-7) + 7.91$

38. $17 - |6| - |-6| + |-17|$

39. $|3 - 11 - (-14)|$

40. $|2 - 6| + |-3 - (-4)| - 5$

41. $81 + [-(-29)] - [-(-29)] - 100$

42. $4 - 7 + (-7) - 22 + 14 - (-31)$

2.6 MULTIPLICATION AND DIVISION OF REAL NUMBERS

From our study of arithmetic we all know how to multiply two positive integers. However, what would happen if one or both of these integers are negative? We will now establish a set of rules that will enable us to multiply *any two real numbers*.

RULE I$_m$ (READ "ONE SUB m," THE m REFERRING
TO MULTIPLICATION)

If a or b or both are 0, then $ab = 0$.

Note

It is also true that if $ab = 0$, then either a or b or both must be 0.

Now let us consider the case when one of the numbers is negative. For example, suppose we wish to multiply $(-4)3$.
We will show that the product $(-4)3$ is the additive inverse of 12, that is, $(-4)3 + 12 = 0$. Upon showing this and knowing that the additive inverse of 12 is -12, and that the *additive inverse is unique*, we will have established that

$$(-4)3 = -12$$

Our line of reasoning is as follows:

(1) Consider the sum $(-4)3 + 12$.
(2) This sum can be written $(-4)3 + (4)3$, since $12 = (4)(3)$.
(3) But by the distributive law

$$(-4)3 + (4)3 = (-4 + 4)3$$

(4) But $-4 + 4 = 0$.   (Additive inverse)
(5) Thus $(-4)3 + 12 = (-4 + 4)3$
$$= (0)3$$
$$= 0$$

We have now shown what we set out to prove, that $(-4)3$ is the additive inverse of 12, and thus $(-4)3 = -12$. Also by the commutative law, $3(-4) = (-4)3 = -12$.

RULE II$_m$

If *one* of the numbers a and b is positive and the other is negative, the *product is netative*. We can write this result as follows:

$$ab = -(|a| \cdot |b|)$$

Now suppose both a and b are negative. For example, consider the product $(-3)(-6)$.
We will show that this product is the additive inverse of -18 and thus that $(-3)(-6) = 18$, the unique additive inverse of -18.

(1) Suppose we add: $(-3)(-6) + (-3)6$.

(2) By the distributive law we would obtain

$$(-3)(-6) + (-3)6 = (-3)(-6 + 6)$$

$$= (-3)(0) \qquad \text{(Why?)}$$

$$= 0$$

(3) Thus $(-3)(-6)$ is the additive inverse of the product $(-3)(6)$, which we know by Rule I_m to be -18.

(4) Therefore $(-3)(-6) = +18$, since the additive inverse is unique.

RULE III_m

If *both numbers a* and *b are negative*, then the *product is positive*. We can write this result as

$$ab = |a| \cdot |b|$$

Example 1

Multiply: $(-7)(3)$.

$$(-7)(3) = -(|-7| \cdot |3|) \qquad \text{(Rule } II_m \text{)}$$

$$= -(7 \cdot 3) \qquad \text{(Definition of absolute value)}$$

$$= -21$$

Example 2

Multiply: $(-6)(-9)$.

$$(-6)(-9) = |-6| \cdot |-9| \qquad \text{(Rule } III_m \text{)}$$

$$= 6 \cdot 9 \qquad \text{(Definition of absolute value)}$$

$$= 54$$

Example 3

Multiply: $(-3)(5)(-4)$.

$$(-3)(5)(-4) = [(-3)5](-4) \qquad \text{(Associative law)}$$

$$= (-15)(-4) \qquad \text{(Rule } II_m \text{)}$$

$$= +60 \qquad \text{(Rule } III_m \text{)}$$

Example 4

Multiply: $(-7)(2)(-3)(-4)$.

$$
\begin{aligned}
(-7)(2)(-3)(-4) &= [(-7)2]\,[(-3)(-4)] & \text{(Associative law)} \\
&= (-14)[(-3)(-4)] & \text{(Rule II}_m) \\
&= (-14)(12) & \text{(Rule III}_m) \\
&= -168 & \text{(Rule II}_m)
\end{aligned}
$$

We will now prove some more general results regarding the multiplication of real numbers.

RESULT A_m

$(-1)a = -a$, for any real number a.

To prove this we need only show that $(-1)a$ is the additive inverse of a, for we know that the unique additive inverse of a is $-a$. Thus we will have established that $(-1)a = -a$.

(1) $(-1)a + a = (-1)a + (1)a$, since $(1)a = a$.
(2) But by the distributive law

$$
\begin{aligned}
(-1)a + (1)a &= [(-1) + 1]a \\
&= (0)a & \text{(Why?)} \\
&= 0
\end{aligned}
$$

(3) Thus $(-1)a$ is the additive inverse of a.
(4) Therefore $(-1)a = -a$.

RESULT B_m

$(-a)b = -ab$, for any real numbers a and b.

This can be shown by using Result A_m in the following manner:

$$
\begin{aligned}
(1)(-a)b &= [(-1)a]\,b & \text{(Result } A_m) \\
&= (-1)(ab) & \text{(Associative law)} \\
&= -(ab) & \text{(Result } A_m)
\end{aligned}
$$

RESULT C_m

$(-a)(-b) = ab$, for any real numbers a and b.

This can also be shown by using Result A_m and Rule III_m in the following manner:

$(1)(-a)(-b)$ $=$ $[(-1)a][(-1)b]$ (Result A_m)

$= (-1)(-1)ab$ (Regrouping using associative and commutative laws)

$= 1(ab)$ (Rule III_m)

$= ab$ (Why?)

DISTRIBUTIVE LAW FOR MULTIPLICATION OVER SUBTRACTION

In light of the results proven thus far we can write the distributive law for multiplication over subtraction. That is, for any real numbers $a, b, c,$ and $d,$

$$a(b - c - d) = ab - ac - ad$$

Recall $b - c - d = b + (-c) + (-d)$ and thus

$a(b - c - d) = a[b + (-c) + (-d)]$

$= ab + a(-c) + a(-d)$ (Why?)

$= ab - ac - ad$ (Result B_m)

Example 5

$5(8 - 2) = 5(8) - 5(2)$

$= 40 - 10$

$= 30$

Example 6

Write the following product as a sum: $7(5 - 2 - 9).$

$7(5 - 2 - 9) = 7(5) - 7(2) - 7(9)$

$= 35 - 14 - 63$

or

$7(5 - 2 - 9) = 35 + (-14) + (-63)$

Example 7

Using the distributive law write the sum $-21 + 7 - 35$ as a product.

$$-21 + 7 - 35 = (-3)7 + (1)7 + (-5)7$$
$$= [-3 + 1 + (-5)]7$$

Exercise Set 2.6A

In exercises 1-10 compute the given product.

1. $5(5)$

2. $3(-2)$

3. $(-4)(0)$

4. $(-13)(-5)$

5. $(-2)(-4)(3)$

6. $(-3)(-3)(-5)$

7. $(|2|)(|-6|)$

8. $(-3)(-3)(-3)(-3)$

9. $(|-6|)(-2)(|+5|)(-4)$

10. $-[3(-5)(-1)(-2)]$

In exercises 11-22 perform the indicated operations.

11. $5(-3) + (-4)(-4)$

12. $(|-3|)(4) + (-3)(4)$

13. $12 + (-4)(-2)$

14. $3(10 - 5)$

15. $-3[10 - (-5)]$

16. $6(|-3| + |0| + |6|)$

17. $(-6)(-2) - (3)(8) - (5)(-3)$

18. $-3(11 - 6 - 8)$

19. $9(-1) - 3(-7) - (-4)(2)$

20. $(-2)(|4 - 6|) - (|5 - (-2)|)(-3)$

21. $8 - 3[6 - (-4)] - 8$

22. $-6 - (3 + 4) - 5(-3 - 4)$

Let us now define division of real numbers.

DIVISION OF REAL NUMBERS

If a and b are any real numbers, $b \neq 0$, then

$$a \div b \text{ (also written } \tfrac{a}{b}) = (\tfrac{1}{b})a$$

(where $a \div b$ is read, "*a* divided by *b*").

Note

$\frac{a}{b}$ is called the *quotient* of a by b. a is called the *numerator* and b, the *denominator*.

Recall that $\frac{1}{b}$ is the multiplicative inverse of b (property VII, Section 2.3). Thus *dividing a* by *b* is the same as *multiplying a by the inverse of b*.

DIVISION BY 0

Now since we know that *zero has no multiplicative inverse* we can see that the expression $\frac{a}{0}$ is meaningless for any real number a. Thus *division by 0 is undefined*.

Example 8

Express the quotient $\frac{7}{15}$ as a product.

$$\frac{7}{15} = (\frac{1}{15})7$$

Example 9

Express the product $(\frac{1}{5})7$ as a quotient.

$$(\frac{1}{5})7 = \frac{7}{5}$$

Example 10

Express the product $(5)(7)$ as a quotient.

$$(5)(7) = \frac{1}{\frac{1}{5}}(7) \qquad (\text{Recall } \frac{1}{\frac{1}{5}} = 5.)$$

$$= \frac{7}{\frac{1}{5}}$$

Note

Following directly from the definition of division, we have that:

$$\frac{c}{c} = 1 \text{ for any real number } c, c \neq 0$$

for

$$\frac{c}{c} = \frac{1}{c}c \qquad (\text{Definition of division})$$

$$= 1 \qquad (\frac{1}{c} \text{ is the multiplicative inverse of } c)$$

This says simply that any real number, *except 0*, divided by itself is 1.

Let us now develop the process for multiplying and dividing fractions. The first result we will need is the following:

RESULT D_m

If a and b are any real numbers, $a \neq 0, b \neq 0$, then

$$\left(\tfrac{1}{a}\right)\left(\tfrac{1}{b}\right) = \tfrac{1}{ab}$$

If we can show that $(\tfrac{1}{a})(\tfrac{1}{b})$ is the multiplicative inverse of ab, we will have established this result, for we know that the *unique* multiplicative inverse of ab is $\tfrac{1}{ab}$.

(1) Since $\tfrac{1}{a}$ and $\tfrac{1}{b}$ are the multiplicative inverses of a and b, respectively, we have that $(\tfrac{1}{a})a = 1$ and $(\tfrac{1}{b})b = 1$.

(2) Thus $[(\tfrac{1}{a})a]\ [(\tfrac{1}{b})b] = 1 \cdot 1 = 1$.

(3) Regrouping the left side of step (2) using the commutative and associative laws, we obtain

$$ab\left(\tfrac{1}{a}\right)\left(\tfrac{1}{b}\right) = 1$$

(4) Thus $(\tfrac{1}{a})(\tfrac{1}{b})$ must be the multiplicative inverse of ab.

(5) Therefore by the uniqueness of the multiplicative inverse

$$\left(\tfrac{1}{a}\right)\left(\tfrac{1}{b}\right) = \tfrac{1}{ab}$$

RESULT E_m

If a, b, c, d are any real numbers with $b \neq 0, d \neq 0$, then

$$\tfrac{a}{b} \cdot \tfrac{c}{d} = \tfrac{ac}{bd}$$

This result follows directly from Result D_m and the definition of division, for

$$\tfrac{a}{b} \cdot \tfrac{c}{d} = \left(\tfrac{1}{b} \cdot a\right)\left(\tfrac{1}{d} \cdot c\right) \qquad \text{(Definition of division)}$$

$$= \left(\tfrac{1}{b} \cdot \tfrac{1}{d}\right)ac \qquad \text{(Regrouping using associative and commutative laws)}$$

$$= \left(\tfrac{1}{bd}\right)ac \qquad \text{(Result } D_m \text{)}$$

$$= \tfrac{ac}{bd} \qquad \text{(Definition of division)}$$

The above result E_m will not only enable us to multiply fractions but to simplify the result as well. This will be shown in the following examples.

Example 11

Multiply $\frac{3}{8} \cdot \frac{4}{9}$ and simplify the result.

$\frac{3}{8} \cdot \frac{4}{9} = \frac{3 \cdot 4}{8 \cdot 9} = \frac{12}{72}$ (Multiplication of fractions using Result E_m)

Now to simplify the result we can write:

$\frac{12}{72} = \frac{1 \cdot 12}{6 \cdot 12} = \frac{1}{6} \cdot \frac{12}{12}$ (Multiplication of fractions)

$\qquad\qquad = \frac{1}{6} \cdot 1$ (Any nonzero number divided by itself is 1.)

$\qquad\qquad = \frac{1}{6}$ (1 is the multiplicative identity.)

Example 12

Simplify the fraction $\frac{14}{63}$.

$\frac{14}{63} = \frac{2 \cdot 7}{9 \cdot 7} = \frac{2}{9} \cdot \frac{7}{7}$ (Multiplication of fractions)

$\qquad\quad = \frac{2}{9} \cdot 1$ (Why?)

$\qquad\quad = \frac{2}{9}$ (Why?)

Example 13

Multiply $(-\frac{5}{9})(\frac{3}{10})$ and simplify the result.

$(-\frac{5}{9})(\frac{3}{10}) = -(\frac{5}{9})(\frac{3}{10})$ (Result B_m)

$\qquad\qquad = -(\frac{15}{90})$ (Why?)

$\qquad\qquad = -(\frac{1}{6} \cdot \frac{15}{15})$ (Why?)

$\qquad\qquad = -\frac{1}{6}$

Example 14

Multiply and simplify: $(-\frac{15}{54})(-\frac{12}{40})$.

If these fractions can be simplified first, it would make the multiplication easier:

$(-\frac{15}{54})(-\frac{12}{40}) = \frac{15}{54} \cdot \frac{12}{40}$ (Result C_m)

Now

$$\frac{15}{54} = \frac{5 \cdot 3}{18 \cdot 3} = \frac{5}{18} \cdot \frac{3}{3} = \frac{5}{18}$$

and

$$\frac{12}{40} = \frac{3 \cdot 4}{10 \cdot 4} = \frac{3}{10} \cdot \frac{4}{4} = \frac{3}{10}$$

Therefore we can now multiply:

$$\frac{5}{18} \cdot \frac{3}{10} = \frac{15}{180}$$

$$= \frac{1 \cdot 15}{12 \cdot 15} \qquad \text{(Further simplification)}$$

$$= \frac{1}{12}$$

Although the following result directly follows from the previous result E_m, it will be very useful in the form given in our further work on fractions.

RESULTS F_m

If a, b, and c are any real numbers, $b \neq 0$, $c \neq 0$, then

$$\frac{a}{b} = \frac{ac}{bc}$$

Exercise Set 2.6B

In exercises 1-6 express each given product as a quotient and each given quotient as a product.

1. $15 \div 4$

2. $(\frac{1}{8})5$

3. $\frac{18}{13}$

4. $(-6)(\frac{2}{5})$

5. $\frac{0}{+7}$

6. $(-\frac{1}{3})(-\frac{7}{2})$

In exercises 7-16 compute the given product and simplify the result.

7. $(\frac{2}{3})(\frac{6}{11})$

8. $(\frac{3}{8})(-\frac{4}{3})$

9. $(-\frac{5}{12})(-\frac{4}{15})$

10. $(|-\frac{1}{2}|)(|\frac{3}{4}|)$

11. $(\frac{2}{3})(-\frac{1}{4})(0)(-\frac{3}{5})$

12. $(-2)(3)(-\frac{1}{6})$

13. $(2\frac{1}{3})(-\frac{3}{5})$

14. $(-8)(-4\frac{2}{3})(-5\frac{1}{4})$

15. $-[(-5)(-\frac{1}{5})(6)(-\frac{1}{6})]$

16. $(|(-\frac{3}{4})(2)|)[-3 - (-5)]$

Since division is defined in terms of multiplication, all the rules and results for division will follow directly from the results already established for multiplication.

RESULT A_d

If a and b are any real numbers, $b \neq 0$, then

$$\frac{-a}{b} = \frac{a}{-b} = -\frac{a}{b}$$

This result can be shown as follows:

$$\frac{-a}{b} = \frac{-1 \cdot a}{1 \cdot b} \qquad \text{(Why?)} \qquad\qquad \frac{-a}{b} = \frac{(-a)(-1)}{(b)(-1)} \qquad \text{(Why?)}$$

$$= \frac{-1}{1} \cdot \frac{a}{b} \qquad \text{(Why?)} \qquad\qquad = \frac{a}{-b} \qquad \text{(Why?)}$$

$$= -1 \cdot \frac{a}{b} \qquad \text{(Why?)}$$

$$= -\frac{a}{b} \qquad \text{(Why?)}$$

Then since $\frac{-a}{b} = -\frac{a}{b}$ and $\frac{-a}{b} = \frac{a}{-b}$, we must also have $-\frac{a}{b} = \frac{a}{-b}$.

Example 15

$$\frac{-5}{4} = \frac{5}{-4} = -\frac{5}{4}$$

RESULT B_d

If a and b are any real numbers, $b \neq 0$, then

$$\frac{-a}{-b} = \frac{a}{b}$$

Try to show that this is true.

Example 16

Simplify the fraction $\frac{-18}{-24}$.

$$\frac{-18}{-24} = \frac{18}{24} \qquad\qquad \text{(Result } B_d \text{)}$$

$$= \frac{3 \cdot 6}{4 \cdot 6} \qquad\qquad \text{(Multiplication of fractions)}$$

$$= \frac{3}{4} \qquad\qquad \text{(Why?)}$$

RESULT C_d
DIVISION OF FRACTIONS

If a, b, c, d are any real numbers, $b \neq 0, c \neq 0, d \neq 0$, then

$$\frac{\frac{a}{b}}{\frac{c}{d}} = \frac{a}{b} \cdot \frac{d}{c}$$

Note

In other words, to divide one fraction by another you "invert the fraction in the denominator" and multiply the resulting inverted fraction by the numerator.

Let us now prove this result.

(1) $\dfrac{\frac{a}{b}}{\frac{c}{d}} = \dfrac{1}{\frac{c}{d}} \cdot \left(\dfrac{a}{b}\right)$ $\qquad$ (Definition of division)

(2) But $\dfrac{1}{\frac{c}{d}} = \dfrac{1}{\left(\frac{1}{d}\right)c}$ $\qquad$ (Definition of division)

$\qquad\qquad = \dfrac{1}{\left(\frac{1}{d}\right)} \cdot \dfrac{1}{c}$ $\qquad$ (Multiplication of fractions, using Result D_m)

$\qquad\qquad = d \cdot \dfrac{1}{c}$ $\qquad$ (d is the multiplicative inverse of $\frac{1}{d}$.)

$\qquad\qquad = \dfrac{d}{c}$ $\qquad$ (Definition of division)

(3) Therefore $\dfrac{\frac{a}{b}}{\frac{c}{d}} = \dfrac{d}{c} \cdot \dfrac{a}{b}$

$\qquad\qquad\qquad = \dfrac{a}{b} \cdot \dfrac{d}{c}$ $\qquad$ (Why?)

Example 17

Divide $\frac{3}{8}$ by $\frac{1}{4}$ and simplify the result.

$$\frac{\frac{3}{8}}{\frac{1}{4}} = \frac{3}{8} \cdot \frac{4}{1} \qquad \text{(Division of fractions)}$$

$$= \frac{12}{8} \qquad \text{(Multiplication of fractions)}$$

$$= \frac{3 \cdot 4}{2 \cdot 4} = \frac{3}{2} \cdot \frac{4}{4} \qquad \text{(Why?)}$$

$$= \frac{3}{2}$$

Example 18

Perform the indicated operation and simplify the result.

$$\frac{-\frac{9}{16}}{3}$$

$$\frac{-\frac{9}{16}}{3} = -\frac{9}{16} \cdot \frac{1}{3}$$ (Note that $3 = \frac{3}{1}$.)

$$= -\frac{9}{16} \cdot \frac{1}{3} = -\frac{9}{16 \cdot 3}$$

$$= -\frac{3}{16} \cdot \frac{3}{3}$$

$$= -\frac{3}{16}$$

Example 19

Perform the indicated operation and simplify the result.

$$-14 \div -\frac{7}{4}$$

$$\frac{-14}{-\frac{7}{4}} = \frac{14}{\frac{7}{4}}$$

$$= \frac{14}{1} \cdot \frac{4}{7}$$

$$= \frac{56}{7}$$

$$= 8$$

There remains only one result which will complete this section. This would be the distributive law for division.

DISTRIBUTIVE LAW FOR DIVISION

If a, b, c, d are any real numbers, $d \neq 0$, then

$$\frac{a + b + c}{d} = \frac{a}{d} + \frac{b}{d} + \frac{c}{d}$$

This follows directly from the definition of division, for

$$\frac{a + b + c}{d} = \frac{1}{d}(a + b + c) \qquad \text{(Definition of division)}$$

$$= (\frac{1}{d} \cdot a) + (\frac{1}{d} \cdot b) + (\frac{1}{d} \cdot c) \quad \text{(Distributive law for multiplication)}$$

$$= \frac{a}{d} + \frac{b}{d} + \frac{c}{d} \qquad \text{(Definition of division)}$$

Example 20

Using the distributive law of division write the quotient $\frac{12 - 6 - 15}{-3}$ as a sum.

$$\frac{12 - 6 - 15}{-3} = \frac{12}{-3} + (\frac{-6}{-3}) + (\frac{-15}{-3})$$

$$= -4 + 2 + 5$$

Exercise Set 2.6C

In exercises 1-16 compute the indicated quotient and simplify the result.

1. $6 \div \frac{3}{4}$

2. $2 \div -\frac{1}{2}$

3. $\frac{2}{3} \div 3$

4. $-\frac{3}{4} \div -3$

5. $|\frac{-6}{2}|$

6. $|\frac{3}{8} \div -\frac{1}{4}|$

7. $\frac{\frac{3}{4}}{\frac{3}{2}}$

8. $\frac{\frac{2}{7}}{\frac{5}{7}}$

9. $\frac{\frac{4}{5}}{-\frac{16}{25}}$

10. $\frac{-\frac{8}{21}}{-\frac{4}{35}}$

11. $\frac{-\frac{5}{6}}{\frac{2}{5}}$

12. $\frac{3\frac{1}{3}}{1\frac{1}{4}}$

13. $\frac{0}{-\frac{4}{3}}$

14. $\frac{-5}{\frac{3}{5}}$

15. $\frac{-\frac{1}{6}}{-6}$

16. $\frac{\frac{3}{5}}{\frac{5}{3}}$

Exercise Set 2.6

In exercises 1-30 perform the operations indicated and simplify the result wherever possible.

1. $5(-3)2$

2. $5(2)(\frac{1}{5})$

3. $[13(-2)] \div -4$

4. $(-3-4-5) \div [(-12)(-2)]$

5. $-153 \div 0.3$

6. $-0.3 \div -0.4$

7. $\dfrac{(\frac{12}{7})(\frac{5}{6})}{(\frac{10}{21})}$

8. $\dfrac{(\frac{2}{5})(\frac{-20}{3})}{(\frac{-1}{9})}$

9. $\dfrac{-(24 + 3)}{6 - (-3)}$

10. $\dfrac{-18 \div 9}{-3 - (-12)}$

11. $\dfrac{3(0)(-2)}{(\frac{3}{5})(\frac{-19}{23})}$

12. $(\frac{-4}{3})(\frac{1}{6})(-\frac{15}{8})$

13. $8(2 + 5 - 4)$

14. $-6[-3-6-(-8)]$

15. $15(\frac{1}{3} + \frac{4}{5} + \frac{13}{15})$

   Hint: Use distributive law.

16. $(-2)(\frac{11}{3})(3)(\frac{-1}{2})$

17. $\dfrac{(-2)(12) - (-4)(-5)}{(-1)(4) + (2)(5)}$

18. $\dfrac{(6\frac{2}{3})(\frac{-7}{8})(\frac{2}{15})}{(\frac{-21}{4})(\frac{-4}{7})}$

19. $-\frac{3}{5}[25 + 0 - (-15)]$

20. $12(-\frac{1}{4} + \frac{1}{2} - \frac{5}{6} + \frac{17}{12})$

21. $\dfrac{(-7\frac{1}{2})(\frac{1}{9})}{|-3\frac{1}{2}|}$

22. $\dfrac{8 - |-5| - (-5)}{|(\frac{1}{4})(\frac{-3}{2})|}$

23. $\dfrac{3 + 6 + 9}{3}$

24. $\dfrac{4 + 8 + (-14)}{4 + 8}$

25. $\dfrac{(3 - 7)(8 - 5)}{(3 - 8)(7 - 5)}$

26. $\dfrac{2 - [-5 + (5 - 2) + 4] + 7}{-7}$

27. $\dfrac{2 - \frac{1}{4}(8 - 12) - \frac{2}{3}(12 + \frac{15}{2})}{-\frac{1}{10}}$

28. $3 \div \dfrac{\frac{-1}{3}}{3}$

29. $\dfrac{4(\frac{1}{2})}{2[-6 - (-6)]}$

30. $\dfrac{(0.7)(-3)}{2(0.3 + 0.4)}$

2.7 ADDITION AND SUBTRACTION OF FRACTIONS

Now that we have developed many rules and results pertaining to fractions, we will easily be able to handle addition and subtraction of fractions.

RESULT A_a

If a, b, and c are any real numbers, $c \neq 0$, then

$$\frac{a}{c} + \frac{b}{c} = \frac{a+b}{c}$$

Note

This is just a case of the distributive law of division.

Example 1

Add: $\frac{-3}{5} + \frac{7}{5}$.

$$\frac{-3}{5} + \frac{7}{5} = \frac{-3+7}{5}$$

$$= \frac{4}{5}$$

Result A_a takes care of the case where both fractions have the same denominator. What would happen if the fractions have different denominators? This will be seen in the following result.

RESULT B_a

If a, b, c, and d are any real numbers, $b \neq 0$, $d \neq 0$, then

$$\frac{a}{b} + \frac{c}{d} = \frac{ad+bc}{bd}$$

To prove result B_a we will obtain two fractions with the same denominator and use Result A_a. Thus

$$\frac{a}{b} + \frac{c}{d} = \frac{ad}{bd} + \frac{cb}{db} \qquad \text{(Multiplication of fractions)}$$

$$= \frac{ad+bc}{bd} \qquad \text{(Result } A_a \text{ and commutative law)}$$

Example 2

Add: $\frac{4}{9} + \frac{2}{15}$ and simplify the result.

$$\frac{4}{9} + \frac{2}{15} = \frac{4(15) + 2(9)}{9 \cdot 15}$$

$$= \frac{60 + 18}{135}$$

$$= \frac{78}{135}$$

$$= \frac{26 \cdot 3}{45 \cdot 3} \qquad \text{(Simplifying)}$$

$$= \frac{26}{45}$$

Note

The addition of the fractions in example 2 may also be done by first multiplying $\frac{4}{9}$ by $\frac{5}{5}$ and $\frac{2}{15}$ by $\frac{3}{3}$, thus obtaining two fractions with the same denominator, and then using result A_a as follows:

$$\frac{4}{9} + \frac{2}{15} = (\frac{4}{9} \cdot \frac{5}{5}) + (\frac{2}{15} \cdot \frac{3}{3})$$

$$= \frac{20}{45} + \frac{6}{45}$$

$$= \frac{26}{45}$$

Example 3

Add and simplify : $\frac{3}{8} + \frac{-7}{12}$

Using Result B_a directly, we obtain:

$$\frac{3}{8} + \frac{-7}{12} = \frac{36 + (-56)}{96}$$

$$= \frac{-20}{96} = -\frac{20}{96} \qquad (\text{Recall } \frac{-a}{b} = -\frac{a}{b})$$

and simplifying

$$= -\frac{5 \cdot 4}{24 \cdot 4}$$

$$= -\frac{5}{24}$$

This can also be done by multiplying $\frac{3}{8}$ by $\frac{3}{3}$ and $\frac{-7}{12}$ by $\frac{2}{2}$ and using result A_a :

$$\frac{3}{8} + \frac{-7}{12} = (\frac{3}{8} \cdot \frac{3}{3}) + (\frac{-7}{12} \cdot \frac{2}{2})$$

$$= \frac{9}{24} + \frac{-14}{24}$$

$$= \frac{9 + (-14)}{24}$$

$$= \frac{-5}{24} = -\frac{5}{24}$$

SUBTRACTION OF FRACTIONS

Since we defined subtraction as addition, there are really *no new results* needed for subtraction of fractions. Thus, as a direct application of Result B_a for addition of fractions we have:

$$\frac{a}{b} - \frac{c}{d} = \frac{ad - bc}{bd} , \ b \neq 0, d \neq 0$$

Example 4

Perform the indicated operation and simplify the result: $\frac{2}{5} - \frac{2}{3}$.

$$\frac{2}{5} - \frac{2}{3} = \frac{2(3) - 2(5)}{5(3)}$$

$$= \frac{6 - 10}{15}$$

$$= \frac{-4}{15}$$

Notice that this result cannot be simplified any further.

Let us now review our work on fractions with a few examples. In the following examples perform the indicated operations and simplify the result.

Example 5

$$\frac{5}{3} - \frac{7}{4} + \frac{2}{5} =$$

$$\frac{5}{3} - \frac{7}{4} + \frac{2}{5} = (\frac{5}{3} - \frac{7}{4}) + \frac{2}{5} \qquad \text{(Associative law)}$$

$$= (\frac{20 - 21}{12}) + \frac{2}{5} \qquad \text{(Addition of fractions)}$$

$$= \frac{-1}{12} + \frac{2}{5}$$

$$= \frac{-5 + 24}{60} \qquad \text{(Addition of fractions)}$$

$$= \frac{19}{60}$$

Example 6

$-\frac{1}{6} \left(\frac{4}{9} - \frac{2}{3} - \frac{3}{4} \right) =$

$-\frac{1}{6}\left(\frac{4}{9} - \frac{2}{3} - \frac{3}{4} \right) = \left(-\frac{1}{6} \cdot \frac{4}{9} \right) - \frac{1}{6}\left(-\frac{2}{3} \right) - \frac{1}{6}\left(-\frac{3}{4} \right)$ (Distributive law)

$\qquad\qquad = \frac{^{-4}}{54} + \frac{2}{18} + \frac{3}{24}$ (Multiplication of fractions)

$\qquad\qquad = -\frac{2 \cdot 2}{27 \cdot 2} + \frac{1 \cdot 2}{9 \cdot 2} + \frac{1 \cdot 3}{8 \cdot 3}$

$\qquad\qquad = -\frac{2}{27} + \frac{1}{9} + \frac{1}{8}$ (Simplifying fractions)

$\qquad\qquad = \left(-\frac{2}{27} + \frac{1}{9} \right) + \frac{1}{8}$ (Associative law)

$\qquad\qquad = \left[\frac{^{-2}}{27} + \left(\frac{1}{9} \cdot \frac{3}{3} \right) \right] + \frac{1}{8}$

$\qquad\qquad = \left(\frac{^{-2}}{27} + \frac{3}{27} \right) + \frac{1}{8}$

$\qquad\qquad = \frac{1}{27} + \frac{1}{8}$ (Addition of fractions, with same denominator)

$\qquad\qquad = \frac{8 + 27}{216}$ (Addition of fractions)

$\qquad\qquad = \frac{35}{216}$

This example can also be done by first adding the three fractions inside the parentheses and multiplying the resulting fraction by $-\frac{1}{6}$ as follows:

$-\frac{1}{6}\left(\frac{4}{9} - \frac{2}{3} - \frac{3}{4} \right) = -\frac{1}{6}\left[\left(\frac{4}{9} \cdot \frac{4}{4} \right) - \left(\frac{2}{3} \cdot \frac{12}{12} \right) - \left(\frac{3}{4} \cdot \frac{9}{9} \right) \right]$

$\qquad\qquad = -\frac{1}{6}\left(\frac{16}{36} - \frac{24}{36} - \frac{27}{36} \right)$

$\qquad\qquad = -\frac{1}{6}\left[\frac{1}{36} (16 - 24 - 27) \right]$ (Distributive law or addition of fractions)

$\qquad\qquad = -\frac{1}{6}\left(\frac{^{-35}}{36} \right)$

$\qquad\qquad = \frac{35}{216}$ (Multiplication of fractions)

Exercise Set 2.7

In exercises 1-10 determine whether or not the given set is closed under the given operation.

1. The set $P = \{x \mid x \text{ is a positive integer}\}$; multiplication

2. The set $P = \{x \mid x \text{ is a positive integer}\}$; subtraction

3. $\{0, 1, -1\}$; multiplication

4. $\{0, 1, -1\}$; addition

5. $N = \{x \mid x \text{ is a negative integer}\}$; multiplication

6. $N = \{x \mid x \text{ is a negative integer}\}$; subtraction

7. $I = \{x \mid x \text{ is an integer}\}$; division

8. $Q = \{x \mid x \text{ is a rational number}\}$; addition

9. $Q = \{x \mid x \text{ is a rational number}\}$; multiplication

10. $\{0, 2, -2, 4, -4\}$; subtraction

In exercises 11-20 find the indicated sum and simplify the result.

11. $\frac{1}{6} + \frac{7}{6} + \frac{11}{6}$

12. $2 - \frac{5}{8} + \frac{7}{8}$

13. $\frac{3}{5} + \frac{1}{3}$

14. $\frac{3}{8} - 2 + \frac{1}{4}$

15. $\frac{1}{3} - \frac{1}{6} - \frac{3}{4}$

16. $5\frac{1}{2} - 3\frac{2}{3}$

17. $\frac{1}{4} - \frac{5}{8} + \frac{1}{6} - \frac{7}{12}$

18. $3 + \frac{7}{18} - \frac{7}{12} - \frac{1}{9}$

19. $3\frac{1}{4} + 5\frac{5}{8} - 2\frac{1}{5}$

20. $-\frac{1}{2} + 2\frac{1}{3} + 3$

In exercises 21-30 perform the indicated operations and simplify the result.

21. $\frac{3}{8} - \frac{1}{2}$

22. $-\frac{2}{15} - \left(-\frac{5}{12}\right)$

23. $\dfrac{\frac{2}{5} - \frac{5}{2}}{\frac{-1}{10} - 2}$

24. $\dfrac{\left|\frac{1}{2} - \frac{2}{3}\right|}{\frac{3}{2} - 3}$

25. $\dfrac{\frac{1}{3} - 4}{\frac{1}{3}}$

26. $-2\left(\frac{1}{2} - \frac{2}{3} - \frac{4}{5}\right)$

27. $\dfrac{-\frac{1}{2}}{\frac{1}{2} - \frac{1}{5}}$

28. $\dfrac{\frac{1}{8} + 0 + \frac{8}{5}}{\frac{1}{10}\left(2 - \frac{5}{2}\right)}$

29. $-\frac{1}{2}\left(\frac{1}{3} - \frac{1}{2} + 3\right)$

30. $\dfrac{\frac{2}{5} \div \left(\frac{1}{2} + \frac{3}{10}\right)}{2 - \frac{2}{5}}$

REVIEW TEST FOR CHAPTER II

Note: This test should be completed in 75 minutes.

For questions 1-10 complete the given statement.

1. The additive identity element of the set R is ___ O ___ .

2. If you add two negative numbers, the sign of the sum will always be ___ neg ___ .

3. The additive inverse of $-(-8-3)$ is ___ -11 ___ .

4. The multiplicative identity element of R is ___ 1 ___ .

5. The multiplicative inverse of $\frac{3}{8}$ is ___ $\frac{8}{3}$ ___ .

6. The sign of the product of two negative numbers will always be ___ $+$ ___ .

7. The property of the real numbers that justifies the statement $-3 + 7(-5+4)$ $= -3 + 7(-5) + 7(4)$ is ___ Distributive ___ .

8. The property of the real numbers that justifies the statement, "$(-3)(8)$ is a real number," is ___ .

9. $\dfrac{-4}{\frac{1}{4}}$ = ___

10. $\dfrac{\frac{-2}{3}}{-3}$ = ___

Answer questions 11-14 true or false.

11. $\dfrac{8 + 7 + 9}{8 + 7} = 9$

12. $\frac{3}{8} > \frac{2}{5}$

13. If a and b are any rational numbers, then $a - b$ is always a rational number.

14. If a and b are any rational numbers, then $\frac{a}{b}$ is always a rational number.

15. Find a rational number between $\frac{1}{6}$ and $\frac{1}{7}$.

16. Arrange the following numbers in order from smallest to largest: $\frac{1}{3}, \frac{5}{6}, \frac{1}{5}, \frac{1}{6}, \frac{1}{2}$.

17. Draw the graph of the set $A = \{x \mid x \in R, x > -4\}$.

18. Let $A = \{x \mid x \in R, x > 3\}$ and
$B = \{x \mid x \in R, -2 \leqslant x \leqslant 5\}$.
Find (a) $A \cup B$ and (b) $A \cap B$.

19. Let $A = \{x \mid x \in I, x < -3 \text{ or } x > 0\}$ and
    $B = \{x \mid x \in I, -5 \leqslant x < 4\}$.
    Find $A \cap B$.

20. Let $A = \{x \mid x \in R, x < -4\}$ and
    $B = \{x \mid x \in R, x \geqslant -1\}$.
    Find $A \cap B$.

21. $3 - [3 - (-4)] - \frac{1}{2}(6 - 8) =$

22. $\frac{1}{3} - \frac{3}{8} + \frac{8}{3} =$

23. $(\frac{3}{5})(\frac{1}{2})(\frac{8}{-3}) =$

24. $\dfrac{\frac{2}{5} \div \frac{3}{5}}{\frac{2}{3} - \frac{5}{6}} =$

25. $\dfrac{\frac{1}{7} - \frac{2}{5} - \frac{9}{14}}{\frac{1}{5} - \frac{3}{10}} =$

III ALGEBRAIC EXPRESSIONS INVOLVING EXPONENTS

3.1 INTRODUCING A VARIABLE

In Chapter I we introduced the roster method and the rule method for describing a set. As you may recall, the set $S = \{1, 2, 3, 4, 5, 6, 7\}$ is an example of the roster method, while the set $O = \{x \mid x$ is an odd integer$\}$ is an example of the rule method.

Suppose we say $x \in S$, where *we do not specify which element of S x is*. Then x could be *any* of the positive integers from 1 through 7. In this case we say that x can *vary* over the set S. Similarly, if we say $y \in O$, then y varies over the set O. That is, y could be *any* odd integer.

VARIABLE

A letter which is used to represent *any* element of a given set is called a variable.

Very often in mathematics the letters at the end of the alphabet, $x, y, z, w, \ldots$, are used as variables.

Note

In the remainder of this book we will take our variables $x, y, z, \ldots$ to be elements of R, the set of real numbers.

84

3.2 INTRODUCING AN EXPONENTIAL EXPRESSION

Now that we have considered multiplication of real numbers, suppose that we consider the following special products:

(1) $2 \cdot 2 = 4$

(2) $(-3)(-3)(-3) = -27$

(3) $(-\frac{1}{3})(-\frac{1}{3})(-\frac{1}{3})(-\frac{1}{3}) = \frac{1}{81}$

(4) $4 \cdot 4 \cdot 4 \cdot 4 \cdot 4 = 1024$

These products are special in that all the real numbers being multiplied are the same. In (1), the number 2 is used twice as a multiplier; in (2) the number -3 is used three times as a multiplier; in (3) the number $-\frac{1}{3}$ is used four times as a multiplier; and in (4) the number 4 is used five times as a multiplier.

We will introduce the following notation to simplify the writing of products where the same number is used as a multiplier more than once.

Notation

(1) $2 \cdot 2$ can be written as 2^2, which is read, "2 to the second power" or "*2* squared."

(2) $(-3)(-3)(-3)$ can be written as $(-3)^3$, which is read, "(−3) to the third power" or "(−3) cubed."

(3) $(-\frac{1}{3})(-\frac{1}{3})(-\frac{1}{3})(-\frac{1}{3})$ can be written as $(-\frac{1}{3})^4$, which is read, "$(-\frac{1}{3})$ to the fourth power."

(4) $4 \cdot 4 \cdot 4 \cdot 4 \cdot 4$ can be written 4^5, which is read, "4 to the fifth power."

Now let x be a variable, where $x \in R$. Then using the same notation we have that:

$$x^2 = x \cdot x$$
$$x^3 = x \cdot x \cdot x$$

and in general

$$x^n = \underbrace{x \cdot x \cdot x \cdots x}_{n \text{ times}}, \qquad \text{where } n \text{ is a positive integer.}$$

Here x is called the *base* and n is called the *exponent*.

Note

$x^1 = x$, where x^1 is read, "x to the first power." Therefore, when the exponent is 1, we usually omit it. Thus $6^1 = 6$ and $y^1 = y$.

   Although the *exponential notation* seems rather straight-forward, it is very important that we be able to distinguish between numbers such as $(2x)^3$ and $2x^3$, or between $-3x^4$ and $(-3x)^4$.

Note

When we multiply a variable by a specific real number, we usually omit the $\cdot$ which represents multiplication. Thus $2x = 2 \cdot x$, and $-3x = -3 \cdot x$.

Example 1

$2x^3$ means $2 \cdot (x^3)$. The number 2 here is called the *coefficient* of x^3. (We will define the word coefficient more explicitly a little later in this chapter.)

In contrast to this, $(2x)^3$ is an exponential expression with base $2x$ and exponent 3. Thus:

$$(2x)^3 = (2x) \cdot (2x) \cdot (2x)$$
$$= (2 \cdot 2 \cdot 2) \cdot (x \cdot x \cdot x)$$

(Using here the commutative and associative laws to regroup the numbers)

$$= 2^3 \cdot x^3$$
$$= 8 \cdot x^3$$

or simply

$$(2x)^3 = 8x^3$$

Notice here that the coefficient of x^3 is 8.

Example 2

$(-3x)^4$ has base $(-3x)$ and exponent 4. Thus:

$$(-3x)^4 = (-3x) \cdot (-3x) \cdot (-3x) \cdot (-3x)$$

$$= (-3) \cdot (-3) \cdot (-3) \cdot (-3) \cdot x \cdot x \cdot x \cdot x$$

(Using again the commutative and associative laws)

$$= (-3)^4 \cdot x^4$$

$$= +81x^4$$

(Remember: A negative multiplied by a negative yields a positive number.)

Here the coefficient of x^4 is 81.

Example 3

In general then we would have

$$(ax)^n = a^n \cdot x^n \qquad \text{(Where } a \text{ is a specific real number)}$$

whereas

$$ax^n = a \cdot x^n$$

Exercise Set 3.2

In exercises 1-14 find the number represented by the given expression.

1. 2^3

2. 3^2

3. $(-2)^5$

4. $(-3)^2$

5. $\left(\frac{3}{4}\right)^3$

6. $\left(-\frac{1}{2}\right)^5$

7. $(-5)^3$

8. $2^3 \cdot 2^5$

9. $3^4 \cdot (-2)$

10. $\frac{3^4}{3^2}$

11. $\frac{(-5)^3}{(-5)^2}$

12. $\frac{4^3}{(-2)^5}$

13. $(2^3)^2$

14. $(4^2 3^2)^2$

In exercises 15-18 explain the difference between each of the given pairs.

15. $-2^4 ; (-2)^4$

16. $\left(\frac{2}{3}\right)^3 ; \frac{2^3}{3}$

17. $5x^3 ; (5x)^3$

18. $-6a^2 ; (-6a)^2$

In exercises 19-28 simplify the given expression using the definition of an exponent, and regrouping properties of the real numbers.

19. $(3x)^3$ **24.** $2^3 \cdot 2^4 \cdot (2y)^3$

20. $(-3y)^3$ **25.** $(x^2 y^3)^2$

21. $(-2x)^4$ **26.** $a^3 \cdot (a^2 b)^2$

22. $(-2) \cdot (-6x)^2$ **27.** $(abc)^2$

23. $4^2 \cdot (5y)^3$ **28.** $(-2ab^2)^3$

29. When will x^5 be a negative number?

30. When will $(-3)^n$ be a positive number?

3.3 LAWS OF EXPONENTS

Now that we know what an exponent is and we also know some of the properties of fractions from Chapter II, we can consider the following examples.

Example 1

$$
\begin{aligned}
x^2 \cdot x^3 &= (x \cdot x)(x \cdot x \cdot x) \\
&= x \cdot x \cdot x \cdot x \cdot x \\
&= x^5
\end{aligned}
$$

We can drop the $\cdot$ in the product on the left side of the above and our result would simply be:

$$x^2 x^3 = x^5$$

Example 2

$$
\begin{aligned}
(x^2)^4 &= (x^2)(x^2)(x^2)(x^2) \\
&= (x \cdot x)(x \cdot x)(x \cdot x)(x \cdot x) \\
&= x \cdot x \cdot x \cdot x \cdot x \cdot x \cdot x \cdot x \\
&= x^8
\end{aligned}
$$

Example 3

$$(xy)^4 = (xy) \cdot (xy) \cdot (xy) \cdot (xy)$$

$$= (x \cdot x \cdot x \cdot x)(y \cdot y \cdot y \cdot y) \qquad \text{(Using commutative and associative laws to regroup)}$$

$$= x^4 y^4$$

Example 4

$$\left(\frac{x}{y}\right)^3 = \left(\frac{x}{y}\right)\left(\frac{x}{y}\right)\left(\frac{x}{y}\right) \qquad \text{(Here } y \text{ cannot be 0.)}$$

$$= \frac{x \cdot x \cdot x}{y \cdot y \cdot y} \qquad \text{(Multiplying fractions)}$$

$$= \frac{x^3}{y^3}$$

Example 5

$$\frac{x^5}{x^2} = \frac{x \cdot x \cdot x \cdot x \cdot x}{x \cdot x} \qquad \text{(Here } x \neq 0.)$$

$$= \frac{x \cdot x}{x \cdot x} \cdot \frac{x \cdot x \cdot x}{1}$$

$$= 1 \cdot \frac{x \cdot x \cdot x}{1} \qquad \text{(Since any number, except 0, divided by itself equals 1)}$$

$$= x^3$$

Example 6

$$\frac{x^2}{x^5} = \frac{x \cdot x}{x \cdot x \cdot x \cdot x \cdot x} \qquad \text{(Again } x \neq 0.)$$

$$= \frac{x \cdot x}{x \cdot x} \cdot \frac{1}{x \cdot x \cdot x}$$

$$= 1 \cdot \frac{1}{x \cdot x \cdot x} \qquad \text{(Again using the fact that any number divided by itself } = 1)$$

$$= \frac{1}{x^3}$$

Example 7

$$\frac{x^5}{x^5} = 1, \quad \text{where } x \neq 0 \qquad \text{(Why?)}$$

The above seven examples illustrate a number of general results, known as the *laws of exponents*.

LAW I

To multiply two exponential expressions with the *same base*, we add exponents; that is,

$$x^m \cdot x^n = x^{m+n} \qquad \text{(This law is exhibited by example 1 above)}$$

LAW II

To obtain a power of an exponential expression we multiply the exponents; that is,

$$(x^m)^n = x^{mn} \qquad \text{(Exhibited by example 2.)}$$

LAW III

To obtain a power of a product of numbers we raise each number in the product to that power and multiply; that is,

$$(xyz)^n = x^n y^n z^n \qquad \text{(Exhibited by example 3.)}$$

LAW IV

To obtain a power of a fraction we simply raise numerator and denominator to that power and divide.

$$\left(\tfrac{x}{y}\right)^n = \frac{x^n}{y^n}, \qquad \text{provided } y \neq 0 \qquad \text{(Exhibited by example 4.)}$$

LAW V

In dividing two exponential expressions with the *same base*, we subtract exponents in the following manner:

(a) $\dfrac{x^m}{x^n} = x^{m-n}$,   if $m > n$ (Recall that this notation simply means m is greater than n.)

(b) $\dfrac{x^m}{x^n} = \dfrac{1}{x^{n-m}}$,   if $m < n$ (m is less than n.)

(c) $\dfrac{x^m}{x^n} = 1$,   if $m = n$ (That is, $\dfrac{x^m}{x^m} = 1$.)

    This law is exhibited by examples 5, 6, and 7 above.

Note 1

In the laws above, x, y, z are real numbers and m, n are *positive integers.*

Note 2

Let us once again stress that to apply Laws I and V above we *must have the same base.* Thus if we have the expression $a^3 b^2$, we can do *nothing* to simplify this expression. However consider the following example which can be simplified.

Example 8

Consider $(a^3 b^2)^5$. This expression can be simplified, for we have

$$(a^3 b^2)^5 = (a^3 b^2)(a^3 b^2)(a^3 b^2)(a^3 b^2)(a^3 b^2)$$

$$= (a^3 a^3 a^3 a^3 a^3)(b^2 b^2 b^2 b^2 b^2) \qquad \text{(Using commutative and associative laws to regroup)}$$

$$= a^{15} b^{10} \qquad \text{(Using here Law I together with the associative law)}$$

Example 9

Simplify $(4x^2 y^3)^4$.

$$(4x^2 y^3)^4 = 4^4 (x^2)^4 (y^3)^4 \qquad \text{(Using Law III)}$$

$$= 256 x^8 y^{12} \qquad \text{(Using Law II)}$$

Example 10

(a) $\dfrac{x^5}{x^4} = x^{5-4} = x^1 = x$ \qquad [Using Law V(a)]

(b) $\dfrac{y^3}{y^8} = \dfrac{1}{y^{8-3}} = \dfrac{1}{y^5}$ \qquad [Using Law V(b)]

(c) $\dfrac{z^3}{z^3} = 1$ \qquad [Using Law V(c)]

Example 11

Simplify $(\frac{4a^2c^4}{3ac^2})^2$

$$(\frac{4a^2c^4}{3ac^2})^2 \ = \ \frac{(4a^2c^4)^2}{(3ac^2)^2} \qquad \text{(Using Law IV)}$$

$$= \ \frac{4^2(a^2)^2(c^4)^2}{3^2a^2(c^2)^2} \qquad \text{(Using Law III)}$$

$$= \ \frac{16a^4c^8}{9a^2c^4} \qquad \text{(Using Law II)}$$

$$= \ (\frac{16}{9})(\frac{a^4}{a^2})(\frac{c^8}{c^4}) \qquad \text{(Properties of fractions)}$$

$$= \ \frac{16}{9}a^2c^4 \qquad \text{[Law V(a)]}$$

Example 12

Multiply $5ab^2$ by $-2a^2b^3$.

$$(5ab^2) \ \cdot \ (-2a^2b^3) \ = \ 5(-2)aa^2b^2b^3 \qquad \text{(Regrouping by using commutative and associative laws)}$$

$$= \ -10a^3b^5 \qquad \text{(Using Law I)}$$

Exercise Set 3.3

In exercises 1-16 simplify using laws of exponents.

1. $2^3 \cdot 2^5$

2. $3^4 \cdot 3^2$

3. $(-3)^2 \cdot (-3)$

4. $\frac{2^5}{2^3}$

5. $\frac{3^5}{3^2}$

6. $\frac{8^6}{8^6}$

7. $\dfrac{(3/4)^8}{(3/4)^6}$

12. $\dfrac{(-5)^6}{(-5)^5}$

8. $\dfrac{3^2}{3^5}$

13. $\dfrac{(-0.3)^3}{(-0.3)^2}$

9. $\dfrac{(0.5)^4}{(0.5)^3}$

14. $\dfrac{-(6)^4}{-(6)^2}$

10. $\dfrac{(-2)^2}{(-2)^3}$

15. $\dfrac{-7^3}{7^4}$

11. $\dfrac{(328)^{15}}{(328)^{16}}$ $\;\;l$

16. $\dfrac{2^3 \cdot (-3)^2 \cdot (-4)^3}{2^4 \cdot (-3)^3 \cdot (-4)^2}$

In exercises 17-30 answer true or false.

17. $3^2 \cdot 3^5 = 3^7$

24. $2^3 + 2^3 + 2^3 = 8^3$

18. $3^2 + 3^3 = 3^5$

25. $4^2 \cdot 3^2 = 12^2$

19. $2^3 + 3^2 = 5^5$

26. $2^2 \cdot 3^2 \cdot 4^2 = 24^2$

20. $4^2 + 5^2 = 9^2$

27. $\dfrac{3^3}{5^3} \not= (\frac{3}{5})^3$

21. $3^2 \cdot 2^3 = 6^5$

28. $\dfrac{2^4}{3^2} = (\frac{2}{3})^2$

22. $3^2 \cdot 3^2 \cdot 3^2 = 27^2$

29. $(2^2)^3 = 2^5$

23. $3^2 \cdot 3^2 \cdot 3^2 = 3^6$

30. $(2^3)^3 = 2^9$

In exercises 31-61 simplify the given expressions. *Note*: All exponents are positive integers and no denominator is zero.

31. $x^3 x^7$

38. $\dfrac{b^5}{b^2}$

32. $(x^2)^4$

39. $(\frac{a}{3})^3$

33. $a^2 a^8$

40. $(\frac{x}{y})^5$

34. $(c^3)^2$

41. $(-3a)^4$

35. $(bx)^4$

42. $(5y^3)^2$

36. $(xy^2)^3$

43. $(-xy^2)^3$

37. $\dfrac{x^3}{x^8}$

44. $(-2a^2x)^2$

45. $(x^a)^b$

46. $(x^2y^3)^d$

47. $(3x^2y) : (3xy^2)$

48. $(2a^2b^3) \cdot (-3a^3b)$

49. $2x^3(xy^5)^2$

50. $x^ax^bx^c$

51. $-3a^2b(a^2b^2)^3$

52. $\left(\dfrac{x^3}{a^2}\right)^4$

53. $\dfrac{x^3y^6}{xy^2}$

54. $\dfrac{-8c^4d^3}{4c^6d^2}$

55. $\dfrac{10xy^2}{5xy}$

56. $\dfrac{-34a^4b^3c^5}{-17ab^2c^4}$

57. $\left(\dfrac{4x^2y}{x^3y^2}\right)\left(\dfrac{5x^2y}{2y^3}\right)$

58. $\left(\dfrac{2x^2y^3}{xy}\right)^4$

59. $\dfrac{(2x^5)(3x^4)}{(x^2)^3}$

60. $(-2xy^2)^5\left(\dfrac{x^8}{8y^2}\right)$

61. $\left(\dfrac{a^2b^3}{c^4}\right) \div \left(\dfrac{ab^2}{c^4}\right)^2$

3.4 THE EXPONENT ZERO AND NEGATIVE EXPONENTS

We would now like to include zero as an exponent and also talk about negative exponents. If we are to include such expressions as x^0, we would like to have the elementary operations with x^0 obey the laws of exponents. Thus, according to Law I we should have:

$$x^0 \cdot x^n = x^{0+n} = x^n$$

or

$$x^n \cdot x^0 = x^{n+0} = x^n$$

Thus

$$x^0 \cdot x^n = x^n \cdot x^0 = x^n$$

And so we see that x^0 must be the *identity element* of the set of real numbers under multiplication. That is, $x^0 = 1$.

ZERO EXPONENT

If x is a real number, $x \neq 0$, then $x^0 = 1$.

Note

We do not define 0^0. This expression would have no useful meaning.

Example 1

$$(a^3 b^4)^0 = 1 \qquad \text{(Here } a \neq 0, b \neq 0.)$$

Example 2

$$3^0 \cdot 5^2 \cdot 6^0 \cdot 3 = 1 \cdot 25 \cdot 1 \cdot 3 = 75$$

Now that we have defined what we mean by x^0, we would also like to define what we mean by x^{-m}, where m is a positive integer, so that $-m$ is negative. As with the 0 exponent, we would also like to have operations with negative exponents satisfy the laws of exponents. Thus again considering Law I we should have:

$$x^m \cdot x^{-m} = x^{m+(-m)} = x^0 = 1$$

or

$$x^{-m} \cdot x^m = x^{-m+m} = x^0 = 1$$

From this we can see that x^{-m} must be the *multiplicative inverse* of x^m. That is,

$$x^{-m} = \frac{1}{x^m}$$

NEGATIVE EXPONENT

If x is a real number, $x \neq 0$, and m is a positive integer, then

$$x^{-m} = \frac{1}{x^m}.$$

Example 3

Write x^{-2} without a negative exponent.

$$x^{-2} = \frac{1}{x^2}$$

Example 4

Write 5^{-3} without the negative exponent and simplify.

$$5^{-3} = \frac{1}{5^3} = \frac{1}{125}$$

Example 5

Write $(\frac{3}{2})^{-2}$ without the negative exponent and simplify.

$(\frac{3}{2})^{-2} = \dfrac{1}{(\frac{3}{2})^2}$ (Definition of negative exponents)

$= \dfrac{1}{\frac{3^2}{2^2}}$ (Law IV of exponents)

$= \dfrac{1}{\frac{9}{4}} = 1 \cdot \frac{4}{9} = \frac{4}{9}$ (Division of fractions)

Example 6

Eliminate negative exponents and simplify: $\dfrac{4^{-2} + 2^{-3}}{3}$

$\dfrac{4^{-2} + 2^{-3}}{3} = \dfrac{\frac{1}{4^2} + \frac{1}{2^3}}{3}$ (Definition of negative exponents)

$= \dfrac{\frac{1}{16} + \frac{1}{8}}{3}$

$= \dfrac{\frac{1 + 2}{16}}{3}$ (Addition of fractions)

$= \dfrac{\frac{3}{16}}{3} = \frac{3}{16} \cdot \frac{1}{3}$ (Division of fractions)

$= \frac{1}{16}$

   With our new knowledge of exponents, including 0 and negative exponents, we can rewrite Law V of Section 3.3, which, to recall, was the following:

$$\frac{x^m}{x^n} = x^{m-n}, \quad m > n$$

$$\frac{x^m}{x^n} = \frac{1}{x^{n-m}} \quad m < n$$

and

$$\frac{x^m}{x^n} = 1, \quad \text{if } m = n$$

Perhaps a few examples will help us see what to do.

Example 7

$$\frac{a^4}{a^2} = a^{4-2} = a^2, \quad a \neq 0$$

Example 8

$$\frac{a^2}{a^4} = \frac{1}{a^2}, \quad (a \neq 0)$$

But we now know that $\frac{1}{a^2} = a^{-2}$, by the definition of negative exponents. And a^{-2} can be written as a^{2-4}, since $2 - 4 = -2$. Thus

$$\frac{a^2}{a^4} = a^{2-4} = a^{-2}$$

Example 9

$$\frac{a^3}{a^3} = 1, \quad a \neq 0$$

But we can now write

$$\frac{a^3}{a^3} = a^{3-3} = a^0 = 1$$

Example 10

$$\frac{a^3}{a^{-2}} = \frac{a^3}{\frac{1}{a^2}} = a^3 \cdot a^2 = a^5$$

Here we used the definition of negative exponents, divided fractions, and then finally applied Law I of exponents. But we could have gotten the same result by simply subtracting the exponent in the denominator from the exponent in the numerator. That is,

$$\frac{a^3}{a^{-2}} = a^{3-(-2)} = a^{3+2} = a^5$$

Example 11

$$\frac{a^{-3}}{a^2} = \frac{\frac{1}{a^3}}{a^2} = \frac{1}{a^3} \cdot \frac{1}{a^2}$$ (Definition of negative exponents followed by division of fractions)

$$= \frac{1}{a^3 \cdot a^2}$$ (Multiplication of fractions)

$$= \frac{1}{a^5}$$ (Law I of exponents)

or simply by subtracting the exponent in the denominator from the exponent in the numerator we would get:

$$\frac{a^{-3}}{a^2} = a^{-3-2} = a^{-5} = \frac{1}{a^5}$$

With these examples in mind, we can now write Law V of exponents simply as follows:

LAW V

If $x \in R$, $x \neq 0$, and m and n are *any* integers, then

$$\frac{x^m}{x^n} = x^{m-n}$$

That is, to divide exponential expressions with the *same base* we merely subtract the exponent in the denominator from the exponent in the numerator.

The first four laws of exponents apply for negative as well as positive exponents. Thus it is well worth repeating all of the laws of exponents here.

LAW I

If $x \in R$ and m, n are *any* integers, then

$$x^m x^n = x^{m+n}$$

LAW II

If $x \in R$ and m, n are *any* integers, then

$$(x^m)^n = x^{mn}$$

LAW III

If x, y, z are real numbers and n is *any* integer,

$$(xyz)^n = x^n y^n z^n$$

LAW IV

If x, y are real numbers, $y \neq 0$, and n is any integer, then

$$\left(\frac{x}{y}\right)^n = \frac{x^n}{y^n}$$

LAW V

If $x \in R, x \neq 0$, and m, n are any integers, then

$$\frac{x^m}{x^n} = x^{m-n}$$

Let us now review all the laws of exponents with a number of examples.

Example 12

Eliminate the negative exponent and simplify: $\left(\frac{2}{5}\right)^{-2}$.

$$\left(\frac{2}{5}\right)^{-2} = \frac{1}{\left(\frac{2}{5}\right)^2} \qquad \text{(Using definition of negative exponents)}$$

$$= \frac{1}{\frac{2^2}{5^2}} \qquad \text{(Using Law IV)}$$

$$= \frac{1}{\frac{4}{25}} = \frac{25}{4} \qquad \text{(Dividing fractions)}$$

Example 13

Simplify: $\dfrac{16^0 + 5}{2^{-3}}$.

$$\frac{16^0 + 5}{2^{-3}} = \frac{1 + 5}{\frac{1}{2^3}} \qquad \text{(Definition of exponent 0 and negative exponents)}$$

$$= \frac{6}{\frac{1}{8}} = 6 \cdot 8 \qquad \text{(Division of fractions)}$$

$$= 48$$

Example 14

Simplify: $\dfrac{(\frac{1}{2})^{-3} + 4}{3^{-2}}$

$$\dfrac{(\frac{1}{2})^{-3} + 4}{3^{-2}} = \dfrac{\dfrac{1}{(\frac{1}{2})^3} + 4}{\dfrac{1}{3^2}}$$
(Definition of negative exponents)

$$= \dfrac{\dfrac{1}{\frac{1^3}{2^3}} + 4}{\frac{1}{9}} = \dfrac{\dfrac{1}{\frac{1}{8}} + 4}{\frac{1}{9}}$$
(Law IV)

$$= \dfrac{8 + 4}{\frac{1}{9}} = \dfrac{12}{\frac{1}{9}}$$
(Why?)

$$= 12 \cdot 9 = 108$$
(Division of fractions)

Example 15

Simplify: $\dfrac{6x^3 y^{-5}}{3x^{-1} y^3}$.

$$\dfrac{6x^3 y^{-5}}{3x^{-1} y^3} = \left(\dfrac{6}{3}\right)\left(\dfrac{x^3}{x^{-1}}\right)\left(\dfrac{y^{-5}}{y^3}\right)$$
(Why?)

$$= 2x^{3-(-1)} y^{-5-3}$$
(Law V)

$$= 2x^4 y^{-8}$$

$$= \dfrac{2x^4}{y^8}$$
(Definition of negative exponents)

Example 16

Simplify: $(x^3 y^{-3})^{-4}$.

$$(x^3 y^{-3})^{-4} = (x^3)^{-4} (y^{-3})^{-4}$$
(Using Law III)

$$= x^{-12} y^{12}$$
(Using Law II)

$$= \dfrac{y^{12}}{x^{12}}$$
(Definition of negative exponents)

Example 17

Simplify: $(3x^{-2}y^3z^4) \cdot (-4x^2y^{-3}z^{-4})$.

$(3x^{-2}y^3z^4) \cdot (-4x^2y^{-3}z^{-4}) = 3(-4)x^{-2}x^2y^3y^{-3}z^4z^{-4}$

(Using commutative and associative laws to regroup)

$= -12x^{-2+2}y^{3+(-3)}z^{4+(-4)}$
(Using Law I)

$= -12x^0y^0z^0$

$= -12 \cdot 1 \cdot 1 \cdot 1 = -12$
(Why?)

Exercise Set 3.4

In exercises 1-14 eliminate negative exponents wherever they appear, and simplify.

1. 2^{-4}

2. 63^0

3. $(\frac{-3}{4})^3$

4. $(\frac{5}{7})^0$

5. $\frac{5^{-7}}{5^{-5}}$

6. $(3^{-2})^2$

7. $(5^0 2^{-3})^{-2}$

8. $(4^2 2^{-3})^{-1}$

9. $2^{-3} + 3^{-1}$

10. $4^{-3} \cdot 3^{-1} \cdot 384$

11. $\frac{10^3 + 10^2}{10^{-2}}$

12. $10^4 \cdot 10^{-2}$

13. $\frac{(\frac{1}{3})^{-2} + (\frac{1}{3})^{-3}}{3^{-2}}$

14. $\frac{5^0 + (\frac{1}{2})^0}{(\frac{1}{2})^{-2}}$

In exercises 15-20 write the given expression without a denominator by using negative exponents.

15. $\frac{1}{x^2}$

16. $\frac{1}{xy^3}$

17. $\frac{a^2}{b^4}$

18. $\frac{6xy^2}{a^2b^5}$

19. $\frac{3^0 ax^2}{b^{-2}y^4}$

20. $\frac{a^5b^6c}{3^{-1}d^{-2}e^{-3}}$

In exercises 21-36 simplify the given expression. Express your answer with positive exponents only.

21. x^{-3}

29. $(x^{-2}y^3) \cdot (2x^{-1}y^{-4})$

22. $\frac{1}{6^{-4}}$

30. $(x^{-2}y^{-1})^{-2}$

23. $x^{-4} \cdot x^2$

31. $(2ab^{-3}c^{-4}) \cdot (-3a^{-4}b^3c^{-1})$

24. $\frac{y^{-3}}{y^{-4}}$

32. $(-3xy^2z) \cdot (-4x^{-1}y^{-2}z^{-1})$

25. $\frac{(xy)^{-4}}{(xy)^{-4}}$

33. $\frac{5x^4y^2}{2xy^5}$

26. $x^{-3} \cdot x^{-5}$

34. $\frac{-6x^{-2}y^0z^{-3}}{-2x^{-4}y^{-2}z^3}$

27. $\frac{a^0}{a^{-3}}$

35. $\left(\frac{a^{-2}b^{-3}}{a^{-1}b^2}\right)^2$

28. $(a^{-2}y^2)^{-5}$

36. $\left(\frac{3x^{-4}y^3z}{2x^2y^{-2}z^{-2}}\right)^{-2}$

3.5 ALGEBRAIC EXPRESSIONS AND THEIR EVALUATION

Suppose we begin with any collection of variables and real numbers. And suppose from this collection we take some of these numbers and variables and combine them by means of a *finite number* of additions, subtractions, multiplications, and divisions. Remembering that a variable itself represents a number, we see that the result of this combination is a *representation of a number*. Any such combination of variables and numbers is called an *algebraic expression*. Let us consider some examples of algebraic expressions.

Examples of Algebraic Expressions

1. 7

6. $x + 3$

2. $6(3 + 4)$

7. $x^2 + y^2$

3. x

8. $x^2 + 3xy - 2y^2$

4. $4x^2$

9. $6x^3 - \frac{3}{5}x - 5$

5. $3xy$

10. $\frac{4}{x} + \frac{3}{y} - \frac{6}{z^2}$

Note in the above examples that when there are no variables present in the algebraic expression (just specific numbers), we know exactly the specific number being represented. This is seen in example 1, where the number 7 is represented, and in example 2, where, when the arithmetic is carried out, we see that the number 42 is represented. However, once there are variables present we certainly do not know what specific number is represented.

But suppose that in a given situation we know, or can determine, or are given a specific value (a specific number) for each of the variables in an algebraic expression. We then could substitute for each letter its given value, wherever it occurs in the algebraic expression. If after making the proper substitutions we perform the indicated arithmetic operations, in the correct order, we will obtain the *number* represented by the algebraic expression *under the given condition*. This procedure is known as the *evaluation* of an algebraic expression.

We are obtaining the *value* of an algebraic expression under given conditions. Let us consider a number of examples.

Example 11

Given $x = 3$, evaluate the expression $x + 7$.

Here we simply substitute for x its given value, 3, and perform the indicated addition.

Thus $x + 7 = 3 + 7 = 10$.

Example 12

Given $x = 4, y = 3$, evaluate the expression $x^2 + y^2$.

Substitute for x the number 4 and for y the number 3 and simplify the resulting expression.

$$x^2 + y^2 = 4^2 + 3^2 = 16 + 9 = 25$$

Example 13

Given $x = 1, y = 2, z = 0$, evaluate the expression

$$xy(y + z) + xz(x + y)$$

Substituting 1 for x wherever it appears, 2 for y, and 0 for z and simplifying, we get:

$$xy(y + z) + xz(x + y) = (1)(2)(2 + 0) + (1)(0)(1 + 2)$$
$$= (1)(2)(2) + (1)(0)(3)$$
$$= 4 + 0$$
$$= 4$$

Example 14

Given $x = 4, y = 5$, evaluate $(y - 2x)^2$.

$$(y - 2x)^2 = [5 - (2 \cdot 4)]^2 = (5 - 8)^2$$
$$= (-3)^2 = (-3)(-3) = 9$$

SUMMARY

Let us now summarize what we have said about evaluating an algebraic expression. To evaluate an algebraic expression:

(1) Substitute the given values for the variables.
(2) Simplify by performing the indicated arithmetic operations in the proper order.

Exercise Set 3.5

In exercises 1-8 let $a = 1$, $b = 3$, $c = 4$. Evaluate the given algebraic expression.

1. $a + b$

2. ab

3. $a + b - c$

4. $3a + 2b$

5. $6(a - b)$

6. $(a + b)(c + b)$

7. $\frac{24}{abc}$

8. $\frac{b^2 + c^2}{5}$

In exercises 9-22 let $x = 1, y = 0, z = -1, u = 3, w = 2$. Evaluate the given expression.

9. z^5

10. x^4

11. $z^8 - x^5$

12. $y(u + w)$

13. $x^5 y^2 (x^2 + 2xy + u^3)$

14. $-3w(u + 2z)$

15. $w^3 - 2w^2 + 3$

16. $(w + u)^3$

17. u^u

18. $(u - w)(3y - z)^2(2x^2 - w)^3$

19. $u^2 + w^2 + z^2$

20. $(u - z)^{2y}$

21. $2w \cdot [(3z)^3 + u^3]$

22. $(x + y + u)(2u - 2w - 3z)$

23. Evaluate $2x^2 - 3x - 5$ when $x = \frac{5}{2}$.

24. Evaluate $x^3 + 3x^2 - 2x + 1$ when $x = -1$.

25. Evaluate $2x^3 - x^2 + 1$ when $x = 2$.

26. Suppose a represents a number. Write an algebraic expression that represents:
    (a) The number increased by 4
    (b) The number decreased by 3
    (c) Three times the number
    (d) 3 more than twice the number
    (e) 2 less than three times the number

27. If John is now x years old:
    (a) What is John's age 3 years from now?
    (b) What was John's age 4 years ago?
    (c) What is 3 times John's age?
    (d) If Ken is 6 years older than John, how old is Ken?
    (e) If John's father is 3 years more than twice John's age, how old is John's father?

28. If John is now 20 years old, find the age represented by each of the expressions in exercise 27.

3.6 INTRODUCING A POLYNOMIAL

In the remainder of this chapter we will restrict ourselves to certain special types of algebraic expressions. Perhaps it will be easier to see the types that we *will* study by first disposing of the ones that we will not consider. We will *not* consider algebraic expressions which involve *negative powers of any of the variables.* For example we will not consider expressions like: (1) x^{-1}, (2) $x^{-2}y$, and (3) $3xyz^{-1}$. We will also not consider expressions like (4) $x + \frac{3}{y}$ since this is actually equal to $x + 3y^{-1}$, or (5) $\frac{4}{x} + \frac{3}{y} - \frac{6}{z^2}$, since this is equal to $4x^{-1} + 3y^{-1} - 6z^{-2}$. (*Note:* This is example 10 of Section 3.5.)

Which expressions will we then consider? We will consider only those algebraic expressions which involve real numbers and *nonnegative integral* powers of the variable.

Note

Nonnegative means *positive or zero.* Remember, $x^0 = 1$, $x \neq 0$. Thus, by nonnegative integral powers we simply mean that we will allow as powers the numbers which are in the set $\{0, 1, 2, 3, 4, \ldots\}$.

MONOMIAL

Suppose we first consider an algebraic expression which consists of a real number and nonnegative integral powers of certain variables, joined only by multiplication. For example, (1) $3x^3$, (2) $5y^2$, (3) $\frac{3}{5} x^2 y$, (4) $\frac{4}{9} xyz^2$. Such an expression is called a *monomial* in the variables involved. Thus, example (1) is a monomial in the variable x; example (2) is a monomial in y; (3) is a monomial in x and y; (4) is a monomial in x, y, and z.

A monomial represents a single quantity. A monomial is also called a *term*. The real number is called the *coefficient* of the monomial. Thus in example (1) the coefficient is 3, in (3) the coefficient is $\frac{3}{5}$, etc.

Note

We have met the word coefficient earlier, in Section 3.2, when we talked about the base and exponent of an exponential expression. To refresh our memory consider the exponential expression $(3x)^3$. Here the base is $3x$ and the exponent is 3. But $(3x)^3 = 3^3 \cdot x^3 = 27x^3$, which is a monomial in the variable x with coefficient 27.

Any real number can be considered a monomial in *any* variable. For example: 16 is a monomial in any variable since 16 can be written as $16x^0$ or $16y^0$ or $16x^0y^0$, etc.

BINOMIAL

A *binomial* is a sum of two monomials.
Examples of binomials are:

(1) $x^2 + 2$
(2) $4x^2 + 2xy$
(3) $x - 2y^2$
(4) $-x - 2yz^2$

Note

You may say that example (3) above is not a binomial because it is a *difference* of two monomials and not a sum, as stated in the definition above. But *remember* any difference $x - y$ can be written as a sum $x + (-y)$. For example, $16 - 3 = 16 + (-3) = 13$. So in example (3) we actually do have a sum of two monomials

$x + (-2y^2)$ where the coefficient of the first term is 1 and the coefficient of the second term is -2. Similarly, example (4) is a binomial $[-1x + (-2yz)]$, where the coefficient of the first term is -1 and the coefficient of the second term is -2.

Naturally a trinomial is a sum of three monomials. However, we usually do not keep going in this way. We use one general name for any sum of monomials, that is, a polynomial.

POLYNOMIAL

A *polynomial* is any sum of monomials.
Some examples of polynomials are:

(1) 5
(2) $5x^2$
(3) $\frac{3}{5}x^2 + \frac{4}{7}$
(4) $2x^2 + \frac{1}{3}xy - y^2$
(5) $x^3 - 5x^2 + 3x - 4$
(6) $xy^5 + 3x^2y^3 - 4x^3y - x^5y - 1$

Note

An algebraic expression like $\frac{3}{x} + \frac{4x}{y}$ is not a polynomial, since it involves negative exponents of the variables. That is, $\frac{3}{x} + \frac{4x}{y}$ can be written $3x^{-1} + 4xy^{-1}$.

Exercise Set 3.6

In exercises 1-16 state whether the given algebraic expression is a monomial, a polynomial of more than one term, or neither.

1. 27

2. $32x$

3. $3(-4)xy$

4. $-3x - 3y$

5. $7x^2 - 3xy + 5y^2$

6. $xy + yu + xv$

7. xyz^2

8. $\frac{3}{4}xy + 5$

9. $\frac{3}{x} + 4x^2 + 2x$

10. $x^3 - \frac{2}{3}x + x^{-1}$

11. $\frac{4x^3}{y^2}$

12. $x^2 - y^2 + 3xyz$

13. $ax^2 + bx + c$

14. $-2ax^2 - 4ax - 7$

15. $\frac{y^2}{6} + 2$

16. 0

In exercises 17-20 name the coefficient of each term in the given polynomial.

17. $3x^2 - 4x$

18. $\frac{2}{3}x^3 - 4x^2 + 7x - 1$

19. $-4xy^2$

20. $2x^2y^2z^2 - 5xyz$

21. Can we say that $\frac{2}{3}$ is a monomial in x? Why?

22. Write the number 727 as a sum of powers of 10.

23. Does the product of two or more monomials yield a monomial?

3.7 ADDITION AND SUBTRACTION OF POLYNOMIALS

We would like to be able to perform the elementary operations (addition, subtraction, multiplication, and division) on algebraic expressions, polynomials in particular. We have already seen how to multiply and divide a monomial by a monomial when we studied the laws of exponents. Let us review by means of a number of examples.

Example 1

Multiply $3x^3$ by $2x^2$.

$$(3x^3)(2x^2) = 3 \cdot 2 \cdot x^3 \cdot x^2 \qquad \text{(Using commutative and asso-}$$
$$\text{ciative laws to regroup}$$
$$= 6x^{3+2} = 6x^5 \qquad \text{(Using Law I of exponents)}$$

Example 2

Multiply $4xy^2$ by $-\frac{1}{2}x^3yz$.

$$(4xy^2)(-\tfrac{1}{2}x^3yz) = 4(-\tfrac{1}{2})xx^3y^2yz \qquad \text{(Regrouping)}$$
$$= -2x^{1+3}y^{2+1}z \qquad \text{(Law I of exponents)}$$
$$= -2x^4y^3z$$

Example 3

Divide $6x^4$ by $3x^2$.

$$\frac{6x^4}{3x^2} = \frac{6}{3}\frac{x^4}{x^2} = 2x^{4-2} = 2x^2 \qquad \text{(Law V)}$$

Example 4

Divide $-8x^3y^4z^3$ by $-2xy^2z$.

$$\frac{-8x^3y^4z^3}{-2xy^2z} = \frac{-8}{-2}\frac{x^3}{x}\frac{y^4}{y^2}\frac{z^3}{z}$$

$$= 4x^2y^2z^2 \qquad \text{(Law V)}$$

Let us see how to add polynomials by first considering some examples.

Example 5

Add $3x^2$ and $5x^2$.

$3x^2 + 5x^2 = (3 + 5)x^2$ (We used the distributive law and simplified.)

$\qquad\qquad = 8x^2$

Example 6

Add $2xy^2$ and $-4xy^2$.

$2xy^2 + (-4xy^2) = 2xy^2 - 4xy^2$

$\qquad\qquad\qquad = (2 - 4)xy^2$ (Using the distributive law)

$\qquad\qquad\qquad = -2xy^2$

Example 7

Find the sum of $3x^3 + 2x^2 - 4x + 5$ and $x^3 - 3x^2 - 3$.

$(3x^3 + 2x^2 - 4x + 5) + (x^3 - 3x^2 - 3)$

$\qquad\qquad = 3x^3 + x^3 + 2x^2 - 3x^2 - 4x + 5 - 3$
$\qquad\qquad$ (Using commutative and associative laws to regroup)

$\qquad\qquad = (3 + 1)x^3 + (2 - 3)x^2 - 4x + (5 - 3)$
$\qquad\qquad$ (Using the distributive law)

$\qquad\qquad = 4x^3 - 1x^2 - 4x + 2$
$\qquad\qquad$ (Simplifying)

$\qquad\qquad = 4x^3 - x^2 - 4x + 2$

Example 8

Subtract $x^3 - 4x^2 + 2x - 1$ from $2x^3 - 3x^2 - x + 2$.

$(2x^3 - 3x^2 - x + 2) - (x^3 - 4x^2 + 2x - 1)$

$$= (2x^3 - 3x^2 - x + 2)$$
$$+ (-1)(x^3 - 4x^2 + 2x - 1)$$

(Writing a difference as a sum)

$$= (2x^3 - 3x^2 - x + 2)$$
$$+ (-x^3 + 4x^2 - 2x + 1)$$

(Using distributive law to multiply through by -1)

$$= 2x^3 - x^3 - 3x^2 + 4x^2 - x - 2x + 2 + 1$$

(Regrouping)

$$= (2 - 1)x^3 + (-3 + 4)x^2 + (-1 - 2)x$$
$$+ (2 + 1)$$

(Distributive law)

$$= 1x^3 + 1x^2 + (-3x) + 3 \qquad \text{(Simplifying)}$$

$$= x^3 + x^2 - 3x + 3$$

Note

The first two steps in example 8 (before the regrouping took place) could have been accomplished by simply changing the signs of the polynomial on the right and finding the sum of the resulting polynomial (the one with signs changed) with the polynomial on the left.

Now let us see if we can summarize what was done. Notice that in examples 5, 6, and 7 we tried to write *like* terms next to each other, using regrouping properties (associative and commutative laws) wherever necessary.

LIKE TERMS

By *like terms* we mean those terms in which the product of variables is *identical*.

Examples of Like Terms

(1) $3x$ and $4x$
(2) $5x^3$ and $-2x^3$
(3) $6xy^2$ and $2xy^2$
(4) $\frac{-1}{2}xy^2z$ and $\frac{-3}{4}xy^2z$

Note the product of variables in each example is identical.

Examples of Unlike Terms

(1) $3x$ and $4y$
(2) $3xy$ and $5xy^2$
(3) $-2xyz$ and $3x^2yz$

The product of variables in each example is *not* identical.

Once we had regrouped, we then applied the distributive law to each set of like terms. For example $2x^3 - x^3 = (2 - 1)x^3$, $-3x^2 + 4x^2 = (-3 + 4)x^2$. After this was accomplished, we just simplified the result.

In the case of example 8 above, where we subtracted one polynomial from another, we first changed the signs in the second polynomial (the one being subtracted) and added, using the same procedure as in the first three examples. Thus we can now write down the following procedure:

To add two polynomials P_1 and P_2:

(1) First group *like* terms together.
(2) Apply distributive law to each set of like terms.
(3) Simplify.

To subtract a polynomial P_2 from a polynomial P_1:

(1) Change the signs of the terms in polynomial P_2 and then add the resulting polynomial to P_1 using the procedure above.

Example 9

Add $3x^4 + 2x^3 - 2x + 5$ and $-x^3 + 3x^2 + 2x$.

$(3x^4 + 2x^3 - 2x + 5) + (-x^3 + 3x^2 + 2x)$

$$= 3x^4 + 2x^3 - x^3 + 3x^2 - 2x + 2x + 5$$
$$\text{(Why?)}$$

$$= 3x^4 + (2 - 1)x^3 + 3x^2 + (-2 + 2)x + 5$$
$$\text{(Using what law?)}$$

$$= 3x^4 + 1x^3 + 3x^2 + 0x + 5$$
$$\text{(Simplifying)}$$

$$= 3x^4 + x^3 + 3x^2 + 5$$

Exercise Set 3.7

In exercises 1-12 perform the indicated operation and state whether or not the result is a monomial.

1. $x \cdot 3x^2$

2. $2xy \cdot 3xy^2$

3. $2xy \cdot 3xy^{-2}$

4. $2xy \cdot 3x^{-1}y^{-1}$

5. $(-6x^2y^3z)(-2)(-3xy)$

6. $(-6x^2y)^2$

7. $\dfrac{8x^3}{2x}$

8. $\dfrac{-6x^3y^2}{3x^2y^2}$

9. $\dfrac{-15x^2y^3}{-5x^3y^2}$

10. $\dfrac{xyz}{xyz^2}$

11. $(-x)(-2x^3yz^2)$

12. $3ax^3y(4ax^2y)$

In exercises 13-18 perform the indicated operations.

13. $3x + 8x$

14. $-3x^2 + 5x^2$

15. $7xy - 3xy$

16. $(-xy^2) + (-3xy^2)$

17. $5xy - 3xy + 6xy$

18. $13y^2 - 15y^2 + 2y^2$

19. Add $3x + 4$ and $2x - 3$.

20. Add $-2x + y$ and $-2x - y$.

21. Combine $3x + 4y - 6z$ and $3x - 4y - 3z$.

22. Subtract $-2x$ from $-8x$.

23. Subtract $3x + 4$ from $2x - 7$.

24. Subtract $2x^2 + xy - 3y^2$ from $3x^2 - 2xy + 3y^2$.

25. John is x years old. John's brother is 4 years older than John. John's father is 2 years more than twice John's age. What is the sum of their ages?

26. If a rectangular pool table is x feet long and $x - 3$ feet wide, what is the total length of the sides?

   In exercises 27-34 perform the indicated operations.

27. $(3x^2 - 5y + 7) + (5x^2 + 3y - 4)$

28. $(-2x^2 + 7xy - 4y^2) + (3x^2 - 4xy + y^2)$

29. $(x^2 + 6x - 12) - (2x^2 - 3x + 7)$

30. $(4a^2 + 9ab - 3b^2) - (-2a^2 + 9ab - 3b^2)$

31. $(x^3 - 3x^2 + 2x - 4) + (2x^3 - 2x^2 + 5)$

32. $(x^4 + 3x^2 - 4x + 1) + (x^3 - 3x^2 - 3x + 4)$

33. $(x^3 - 5 + 3x^2 + 4x) - (x^3 - 3x + 2x^2 - 5)$

34. $(x - x^4 + 3x^3 - 4) - (-x^3 + 2x^2 + x - 3)$

3.8 MULTIPLICATION AND DIVISION OF POLYNOMIALS

To multiply polynomials we will make repeated use of the distributive law of multiplication. *Remember: $a(b + c + d) = ab + ac + ad$, where a, b, c, d are real numbers.* Once the distributive law is used we will use the laws of exponents to simplify.

Example 1

Multiply: $2x^2 - 3x + 4$ by $2x$.

$(2x)(2x^2 - 3x + 4) = (2x)(2x^2) + (2x)(-3x) + (2x)(4)$
$$\text{(Distributive law)}$$

$$= (2)(2)(x)(x^2) + (2)(-3)(x)(x) + (2)(4)(x)$$
$$\text{(Regrouping)}$$

$$= 4x^3 - 6x^2 + 8x \quad \text{(Law I of exponents)}$$

Example 2

Multiply: $-3x^2y(4xy^2 - 2y^3)$.

$-3x^2y(4xy^2 - 2y^3) = (-3x^2y)(4xy^2) - (-3x^2y)(2y^3)$
$$\text{(Distributive law)}$$

$$= (-3)(4)(x^2)(x)(y)(y^2) - (-3)(2)(x^2)(y)(y^3)$$
$$\text{(Regrouping)}$$

$$= -12x^3y^3 - (-6x^2y^4) \text{ (Law I of exponents)}$$

$$= -12x^3y^3 + 6x^2y^4 \quad \text{(Why?)}$$

In the above two examples we multiplied a polynomial by a monomial. Let us now consider an example where both polynomials have more than one term.

Example 3

Multiply: $(x - 2)(3x^2 - 2x + 1)$.

$$(x - 2)(3x^2 - 2x + 1) = x(3x^2 - 2x + 1) - 2(3x^2 - 2x + 1)$$
$$\text{(Distributive law)}$$

$$= x(3x^2) - x(2x) + x(1) + (-2)(3x^2)$$
$$+ (-2)(-2x) + (-2)(1)$$
$$\text{(Using distributive law}$$
$$\text{again)}$$

$$= 3x^3 - 2x^2 + x - 6x^2 + 4x - 2$$
$$\text{(Using Law I of expo-}$$
$$\text{nents)}$$

$$= 3x^3 - 2x^2 - 6x^2 + x + 4x - 2$$
$$\text{(Grouping like terms}$$
$$\text{together)}$$

$$= 3x^3 + (-2 - 6)x^2 + (1 + 4)x - 2$$
$$\text{(Distributive law)}$$

$$= 3x^3 - 8x^2 + 5x - 2$$
$$\text{(Simplifying)}$$

SUMMARY

So we see that to multiply two polynomials we must:

(1) Use the distributive law as often as needed.
(2) Use Law I of exponents.
(3) Group like terms together and combine them.
(4) Simplify the result.

Example 4

Multiply: $(x - y)(x^2 + y^2)$.

$$(x - y)(x^2 + y^2) = x(x^2 + y^2) - y(x^2 + y^2) \qquad \text{(What law?)}$$

$$= x(x^2) + x(y^2) - y(x^2) - y(y^2)$$

$$\text{(What law?)}$$

$$= x^3 + xy^2 - yx^2 - y^3 \qquad \text{(What law?)}$$

This is the simplest answer since there are no like terms to combine.

If we want to divide a polynomial by a monomial, we just have to realize that division can be expressed as multiplication. For example:

$$\frac{a + b + c}{d} = \tfrac{1}{d}(a + b + c) = \tfrac{1}{d}(a) + \tfrac{1}{d}(b) + \tfrac{1}{d}(c)$$

$$= \frac{a}{d} + \frac{b}{d} + \frac{c}{d}$$

Thus we have

$$\frac{a + b + c}{d} = \frac{a}{d} + \frac{b}{d} + \frac{c}{d}$$

Recall that this is referred to as the *distributive law of division*. Let us now consider a number of examples.

Example 5

Divide $6x^4 + 8x^3 - 14x^2$ by $2x^2$.

$$\frac{6x^4 + 8x^3 - 14x^2}{2x^2} = \frac{6x^4}{2x^2} + \frac{8x^3}{2x^2} - \frac{14x^2}{2x^2} \qquad \text{(Distributive law of division)}$$

$$= 3x^{4-2} + 4x^{3-2} - 7x^{2-2} \qquad \text{(Law V of exponents)}$$

$$= 3x^2 + 4x^1 - 7x^0$$

$$= 3x^2 + 4x - 7$$

Example 6

Divide $5x^3y^2 - 15xy^3 + 10x^2y^3$ by $5xy^2$.

$$\frac{5x^3y^2 - 15xy^3 + 10x^2y^3}{5xy^2} = \frac{5x^3y^2}{5xy^2} - \frac{15xy^3}{5xy^2} + \frac{10x^2y^3}{5xy^2}$$

$$\text{(Distributive law of division)}$$

$$= 1x^{3-1}y^{2-2} - 3x^{1-1}y^{3-2} + 2x^{2-1}y^{3-2}$$

$$\text{(Law V of exponents)}$$

$$= x^2 - 3y + 2xy$$

(Simplifying using the fact
that $y^0 = 1, x^0 = 1$)

SUMMARY

Let us now summarize what we have seen in the previous two examples. To divide a polynomial by a monomial we:

(1) Use the distributive law of division.
(2) Use Law V of exponents.
(3) Simplify.

Note

We will not consider here division of a polynomial by a polynomial of more than one term.

Exercise Set 3.8

In exercises 1-12 write the given product as a sum.

1. $3(6x + 3y)$

2. $-2(3a - 4b)$

3. $-15[-\frac{1}{5}c + \frac{1}{3}d]$

4. $2x(3x - 7)$

5. $-y(a - 3y)$

6. $-3x(x^2 - 4)$

7. $xy(x^2 + y^2)$

8. $2xy^2(xy + x^3)$

9. $3xy(x - 4y + 3xy)$

10. $-2x^2y(x^2y^2 + 2xy^3 - 3)$

11. $-5z(z^3 - 4xz^2 - 3)$

12. $-x^2yz(x^2 + y^2 + z^2)$

In exercises 13-34 multiply and collect like terms.

13. $(x - 2)(x + 5)$

14. $(x + 7)(x + 3)$

15. $(2x - 3)(3x - 1)$

16. $(x - 5)(x + 5)$

17. $(y - a)(y + a)$

18. $(x - y)(x + y)$

19. $(y - 6)^2$

20. $(2x + 5)^2$

21. $(x - y)^2$

22. $(3y - 2x)^2$

23. $(2x - 5y)(-x + 4y)$

24. $(x^2 - y^2)(x - y)$

25. $(s^2 - 2)(s^2 + 2)$

26. $(r^3 - s^3)(r^3 + s^3)$

27. $(x - 3)(x^2 + 3x + 2)$

28. $(y + 4)(2y^2 - 2y - 1)$

29. $(x - 2y)(x^2 + 3xy + 5)$

30. $(a - b)(a^2 + ab + b^2)$

31. $(1 - x)(x^2 + x + 1)$

32. $(x + 2)(x + 3)(x - 4)$

33. $(5 - 2x)(3 - 4x - x^2)$

34. $(x^2 + xy - y^2)(x^2 + y^2)$

35. If a basketball costs $x + 3$ dollars, what would be the cost of 10 basket-balls?

36. If a car travels $2x + 7$ miles an hour, how far would it travel in 10 hours? How far will it travel in $(2x + 3)$ hours?

In exercises 37-50 perform the indicated division; assume no denominator is zero.

37. $\dfrac{8x + 4y}{2}$

38. $\dfrac{18a - 6b}{-3}$

39. $\dfrac{x^2 + 9x}{x}$

40. $\dfrac{2y^2 - 6y}{-y}$

41. $\dfrac{9rs^2 + 6r^2}{3r}$

42. $\dfrac{15x^2y^2 - 10x^3y}{-5x^2}$

43. $\dfrac{-5a^2b - 20ab^2}{-5ab}$

44. $\dfrac{3x^3y^2 - 4x^2y^3}{x^2y}$

45. $\dfrac{2x^3 + 3x^2 - x}{x}$

46. $\dfrac{6x^3y + 5x^2y - 3xy}{xy}$

47. $\dfrac{-14x^2y^3 + 7x^5y^8 - x^6y^7}{7xy^3}$

48. $\dfrac{(r^2s + s^2)(rs^3 - r^2s)}{rs^2}$

49. $\dfrac{6a^4b^4 - 12a^3b^3 - 18a^2b^2}{-3a^2b^2}$

50. $\dfrac{16x^4 - 8x^3 + 12x^2}{-4x^2}$

3.9 ROOTS

SQUARE ROOT

If $a^2 = r$, where a and r are real numbers, then a is said to be a *square root* of r.

Example 1

4 is a square root of 16, since $4^2 = 16$. Also, -4 is a square root of 16, since

$$(-4)^2 = (-4)(-4) = +16$$

Example 2

$\frac{2}{5}$ is a square root of $\frac{4}{25}$, since

$$\left(\tfrac{2}{5}\right)^2 = \left(\tfrac{2}{5}\right)\left(\tfrac{2}{5}\right) = \tfrac{4}{25}$$

Also, $-\frac{2}{5}$ is a square root of $\frac{4}{25}$, since

$$\left(-\tfrac{2}{5}\right)^2 = \left(-\tfrac{2}{5}\right)\left(-\tfrac{2}{5}\right) = +\tfrac{4}{25}$$

Note

(1) Every *positive* real number r has *two square roots*, one positive and one negative.

(2) 0 has only one square root, namely 0, for only $0^2 = 0$.

Example 3

-16 has *no real square roots*, since there is no real number a such that $a^2 = -16$, for we know that the square of any real number is a *positive* real number.

Note

(3) Negative numbers have no real square roots.

Notation

The positive square root of r will be denoted by $\sqrt{r}$ and the negative square root by $-\sqrt{r}$. The symbol $\sqrt{}$ is called a *radical*.

Example 4

(a) $\sqrt{36} = +6$ (c) $\sqrt{\tfrac{16}{25}} = \tfrac{4}{5}$

(b) $-\sqrt{36} = -6$ (d) $-\sqrt{\tfrac{16}{25}} = -\tfrac{4}{5}$

(e) $\sqrt{6.25} = 2.5$, since $(2.5)^2 = (2.5)(2.5) = 6.25$.

(f) $-\sqrt{6.25} = -2.5$

CUBE ROOT

If $a^3 = r$, where a and r are real numbers, then a is called a *cube root* of r.

Example 5

3 is a cube root of 27, since

$$3^3 = 3 \cdot 3 \cdot 3 = 27$$

Example 6

-4 is a cube root of -64, since

$$(-4)^3 = (-4)(-4)(-4) = -64$$

Note

For *any* real number r there is only one real cube root. If r is positive, the cube root is positive, and if r is negative, the cube root is negative.

Notation

In either case, the cube root of r will be denoted by $\sqrt[3]{r}$.

In a similar manner, we can define a fourth root, fifth root, sixth root, etc. For example, 2 is a fourth root of 16, since $2^4 = 2 \cdot 2 \cdot 2 \cdot 2 = 16$; -3 is a fifth root of -243, since $(-3)^5 = (-3)(-3)(-3)(-3)(-3) = -243$.

In general, we will define an nth root of a real number r, where n is an integer greater than 1, as follows:

nth ROOT

If $a^n = r$, where a and r are real numbers and n is an integer greater than 1, then a is called an nth *root* of r, and is denoted by $\sqrt[n]{r}$.

Note

As we have already seen, in the case of a square root we *leave out the 2* in the notation $\sqrt[2]{r}$ and simply write $\sqrt{r}$.

The above definition presents a number of cases:

Case I

If r is positive, then $\sqrt[n]{r}$ will denote the positive nth root of r.

Example 7

(a) $\sqrt{16}$ (read "the square root of 16") $= 4$

(b) $\sqrt[3]{8}$ (read "the cube root of 8") $= 2$

(c) $\sqrt[4]{81}$ (read "the fourth root of 81") $= 3$

(d) $\sqrt[5]{32}$ (read "the fifth root of 32") $= 2$

Case II

If r is negative and *n is odd*, then $\sqrt[n]{r}$ denotes the negative nth root of r.

Example 8

(a) $\sqrt[3]{-125} = -5$ (b) $\sqrt[5]{-32} = -2$

Case III

If r is negative and *n is even*, there is *no real nth root of r*.

Note

Thus in the remainder of this chapter, whenever we will deal with expressions such as $\sqrt[4]{x}, \sqrt[6]{x}$, etc. it will be assumed that x can take on *only nonnegative values*.

Example 9

There is no real fourth root of -81, since there is no real number a such that $a^4 = -81$, for an *even power of any real number* will be a *positive* real number. For example, $(-3)^4 = +81$.

Exercise Set 3.9

Find the value of each of the following expressions if it is a real number. If it is not a real number, explain why.

1. $\sqrt{64}$ 7. $-\sqrt{\frac{9}{49}}$ 13. $\sqrt[7]{-1}$ 19. $-\sqrt[6]{3^6}$

2. $-\sqrt{36}$ 8. $\sqrt{37^2}$ 14. $\sqrt[4]{256}$ 20. $\sqrt[5]{\frac{32}{243}}$

3. $\sqrt{400}$ 9. $-\sqrt{(\frac{7}{16})^2}$ 15. $-\sqrt[4]{1}$ 21. $\sqrt{1.44}$

4. $-\sqrt{121}$ 10. $-\sqrt{(3)^4}$ 16. $\sqrt[3]{-\frac{8}{27}}$ 22. $-\sqrt{0.0081}$

5. $\sqrt{-9}$ 11. $\sqrt[3]{-27}$ 17. $\sqrt[3]{(-7)^3}$ 23. $\sqrt[3]{0.008}$

6. $\sqrt{\frac{1}{81}}$ 12. $\sqrt[5]{243}$ 18. $\sqrt[4]{-16}$ 24. $\sqrt[3]{-0.064}$

3.10 FRACTIONAL EXPONENTS

We would now like to extend the laws of exponents of Section 3.4 to include all rational exponents of the form $\frac{p}{q}$, where p and q are integers, $q \neq 0$. If fractional exponents are to obey the laws of exponents, then according to Law I we should have, for example,

$$x^{1/2} \cdot x^{1/2} = x^{1/2 + 1/2} = x^1 = x$$

or

$$(x^{1/2})^2 = x, \quad \text{since } x^{1/2} \cdot x^{1/2} = (x^{1/2})^2$$

Thus by our definition of square root in Section 3.9, $x^{1/2}$ must be a square root of x, so that we can now write

$$x^{1/2} = \sqrt{x}$$

Now directly from Law II of exponents we should have

$$(x^{1/3})^3 = x^{1/3 \cdot 3} = x^1 = x$$

Thus $x^{1/3}$ must be the cube root of x and we can write

$$x^{1/3} = \sqrt[3]{x}$$

In general we should have

$$(x^{1/n})^n = x^{1/n \cdot n} = x$$

$x^{1/n}$

Thus we will define

$$x^{1/n} = \sqrt[n]{x}$$

Similarly, according to Law II we should have

$$(x^{3/2})^2 = x^{3/2 \cdot 2} = x^3$$

Thus $x^{3/2}$ must be a square root of x^3, and we will write

$$x^{3/2} = \sqrt{x^3}$$

According to Law II we should also have, for example,

$$(x^{5/3})^3 = x^{5/3 \cdot 3} = x^5$$

Thus $x^{5/3}$ must be the cube root of x^5, and we will write

$$x^{5/3} = \sqrt[3]{x^5}$$

In general we should have

$$(x^{p/q})^q = x^{p/q \cdot q} = x^p$$

$x^{p/q}$

Thus we will define $x^{p/q} = \sqrt[q]{x^p}$

Also since $x^{p/q}$ can be written as $x^{1/q \cdot p}$, then according to Law II of exponents we should also be able to write

$$x^{p/q} = x^{1/q \cdot p} = (x^{1/q})^p$$

But we have established above that $x^{1/q} = \sqrt[q]{x}$. Therefore we can also write

$$x^{p/q} = (x^{1/q})^p = (\sqrt[q]{x})^p$$

ANOTHER DEFINITION OF $x^{p/q}$

Thus we can also define $x^{p/q} = (\sqrt[q]{x})^p$

Note

What we have in essence established is that any radical expression can be replaced by an expression involving a fractional exponent, and any expression involving a fractional exponent can be replaced by a radical expression.

Examples

1. $(-8)^{1/3} = \sqrt[3]{-8} = -2$

2. $625^{1/4} = \sqrt[4]{625} = 5$

3. $8^{2/3} = \sqrt[3]{8^2} = \sqrt[3]{64} = 4$, or we can write

$$8^{2/3} = (\sqrt[3]{8})^2 = 2^2 = 4$$

4. Consider $4^{5/2}$. We could write

$$4^{5/2} = \sqrt{4^5} = \sqrt{(2^2)^5} = \sqrt{2^{10}} = 2^{10/2} = 2^5 = 32$$

However it would have been much more convenient to evaluate this quantity by writing

$$4^{5/2} = (\sqrt{4})^5 = 2^5 = 32$$

5. $(-27)^{5/3} = (\sqrt[3]{-27})^5 = (-3)^5 = -243$

6. $x^{5/8} = \sqrt[8]{x^5}$ or $x^{5/8} = (\sqrt[8]{x})^5$

7. $x^{5/4} = \sqrt[4]{x^5}$ or $x^{5/4} = (\sqrt[4]{x})^5$

Since we are dealing here with an *even root*, we are assuming x can take on *only positive values*.

Exercise Set 3.10A

In exercises 1-8 express each fractional power as a radical.

1. $x^{1/2}$

2. $x^{5/7}$

3. $xy^{1/5}$

4. $(3xy)^{3/2}$

5. $3x^{5/3}$

6. $(x + y)^{1/4}$

7. $-2x^{1/2}$

8. $(2x^3)^{3/5}$

In exercises 9-16 express each radical as a fractional power.

9. $\sqrt{x}$ 13. $(\sqrt[8]{x})^5$

10. $\sqrt[8]{x}$ 11. $\sqrt[5]{x^8}$ 14. $\sqrt[4]{xy}$

15. $\sqrt[3]{(x+y)^2}$

12. $\sqrt[8]{x^5}$ 16. $\sqrt[7]{x^{12}y^7}$

In exercises 17-36 find the value of the given expression.

17. $100^{1/2}$ 27. $(\frac{16}{25})^{3/2}$

18. $(-216)^{1/3}$ 28. $(0.000008)^{2/3}$

19. $(\frac{1}{27})^{1/3}$ 29. $(8)^{-1/3}$

20. $(\frac{1}{4})^{1/2}$ 30. $(64)^{-1/2}$

21. $(-8)^{5/3}$ 31. $(4)^{-3/2}$

22. $(16)^{3/4}$ 32. $(27)^{-2/3}$

23. $(\frac{8}{27})^{2/3}$ 33. $(-1)^{-1/3}$

24. $(243)^{4/5}$ 34. $(81)^{-3/4}$

25. $(0.01)^{3/2}$ 35. $(\frac{1}{9})^{-1/2}$

26. $(-0.027)^{4/3}$ 36. $(\frac{8}{27})^{-2/3}$

Once again we will repeat the laws of exponents. However, now we will allow for any rational exponents. We will also write special cases of two of these laws which involve radicals.

LAW I

If $x \in R$ and m, n are *any rational numbers*, then

$$x^m x^n = x^{m+n}$$

LAW II

If $x \in R$ and m, n are *any rational numbers*, then

$$(x^m)^n = x^{mn}$$

LAW III

If x, y, z are real numbers and m is *any rational number*, then

$$(xyz)^m = x^m y^m z^m$$

LAW III(a)

$\sqrt[n]{xy} = \sqrt[n]{x}\sqrt[n]{y}$ where n is any integer greater than 1.

This is a direct result of Law III and the definition of a fractional exponent, for

$$\sqrt[n]{xy} = (xy)^{1/n} = x^{1/n}y^{1/n} = \sqrt[n]{x}\,\sqrt[n]{y}$$

LAW IV

If x and y are real numbers, $y \neq 0$, and m is *any rational number*, then

$$\left(\frac{x}{y}\right)^m = \frac{x^m}{y^m}$$

LAW IV(a)

$\sqrt[n]{\dfrac{x}{y}} = \dfrac{\sqrt[n]{x}}{\sqrt[n]{y}}$, where n is any integer greater than 1.

This is a direct result of Law IV and the definition of a fractional exponent, for

$$\sqrt[n]{\frac{x}{y}} = \left(\frac{x}{y}\right)^{1/n} = \frac{x^{1/n}}{y^{1/n}} = \frac{\sqrt[n]{x}}{\sqrt[n]{y}}$$

LAW V

If $x \in R$, $x \neq 0$, and m, n are *any rational numbers*, then

$$\frac{x^m}{x^n} = x^{m-n}$$

Although Laws III(a) and IV(a) are direct results of Laws III and IV, and thus could have been omitted, they were worth special mention as you shall see in the first three of the following examples.

Example 1

Using Law III(a), simplify the following roots.

(a) $\sqrt[3]{50}$ (b) $\sqrt{48}$ (c) $\sqrt[3]{54}$ (d) $\sqrt{45x^3}$

(a) $\sqrt{50} = \sqrt{25 \cdot 2}$

$\qquad = \sqrt{25}\,\sqrt{2}$ [Law III(a)]

$\qquad = 5\sqrt{2}$

(b) $\sqrt{48} = \sqrt{16 \cdot 3}$

$\qquad = \sqrt{16}\,\sqrt{3}$ [Law III(a)]

$\qquad = 4\sqrt{3}$

(c) $\sqrt[3]{54} = \sqrt[3]{27 \cdot 2}$

$\qquad = \sqrt[3]{27}\,\sqrt[3]{2}$ [Law III(a)]

$\qquad = 3\sqrt[3]{2}$

(d) $\sqrt{45x^3} = \sqrt{5 \cdot 9 \cdot x^2 \cdot x}$

$\qquad = \sqrt{5}\,\sqrt{9}\,\sqrt{x^2}\,\sqrt{x}$ [Law III(a)]

$\qquad = 3x\sqrt{5}\,\sqrt{x}$

$\qquad = 3x\sqrt{5x}$ [Law III(a)]

Example 2

Use Law III(a) to simplify the following products.

(a) $\sqrt{3}\,\sqrt{27}$ (b) $\sqrt[3]{25}\,\sqrt[3]{5}$ (c) $\sqrt{6}\,\sqrt{72}$ (d) $\sqrt{3x}\,\sqrt{12x^3}$

(a) $\sqrt{3}\,\sqrt{27} = \sqrt{3 \cdot 27}$ [Law III(a)]

$\qquad = \sqrt{81}$

$\qquad = 9$

(b) $\sqrt[3]{25} \ \sqrt[3]{5} = \sqrt[3]{125}$ [Law III(a)]

　　　　　　　$= 5$

(c) $\sqrt{6} \ \sqrt{72} = \sqrt{6} \ \sqrt{2 \cdot 36}$

　　　　　　　$= \sqrt{6} \ \sqrt{2} \ \sqrt{36}$ [Law III(a)]

　　　　　　　$= \sqrt{6 \cdot 2} \cdot 6$ [Law III(a)]

　　　　　　　$= 6\sqrt{12}$

　　　　　　　$= 6\sqrt{4 \cdot 3}$

　　　　　　　$= 6\sqrt{4} \ \sqrt{3}$ [Law III(a)]

　　　　　　　$= 6 \cdot 2\sqrt{3}$

　　　　　　　$= 12\sqrt{3}$

(d) $\sqrt{3x} \ \sqrt{12x^3} = \sqrt{36x^4}$ [Law III(a)]

　　　　　　　$= \sqrt{36} \ \sqrt{x^4}$ [Law III(a)]

　　　　　　　$= 6\sqrt{x^2 \cdot x^2}$

　　　　　　　$= 6\sqrt{x^2} \ \sqrt{x^2}$ [Law III(a)]

　　　　　　　$= 6x \cdot x$

　　　　　　　$= 6x^2$

Example 3

Use Law IV(a) to simplify the following square roots.

(a) $\sqrt{\frac{9}{49}}$　　　　　　　　　　　　　(b) $\sqrt{\frac{8}{81}}$

(a) $\sqrt{\frac{9}{49}} = \dfrac{\sqrt{9}}{\sqrt{49}}$ [Law IV(a)]

　　　　　$= \frac{3}{7}$

(b) $\sqrt{\frac{8}{81}} = \dfrac{\sqrt{8}}{\sqrt{81}}$ [Law IV(a)]

　　　　　$= \dfrac{\sqrt{4 \cdot 2}}{9}$

$$= \frac{\sqrt{4}\ \sqrt{2}}{9} \qquad \text{[Law III(a)]}$$

$$= \frac{2\ \sqrt{2}}{9}$$

Example 4

Simplify each of the following expressions, and write the result free of radicals.

(a) $(5x^{1/3}y^{3/2})(2x^{5/3}y^{1/2})$ (b) $(3\sqrt[3]{x^2}\,y)(\sqrt{9y}\ x^2)$

(a) $(5x^{1/3}y^{3/2})(2x^{5/3}y^{1/2}) = 2 \cdot 5x^{1/3}x^{5/3}y^{3/2}y^{1/2}$ (Regrouping)

$$= 10x^{1/3+5/3}y^{3/2+1/2} \qquad \text{(Law I)}$$

$$= 10x^{6/3}y^{4/2}$$

$$= 10x^2y^2$$

(b) $(3\sqrt[3]{x^2}y)(\sqrt{9y}\ x^2) = (3x^{2/3}y)(\sqrt{9}\sqrt{y}\ x^2)$ [Definition of fractional exponents and Law III(a)]

$$= (3x^{2/3}y)(3y^{1/2}x^2) \qquad \text{(Definition of } y^{1/2})$$

$$= 3 \cdot 3x^{2/3}x^2yy^{1/2} \qquad \text{(Regrouping)}$$

$$= 9x^{2/3+2}y^{1+1/2} \qquad \text{(Law I)}$$

$$= 9x^{8/3}y^{3/2}$$

Example 5

Simplify each of the following and write the result free of radicals.

(a) $(36x^2y^6)^{3/2}$ (b) $\sqrt[3]{27x^2y^{12}}$

(a) $(36x^2y^6)^{3/2} = (36)^{3/2}(x^2)^{3/2}(y^6)^{3/2}$ (Law III)

$$= (36^{1/2})^3 x^{2\cdot 3/2}y^{6\cdot 3/2} \qquad \text{(Law II)}$$

$$= 6^3x^3y^9$$

$$= 216x^3y^9$$

(b) $\sqrt[3]{27x^2y^{12}}$ $= (27x^2y^{12})^{1/3}$ (Definition of fraction-
                                                            al exponents)

$\qquad\qquad\quad = 27^{1/3}(x^2)^{1/3}(y^{12})^{1/3}$ (Law III)

$\qquad\qquad\quad = 3x^{2\cdot1/3}y^{12\cdot1/3}$ (Law II)

$\qquad\qquad\quad = 3x^{2/3}y^4$

Example 6

Simplify the expression $\sqrt[3]{\dfrac{-64y^9}{27x^6}}$ and write the result free of radicals.

$$\sqrt[3]{\dfrac{-64y^9}{27x^6}} = \dfrac{\sqrt[3]{-64y^9}}{\sqrt[3]{27x^6}} \qquad \text{[Law IV(a)]}$$

$$= \dfrac{\sqrt[3]{-64}\ \sqrt[3]{y^9}}{\sqrt[3]{27}\ \sqrt[3]{x^6}} \qquad \text{[Law III(a)]}$$

$$= \dfrac{-4y^{9/3}}{3x^{6/3}} \qquad \text{(Definition of fractional exponents)}$$

$$= \dfrac{-4}{3}\dfrac{y^3}{x^2}$$

Example 7

Simplify the expression $\dfrac{\sqrt[3]{16x^8}}{\sqrt[3]{2x^5}}$ and write the result free of radicals.

$$\dfrac{\sqrt[3]{16x^8}}{\sqrt[3]{2x^5}} = \sqrt[3]{\dfrac{16x^8}{2x^5}} \qquad \text{[Law IV(a)]}$$

$$= \sqrt[3]{8x^{8-5}} \qquad \text{(Law V)}$$

$$= \sqrt[3]{8x^3}$$

$$= \sqrt[3]{8}\ \sqrt[3]{x^3} \qquad \text{[Law III(a)]}$$

$$= 2x$$

Example 8

Simplify the expression $\dfrac{\sqrt{x^3 y^3}}{\sqrt[3]{x^2 y^2}}$ and write the result free of radicals.

$$\frac{\sqrt{x^3 y^3}}{\sqrt[3]{x^2 y^2}} = \frac{(x^3 y^3)^{1/2}}{(x^2 y^2)^{1/3}} \qquad \text{(Definition of fractional exponents)}$$

$$= \frac{(x^3)^{1/2}(y^3)^{1/2}}{(x^2)^{1/3}(y^2)^{1/3}} \qquad \text{(Law III)}$$

$$= \frac{x^{3/2} y^{3/2}}{x^{2/3} y^{2/3}} \qquad \text{(Law II)}$$

$$= x^{3/2 - 2/3} \, y^{3/2 - 2/3} \quad \text{(Law V)}$$

$$= x^{5/6} y^{5/6}$$

Exercise Set 3.10B

In exercises 1-20 use Laws III(a) and IV(a) to simplify the given expression.

1. $\sqrt{8}$

2. $\sqrt{32}$

3. $\sqrt{300}$

4. $\sqrt{108}$

5. $\sqrt[3]{24}$

6. $\sqrt[3]{108}$

7. $\sqrt[4]{48}$

8. $\sqrt[3]{0.024}$

9. $\sqrt{\frac{8}{49}}$

10. $\sqrt{\frac{2}{50}}$

11. $\sqrt[3]{\frac{128}{27}}$

12. $\sqrt[4]{\frac{162}{16}}$

13. $\sqrt{5} \, \sqrt{10}$

14. $\sqrt{6} \, \sqrt{12}$

15. $\sqrt{45} \, \sqrt{5}$

16. $\sqrt{2} \, \sqrt{24}$

17. $\sqrt[3]{54} \, \sqrt[3]{2}$

18. $\sqrt[3]{192} \, \sqrt[3]{-9}$

19. $\sqrt{2} \, \sqrt{3} \, \sqrt{6}$

20. $\sqrt{3} \, \sqrt{6} \, \sqrt{8}$

21. True or false: $\sqrt{2} \, \sqrt{4} = 8$

22. True or false: $\sqrt{3} \, \sqrt{3} = 9$

23. True or false: $\sqrt[3]{-1} \, \sqrt[3]{-1} = 1$

24. True or false: $(4)^{-3/2} = -8$

25. True or false: $\sqrt{4} + \sqrt{4} = 4$

26. True or false: $\sqrt{8} + \sqrt{8} = 8$

In exercises 27-48 simplify the given expression, writing the result free of radicals and free of negative exponents.

27. $\sqrt{3x}\ \sqrt{12x}$

28. $(\sqrt{x}\,)^4$

29. $\sqrt{x}\ \sqrt{x^3}$

30. $x^{1/3}x^{5/3}$

31. $\dfrac{x^{5/6}}{x^{1/12}}$

32. $\sqrt{\dfrac{x^8}{x^2}}$

33. $\sqrt{x}\ \sqrt{2x}\ \sqrt{8x}$

34. $(3\sqrt{2x}\,)^2$

35. $(3\sqrt[3]{3x})^3$

36. $\sqrt[3]{5x}\ \sqrt[3]{25x^5y^4}$

37. $\sqrt{xy^3}\ \sqrt[3]{x^2y}$

38. $(3x^{2/3}y^{1/2})(4x^{1/3}y^{5/2})$

39. $(x^{5/2}y^{-2/3})(x^{-3/2}y)$

40. $(27x^6y^9)^{2/3}$

41. $\left(\dfrac{x^2y^3}{x^8}\right)^{2/3}$

42. $\left(\dfrac{81y^{-2}x^5}{3x^2}\right)^{1/3}$

43. $\sqrt{\dfrac{49x^7y^4}{x^3z^2}}$

44. $\left(\dfrac{27x^3y^4}{8x^{-3}y}\right)^{1/3}$

45. $\sqrt{(x^6y^{-2}z^2)^3}$

46. $\sqrt[3]{\left(\dfrac{x^6y}{x^3y^4}\right)^2}$

47. $\left(\dfrac{x^6}{y^3}\right)^{-2/3}$

48. $\left(\dfrac{x^{-2}y^{10}}{x^4}\right)^{-5/2}$

REVIEW TEST FOR CHAPTER III

Note: This test should be completed in 2 hours.

Answer questions 1-5 true or false.

1. $\dfrac{a+b+c}{a+b} = c$, for any real numbers a, b, c, where $a + b \neq 0$

2. $a^2 + a^3 = a^5$, for any $a \in R$

3. $a^2 + a^2 + a^2 = 3a^2$, for any $a \in R$

4. $a^2 + b^2 = (a + b)^2$, for any $a, b \in R$

5. $(a^3)^3 = a^6$, for any $a \in R$

In questions 6-9 find the number represented by the given expression.

6. $\left(\frac{2}{5}\right)^{-3}$

7. $(2^{-1} + 2^2)^{-2}$

8. $\dfrac{(2^{-2} \cdot 3 \cdot 2^2)^{-4}}{3^{-2}}$

9. $\dfrac{4^{-1} + 3^{-1}}{3^{-2} - 3^{-1}}$

10. Evaluate $x^3 - 3x^2 - 2xy - y^2$, when $x = -2, y = -1$.

11. Evaluate $(2a + b)^3 + (3a - 2b)^2 - 2(2a - b)$, when $a = 1, b = -2$.

In questions 12-16 simplify the given expression and express the result using positive exponents only. (Assume no denominator is 0.)

12. $(-3x^2y^3)(\frac{2}{3}xy^{-1})$

13. $\dfrac{6x^2y^{-3}z^3}{\frac{1}{6}x^4z^{-3}}$

14. $(x^2y^2z)^3(x^2y^2z^2)^{-3}$

15. $(-2x^{-2}y^2)^{-2}$

16. $\dfrac{(x + y)^3x^{-3}}{x + y}$

In questions 17-21 perform the indicated operations and simplify the result, collecting like terms wherever possible.

17. $(7x - 4y + 3z) - 2(4x + 3y - 2z)$

18. $5x^3 - 3xy + y^2 - 3(-3x^3 - 4y^2) + 5xy$

19. $(a^2 - b^2)(a^2 + b^2)$

20. $\dfrac{xy - 3x^2y^3 + 4x^3y^2}{xy}$

21. $(-3s^2 - 2s + 4)(s^2 - s + 2)$

22. Write the number 1092 as a sum of powers of 10.

23. Let x stand for Beverly's present age. Write an algebraic expression for two times her age four years ago.

24. If Oscar scored x points in the last basketball game and John scored $x - 3$ points and Jim scored twice as many points as John, what is the total points that these three players scored?

25. Simplify $\dfrac{(-2x^{-3}y^5z^{-2})^3}{(-\frac{1}{4}x^{-3}y^0z^{-1})^2}$

26. Find the value of $\left(\frac{4}{9}\right)^{-3/2}$.

27. Simplify the expression $\sqrt[4]{25}\ \sqrt[4]{50}$.

28. Simplify the expression $\sqrt[3]{xy^2}\ \sqrt[3]{x^2y^4}$, writing the result free of radicals.

In questions 29-32 simplify the given expression, writing the result free of radicals and negative exponents.

29. $(3x^{3/8}y^{-2/3})(2x^{3/4}yz^{1/2})$

30. $\left(\dfrac{5x^{1/3}}{25x^{1/2}}\right)^2$

31. $\dfrac{(4x^3y^{5/2})^2}{x^6y^{3/2}}$

32. $\left(\dfrac{x^6y^4}{x^8y^{-2}}\right)^{-1/2}$

IV LINEAR EQUATIONS AND INEQUALITIES IN ONE VARIABLE

4.1 DEFINITION OF AN EQUATION

AN EQUATION

An *equation* is a mathematical statement that *two algebraic expressions are equal.* The two expressions are called the *sides* or *members* of the equation.

Examples of Equations

1. $7 + 3 = 10$
2. $6 + 1 = 9$
3. $x + 3 = 7$
4. $3x + 7 = 3x + 6$
5. $-2(x^2 - 3x - 1) = -2x^2 + 6x + 2$
6. $x^2 + y^2 = 25$
7. $x^3 + \frac{4}{x} = 3x + \frac{4}{x^2}$

In the case of examples 1 and 2, where no variables are involved, we can obviously determine whether or not the given statement (equation) is true or false. We will therefore not consider such equations and concern ourselves only with equations involving one or more variables.

In examples 3-7, the given statements (equations) are neither true nor false. However, they become true or false when the variable (or variables) is replaced by some real number.

Example 8

Let us consider the equation $2x + 1 = 7$.

If x is here replaced by the number 2, then the equation is false, for $(2 \cdot 2) + 1 = 5$ and $5 \neq 7$. However if x is replaced by the number 3, the equation is then true, for $(2 \cdot 3) + 1 = 6 + 1 = 7$. The number 3 is said to *satisfy* the equation and is called a solution of the equation.

Example 9

Consider the equation $(x + 1)(x + 2) = x^2 + 3x + 2$.

Since we know that the product of the two binomials $x + 1$ and $x + 2$ is $x^2 + 3x + 2$, we then can see that this equation is true if x is replaced by any real number. Here we say that *every real number satisfies this equation* and thus each real number is a solution of this equation.

Example 10

Consider the equation $x + 5 = x + 3$.

Whenever x is replaced by any real number, we can see that the sum of that number and 5 cannot possibly equal the sum of that same number and 3. Thus this equation is false whenever x is replaced by any real number. We then say that this equation has no solutions.

The equations of examples 8 and 10 are called *conditional equations*, while the equation of example 9 is called an *identity*.

AN IDENTITY

An equation which is satisfied by *every permissible value* of the variables involved is called an *identity*.

CONDITIONAL EQUATION

A *conditional equation* is one which is *not satisfied by every permissible value* of the variables involved.

Note

A *permissible value* of a variable is a number which when used to replace the variable in each side of the equation *produces a real number.*

Example 11

Consider the equation $\frac{1}{x} = \frac{x}{x^2}$.

Here every real number is permissible, *except $x = 0$*, for when x is replaced by 0 both sides of the equation are not defined.

This equation is an *identity*, for when $x \neq 0$ we know by the laws of exponents that:

$$\frac{x}{x^2} = x^{1-2} = x^{-1} = \frac{1}{x}$$

Example 12

Consider the equation $\frac{1}{(x-1)(x-4)} = 3$

Here $x = 1$ and $x = 4$ are not permissible values of the variable, for when x is replaced by either 1 or 4 the denominator of the left side of the above equation is 0 and thus the left side is not defined.

This is a conditional equation, for we need only see that $x = 5$, for example, (a permissible value) does not satisfy the equation.

Let us now define the *solution set* of an equation in *one variable.*

SOLUTION

If an equation becomes a true statement when the variable is replaced by a specific number, then that number is called a solution of the equation, and is said to satisfy the equation.

THE SOLUTION SET OF AN EQUATION IN ONE VARIABLE

The *solution set* of an equation is the set of all the solutions of the equation.

Note

Finding the solution set of an equation is referred to as *solving the equation.*

Example 13

Consider the equation $2x + 1 = 7$. (This was example 8.)

We saw that the number 3 is a solution of this equation. 3 is the only real number that satisfies this equation. Therefore, the solution set would be $\{3\}$.

Example 14

Consider again the equation $(x + 1)(x + 2) = x^2 + 3x + 2$ (example 9).

We saw that this equation is an identity for all real numbers. Thus the solution set is:

$$R = \{x \mid x \text{ is a real number}\}$$

Example 15

Consider again the equation $x + 5 = x + 3$ (example 10).

This equation has no solutions. Therefore, the solution set is $\emptyset$, the null set.

Exercise Set 4.1

In exercises 1-8, state whether the given equation is a conditional equation or an identity.

1. $x + 3 = 3 + x$

2. $x + 4 = 10 + 2x$

3. $y + 2 + 5 = y + 7$

4. $(x + 1)(x - 1) = x^2 - 1$

5. $3x + 1 = 4(x - 2)$

6. $2(x + 4) = 2x + 4$

7. $3(x + 1) = \frac{1}{2}(6x + 6)$

8. $(x - 2)(x - 2) = x^2 - 4$

9. Is 2 a solution of the equation $2x + 9 = 27$?

10. Is 3 a solution of the equation $3x - 10 = 1$?

11. Is -5 a solution of the equation $4x - 5 = 2x - 15$?

12. Is 3 a solution of the equation $\dfrac{2}{x - 3} + \dfrac{5}{x(x - 3)} = \dfrac{11}{3(x - 3)}$?

13. Is 0 a solution of the equation $\dfrac{x}{x - 2} + x(x - 3) = 0$?

In exercises 14-21 solve the given equation by inspection.

14. $x + 5 = 6$ **18.** $x - 5 = x + 5$

15. $6x = 36$ **19.** $\frac{x}{7} = 3$

16. $x - 1 = 7$ **20.** $15x = -45$

17. $x - 2 = -9$ **21.** $x + 3 = -6$

4.2   LINEAR EQUATIONS IN ONE VARIABLE

LINEAR EQUATION IN ONE VARIABLE

An equation in one variable which contains the first power of the variable, and no higher power, and which contains *no fractions that have the variable in the denominator* is called a *linear equation in one variable.*

Examples

1. $2x + 5 = 9$ is a linear equation in one variable.
2. $\frac{2}{3}(y + 3) = \frac{4}{5} - 1$ is a linear equation in one variable.
3. $\frac{2}{x} + 1 = 5$ is *not* a linear equation in one variable, for the variable x is involved in the denominator.
4. $x^2 + x + 1 = 5$ is *not* a linear equation in one variable, for it contains the second power of the variable x.

Finding a solution of an equation involves finding a number which, when replacing the variable, produces a true statement. In an equation like $x + 3 = 7$, this can be done simply by inspection. That is, we can see that the number 4 is a solution of this equation, and is *the only solution*, for if we replace x by 4 we get $4 + 3 = 7$ or $7 = 7$.

However, not all linear equations are in this simple a form. For example, consider the equation:

$$\frac{2}{3}(2x - 5) + \frac{1}{2}(4 - 7x) = \frac{7}{4}$$

It is obvious that it would be much more difficult to find a solution of this equation merely by inspection or guessing. Thus we should develop a procedure to solve any linear equation in one variable.

SOME PROPERTIES OF AN EQUALITY

Before we consider the procedure for solving a linear equation in one variable, we will need the following basic results regarding an equality:

A. If $a = b$, then $a + c = b + c$,   where a, b, and c
B. If $a = b$, then $ac = bc$ *are real numbers.*

Example 5

$$7 = 3 + 4$$

then

$$7 + 5 = 3 + 4 + 5 \qquad \text{(Result A)}$$

Also

$$7 - 2 = 3 + 4 - 2 \qquad \text{[Recall } 7 - 2 = 7 + (-2) \text{ and } 3 + 4 - 2 = 3 + 4 + (-2)\text{].}$$

Example 6

$$7 = 3 + 4$$

then

$$7(2) = (3 + 4)2 \qquad \text{(Result B)}$$

Also

$$7(\tfrac{1}{2}) = (3 + 4)\tfrac{1}{2} \qquad \text{(Result B)}$$

Now suppose we consider again the equation $x + 3 = 7$, which we've seen, by inspection, has 4 as its only solution. Since 4 is a solution of $x + 3 = 7$, 4 must also be a solution of the following equations:

(1) $x + 3 + c = 7 + c$ (c is any real number.)

and

(2) $k(x + 3) = k(7)$ (k is any nonzero real number.)

If we replace x by 4 in equation (1), we obtain:

$$4 + 3 + c = 7 + c$$

or

$$7 + c = 7 + c \qquad \text{(Which is true by Result A above)}$$

If we replace x by 4 in equation (2), we obtain:

$$k(4 + 3) = k(7)$$

or

$$k(7) = k(7) \qquad \text{(Which is true by Result B above)}$$

Note

This procedure, that of adding the same real number to *both sides* of an equation or multiplying *both sides* of an equation by the same *nonzero* real number, thus producing a new equation with the same solution as the original equation, opens the door to solving any linear equation in one variable. The idea is to use the *appropriate* real numbers so as to simplify the form of the given equation.

In the case of the equation $x + 3 = 7$, if we add -3 to *both sides* of the equation, we obtain:

$$x + 3 + (-3) = 7 + (-3)$$

or

$$x + 0 = 4 \qquad \text{(Why?)}$$

and thus.

$$x = 4$$

This is the simplest form that any linear equation in one variable can be converted to. In this simple form, we see that the *only* number that the variable x can be replaced by to make the *original* equation true is 4. Thus 4 is the only solution of the equation $x + 3 = 7$.

Example 7

Find the solution set of the equation

$$3x - 7 = 11$$

and check the result.

$$3x - 7 = 11$$

Adding 7 to *both* sides, we obtain

$$3x - 7 + 7 = 11 + 7$$

or

$$3x = 18$$

Now, multiplying both sides by $\frac{1}{3}$, the multiplicative inverse of 3, we obtain

$$\tfrac{1}{3}(3x) = \tfrac{1}{3}(18)$$

or

$$1x = 6$$

or simply

$$x = 6$$

Thus we see that 6 is the only solution and therefore the solution set is $\{6\}$.

To *check* our result we will replace x by 6 in the *original* equation, thus obtaining:

$$3x - 7 = 11$$

$$3(6) - 7 \overset{?}{=} 11$$

$$18 - 7 \overset{?}{=} 11$$

$$11 = 11$$

Example 8

Find the solution set of the equation $-3x - 5 = 2x + 5$ and check your result.

$$-3x - 5 = 2x + 5$$

$$-2x - 3x - 5 = -2x + 2x + 5 \qquad \text{(Adding } -2x \text{ to both sides)}$$

or

$$(-2-3)x - 5 = (-2 + 2)x + 5$$

or

$$-5x - 5 = 0 \cdot x + 5 \qquad \text{(Using the distributive law to combine like terms)}$$

or

$$-5x - 5 = 5$$

$$-5x - 5 + 5 = 5 + 5 \qquad \text{(Adding 5 to both sides)}$$

or

$$-5x = 10$$

$$-\tfrac{1}{5}(-5x) = -\tfrac{1}{5}(10) \qquad \text{(Multiplying both sides by } -\tfrac{1}{5}\text{, the multiplicative inverse of } -5\text{)}$$

or

$$1x = -2$$

or simply

$$x = -2$$

Thus the solution set is $\{-2\}$.

To check our result we replace x by -2 in the *original* equation.

$$-3x - 5 = 2x + 5$$

$$(-3)(-2) - 5 \overset{?}{=} 2(-2) + 5$$

$$6 - 5 \overset{?}{=} -4 + 5$$

$$1 = 1$$

We could have also solved this equation in the following way:

$$-3x - 5 = 2x + 5$$

$$3x - 3x - 5 = 3x + 2x + 5 \qquad \text{(Adding } 3x \text{ to both sides)}$$

or

$$-5 = 5x + 5 \qquad \text{(Adding like terms)}$$

$$-5 - 5 = 5x + 5 - 5 \qquad \text{(Adding } -5 \text{ to both sides)}$$

or

$$-10 = 5x$$

$$-10(\tfrac{1}{5}) = \tfrac{1}{5}(5x) \qquad \text{(Multiplying both sides by } \tfrac{1}{5},$$

$$-2 = x \qquad\qquad\quad \text{the multiplicative inverse of 5)}$$

SUMMARY

Now we are ready to outline a procedure for solving a linear equation in one variable.

(1) Add the appropriate algebraic expressions to *both sides* of the equation in order to get an expression involving the variable on one side and the constant terms on the other side.
(2) Combine like terms.

(3) To obtain a coefficient of 1 for the variable, multiply *both sides* by the multiplicative inverse of the existing coefficient of the variable.
(4) Check your result by substituting the solution for the variable in the *original* equation.

Example 9

Solve the equation $\frac{x}{7} + 6 = 14$ and check your result.

$$\frac{x}{7} + 6 = 14$$

$$\frac{x}{7} + 6 - 6 = 14 - 6 \qquad \text{(Adding } -6 \text{ to both sides)}$$

or

$$\frac{x}{7} = 8$$

$$7 \cdot \frac{x}{7} = 7 \cdot 8 \qquad \text{(Multiplying both sides by 7,}$$
$$\text{the multiplicative invers of } \tfrac{1}{7})$$

or

$$x = 56$$

Thus the solution set is $\{56\}$.
Check:

$$\frac{x}{7} + 6 = 14$$
$$\frac{56}{7} + 6 \overset{?}{=} 14$$
$$8 + 6 \overset{?}{=} 14$$
$$14 = 14$$

Example 10

Solve the equation $\frac{x}{5} + 3 = 11 - \frac{x}{3}$ and check your result.

$$\frac{x}{5} + 3 = 11 - \frac{x}{3}$$

$$\frac{x}{5} + \frac{x}{3} + 3 = 11 - \frac{x}{3} + \frac{x}{3} \qquad \text{(Adding } \tfrac{x}{3} \text{ to both sides)}$$

or

$$\frac{x}{5} + \frac{x}{3} + 3 = 11$$

$$\frac{x}{5} + \frac{x}{3} + 3 - 3 = 11 - 3 \qquad \text{(Adding } -3 \text{ to both sides)}$$

or

$$\tfrac{x}{5} + \tfrac{x}{3} = 8$$

$(\tfrac{1}{5} + \tfrac{1}{3})x = 8$ (Using the distributive law to combine like terms)

$$\tfrac{8}{15}x = 8 \qquad \text{(Adding fractions)}$$

$\tfrac{15}{8}(\tfrac{8}{15}x) = (\tfrac{15}{8})8$ (Multiplying both sides by $\tfrac{15}{8}$, the multiplicative inverse of $\tfrac{8}{15}$)

$$x = 15 \qquad \text{(Multiplying fractions)}$$

Thus the solution set is $\{15\}$.
Check:

$$\tfrac{x}{5} + 3 = 11 - \tfrac{x}{3}$$

$$\tfrac{15}{5} + 3 \overset{?}{=} 11 - \tfrac{15}{3}$$

$$3 + 3 \overset{?}{=} 11 - 5$$

or

$$6 = 6$$

Example 11

Solve the equation $2(7 + x) = 1 - 7x$ and check the result.

$$2(7 + x) = 1 - 7x$$

$14 + 2x = 1 - 7x$ (Distributive law)

$14 + 2x + 7x = 1 - 7x + 7x$ (Adding $7x$ to both sides)

or

$14 + 9x = 1$ (Combining like terms)

$-14 + 14 + 9x = -14 + 1$ (Adding -14 to both sides)

or

$9x = -13$

$\tfrac{1}{9}(9x) = \tfrac{1}{9}(-13)$ (Multiplying both sides by $\tfrac{1}{9}$)

or

$$x = \tfrac{-13}{9}$$

The solution set is $\{\frac{-13}{9}\}$.
Check:

$$2(7 + x) = 1 - 7x$$

$$2(7 + \tfrac{-13}{9}) \overset{?}{=} 1 - 7(\tfrac{-13}{9})$$

$$2(\tfrac{63}{9} - \tfrac{13}{9}) \overset{?}{=} 1 + \tfrac{91}{9}$$

$$2(\tfrac{50}{9}) \overset{?}{=} \tfrac{9}{9} + \tfrac{91}{9}$$

$$\tfrac{100}{9} = \tfrac{100}{9}$$

Exercise Set 4.2

In exercises 1-8 state whether the given equation is linear.

1. $-3x + 4 = 2x - 1$

2. $2(x + 1) = 7x + 5$

3. $2x + \frac{x}{2} = 7$

4. $\frac{3}{x} + \frac{1}{2} = 7$

5. $2x + 5x = \frac{1}{2} + \frac{1}{3}x$

6. $x + 3 = x^2 - 7$

7. $3x + 4x^{-1} = 3$

8. $\frac{x^2}{x} + 3x = 5$

In exercises 9-30 find the solution set of the given equation and check the result.

9. $3x - 5 = 7$

10. $3(x - 5) = 7$

11. $70 = 6x + 10$

12. $-5y + 17 = 47$

13. $x + 3 = 4x + 1$

14. $2x - 5 = x - 8$

15. $2(x + 5) = 10 - x$

16. $5(y - 2) = -2(y - 2)$

17. $6x + 3x - 12 = 2x$

18. $9x + 3(2x - 1) = 12$

19. $-2x - 3(2x - 4) = 4x + 8$

20. $\frac{1}{3}x - 3 = 4$

21. $y - \frac{1}{4} = 5\frac{3}{4}$

22. $2(x + 1) = 7x - 8$

23. $z - \frac{5}{4} = \frac{13}{2}$

24. $\frac{3x}{4} - 6 = \frac{x}{12}$

25. $\frac{2x}{3} + \frac{x}{4} = 22$

26. $\frac{x}{3} - \frac{3x}{8} = 5 + \frac{3x}{4}$

27. $\frac{3x - 2}{5} = 1$

28. $\frac{1 - 2x}{4} = 2$

29. $3(y - 2) - 2 = 5(y + 3) - 7(y - 1)$

30. $2(x - 1) + 2 + 3(x - \frac{1}{3}) + 1 = -4(x - \frac{9}{4})$

4.3 MORE ON FRACTIONS

In Section 2.7 we saw that we could add fractions by first writing them with the same denominator. For example, suppose we add $\frac{3}{10}$ and $\frac{4}{15}$. We could first multiply $\frac{3}{10}$ by $\frac{15}{15}$ and $\frac{4}{15}$ by $\frac{10}{10}$, thus producing two fractions with the same denominator, 150.

$$
\begin{aligned}
\tfrac{3}{10} + \tfrac{4}{15} &= (\tfrac{3}{10} \cdot \tfrac{15}{15}) + (\tfrac{4}{15} \cdot \tfrac{10}{10}) \\[4pt]
&= \tfrac{45}{150} + \tfrac{40}{150} \\[4pt]
&= \tfrac{85}{150} \\[4pt]
&= \tfrac{17 \, \cdot \, 5}{30 \, \cdot \, 5} \qquad\qquad \text{(Simplifying fractions)} \\[4pt]
&= \tfrac{17}{30}
\end{aligned}
$$

You may have noticed that we could have multiplied $\frac{3}{10}$ by $\frac{6}{6}$ and $\frac{4}{15}$ by $\frac{4}{4}$, thus obtaining 60 as a common denominator; or we could have multiplied $\frac{3}{10}$ by $\frac{3}{3}$ and $\frac{4}{15}$ by $\frac{2}{2}$ to obtain still a smaller common denominator, 30, which would at the same time simplify the arithmetic involved.

$$
\begin{aligned}
\tfrac{3}{10} + \tfrac{4}{15} &= (\tfrac{3}{10} \cdot \tfrac{3}{3}) + (\tfrac{4}{15} \cdot \tfrac{2}{2}) \\[4pt]
&= \tfrac{9}{30} + \tfrac{8}{30} \\[4pt]
&= \tfrac{17}{30}
\end{aligned}
$$

Thus we can see that the smaller the common denominator, the simpler the arithmetic becomes. The question is, how do we determine the *least common denominator*?

As in the example above, the least common denominator can often be determined by inspection. However this is not always as easy as it may seem, and may require much guesswork. We will therefore develop a procedure to find the least common denominator. To do this we will need a number of definitions.

INTEGRAL DIVISOR, OR FACTOR

If a, b, and c are integers such that $c = a \cdot b$, then a and b are said to be *integral divisors* or *factors* of c.

Example 1

Find all the integral divisors of 12.

12 can be written as the product of two integers in the following ways:

12 · 1, 6 · 2, 4 · 3, (–1) · (–12), (–2) · (–6), (–4) · (–3)

Thus the integral divisors of 12 are:

1, 2, 3, 4, 6, 12, –1, –2, –3, –4, –6, –12

Note 1

In the remainder of this section we will concern ourselves solely with the *positive* integral divisors of a number.

Note 2

An integral divisor or factor of a number c is essentially any integer which "*divides evenly into c.*"

INTEGRAL MULTIPLE

If a number a is an integral divisor of a number c, then c is said to be an integral multiple of a.

Example 2

Find the positive factors of 15.

Since $15 = 1 \cdot 15 = 3 \cdot 5$, the positive factors of 15 are 1, 3, 5, and 15.

We can also say that 15 is an integral multiple of 1, 3, 5, and 15.

Example 3

Find the positive factors of 36.

Since $36 = 1 \cdot 36 = 2 \cdot 18 = 3 \cdot 12 = 4 \cdot 9 = 6 \cdot 6$, the positive factors of 36 are 1, 2, 3, 4, 6, 9, 12, 18, 36.

We can also say that 36 is an integral multiple of each of the above numbers.

PRIME NUMBER

A prime number is a *positive integer, different from* 1, whose only positive integral divisors are the number 1 and itself.

Examples of Prime Numbers

4. 2 is a prime number, for its only positive factors are the number 1 and the number 2 itself.
5. 3 is also a prime number, for its only positive factors are 1 and 3.
6. The first nine prime numbers are: 2, 3, 5, 7, 11, 13, 17, 19, 23. Can you think of other prime numbers?

Example 7

The number 6 is not a prime number for its positive factors are 1, 2, 3, and 6.

Note

2 is the only *even prime number,* since any other even number will have 2 as one of its factors.

FACTORING A NUMBER COMPLETELY

A positive integer, different from 1, is said to be *completely factored* if it is written as a product of its prime factors.

Example 8

Factor the number 120 completely.

$$120 = 2 \cdot 60$$
$$= 2 \cdot 2 \cdot 30$$
$$= 2 \cdot 2 \cdot 2 \cdot 15$$
$$= 2 \cdot 2 \cdot 2 \cdot 3 \cdot 5 \qquad \text{(Notice that we have now obtained all the prime factors of 120.)}$$

This may also be written:

$$120 = 2^3 \cdot 3 \cdot 5$$

Example 9

Factor the number 252 completely.

$$252 = 2 \cdot 126$$
$$= 2 \cdot 2 \cdot 63$$
$$= 2 \cdot 2 \cdot 3 \cdot 21$$
$$= 2 \cdot 2 \cdot 3 \cdot 3 \cdot 7$$

Thus:

$$252 = 2^2 \cdot 3^2 \cdot 7$$

We are now ready to describe a procedure to find the *least common denominator* (L.C.D.) of any number of fractions.

TO FIND THE L.C.D.

(1) Factor each denominator completely.
(2) The L.C.D. is the *product* of all the *different* prime factors involved, each with the *highest exponent* that appears in any of the denominators.

Example 10

Find the L.C.D. and add: $\frac{1}{2} + \frac{2}{3} + \frac{3}{4} + \frac{1}{9}$.

Here we may see by inspection that the L.C.D. is 36. However let us use the above procedure.

2 and 3 are completely factored since they are prime numbers.

$$4 = 2 \cdot 2 = 2^2$$
$$9 = 3 \cdot 3 = 3^2$$

The different prime factors are then 2, with highest exponent 2; and 3, with highest exponent 2.

Thus the L.C.D. is:

$$2^2 \cdot 3^2 = 4 \cdot 9 = 36$$

Now:

$$\frac{1}{2} + \frac{2}{3} + \frac{3}{4} + \frac{1}{9} = (\frac{1}{2} \cdot \frac{18}{18}) + (\frac{2}{3} \cdot \frac{12}{12}) + (\frac{3}{4} \cdot \frac{9}{9}) + (\frac{1}{9} \cdot \frac{4}{4})$$
$$= \frac{18}{36} + \frac{24}{36} + \frac{27}{36} + \frac{4}{36}$$
$$= \frac{73}{36}$$

Example 11

Find the L.C.D. and add: $\frac{5}{12} - \frac{8}{15} + \frac{7}{18}$.

$$12 = 2 \cdot 6 = 2 \cdot 2 \cdot 3 = 2^2 \cdot 3$$

$$15 = 3 \cdot 5$$

$$18 = 2 \cdot 9 = 2 \cdot 3 \cdot 3 = 2 \cdot 3^2$$

The different prime factors are 2, with highest exponent 2; 3, with highest exponent 2; and 5, with highest exponent 1.

Thus the L.C.D. is:

$$2^2 \cdot 3^2 \cdot 5 = 4 \cdot 9 \cdot 5 = 180$$

Now:

$$\frac{5}{12} - \frac{8}{15} + \frac{7}{18} = (\frac{5}{12} \cdot \frac{15}{15}) - (\frac{8}{15} \cdot \frac{12}{12}) + (\frac{7}{18} \cdot \frac{10}{10})$$

$$= \frac{75}{180} - \frac{96}{180} + \frac{70}{180}$$

$$= \frac{49}{180}$$

Note (Least Common Multiple)

The least common denominator is actually the *least common multiple* (L.C.M.) of the denominators, where the least common multiple of two or more positive integers is the *smallest* positive integer that is *exactly divisible* by each of the given numbers.

Example 12

Find the L.C.M. of the numbers: 4, 8, 9, 15, 21.

$$4 = 2 \cdot 2 = 2^2$$

$$8 = 2 \cdot 4 = 2 \cdot 2 \cdot 2 = 2^3$$

$$9 = 3 \cdot 3 = 3^2$$

$$15 = 3 \cdot 5$$

$$21 = 3 \cdot 7$$

The different prime factors involved are 2, with highest exponent 3; 3, with highest exponent 2; 5 with highest exponent 1; and 7, with highest exponent 1.

The L.C.M. is then:

$$2^3 \cdot 3^2 \cdot 5 \cdot 7 = 8 \cdot 9 \cdot 5 \cdot 7 = 2520$$

Exercise Set 4.3A

1. Give all the positive integral divisors of:

    (a) 18   (b) 24   (c) 128   (d) 225   (e) 243

2. If $A = \{x \mid x$ is an integral multiple of $3\}$ and $B = \{x \mid x$ is an integral multiple of $2\}$, find $A \cap B$.

3. If $A = \{x \mid x$ is an integral multiple of $3\}$ and $B = \{x \mid x$ is an integral multiple of $6\}$, find $A \cap B$ and $A \cup B$.

4. If $A = \{x \mid x$ is an integral multiple of $5\}$ and $B = \{x \mid x$ is an integral multiple of $7\}$, find $A \cap B$.

5. Factor the following numbers completely:

    (a) 24   (b) 81   (c) 180   (d) 490   (e) 819

In exercises 6-12 find the L.C.M. of the given numbers.

6. 3, 7, 21

7. 8, 7, 6

8. 2, 8, 7

9. 4, 6, 18

10. 15, 20, 24, 75

11. 12, 26, 36, 45

12. 15, 18, 27, 33, 36

In exercises 13-22 perform the indicated addition and simplify the result.

13. $\frac{1}{5} + \frac{2}{3}$

14. $\frac{1}{8} - \frac{3}{2}$

15. $3 - \frac{1}{12} + \frac{9}{30}$

16. $\frac{1}{4} - \frac{3}{8} - \frac{1}{6}$

17. $5 - \frac{5}{12} + \frac{7}{30} - \frac{7}{4}$

18. $2 - \frac{5}{24} - \frac{7}{18} + \frac{1}{36}$

19. $\frac{2}{15} + \frac{3}{20} - \frac{3}{5} - \frac{1}{12}$

20. $4\frac{2}{3} + 5\frac{3}{7}$

21. $2\frac{1}{4} - 4\frac{3}{8} - 2\frac{1}{5}$

22. $\frac{5}{8} - \frac{5}{6} - \frac{4}{9} + \frac{11}{18}$

Now suppose we consider fractions which have in their denominators polynomials which involve a variable. To add such fractions involves a similar procedure as that which is used when the variable is not present. That is, we must still find the L.C.D. To do this let us define the *factors* of a polynomial in general.

Note

Recall from Section 3.6 that a polynomial in one variable is any sum of algebraic expressions which consists of a real number and *nonnegative integral* powers of the variable joined by multiplication.

FACTORS OF A POLYNOMIAL

If a polynomial can be expressed as the product of two or more algebraic expressions, each expression of the product is a *factor* of the original polynomial.

Note

In this section we will deal only with polynomials with *integral coefficients*. We will require the factors to be monomials or polynomials with *integral coefficients*. We also will *exclude factors which are negative integers*.

Example 13

Since $x^3 = x^3 \cdot 1 = x^2 \cdot x$, then the factors of x^3 are $1, x, x^2$, and x^3.

Example 14

Find the factors of $3x + 6$.

$$3x + 6 = 1(3x + 6)$$

and

$$3x + 6 = 3(x + 2) \qquad \text{(Distributive law)}$$

Since we cannot find two more polynomials whose product is $x + 2$, we have now found all the factors of $3x + 6$, namely, $1, 3, x + 2$, and $3x + 6$.

PRIME POLYNOMIAL

A polynomial with integral coefficients is said to be *prime* if it has no other factors but itself and 1.

Examples of Prime Polynomials

15. $2, 3, 5$, and any other prime number
16. x
17. $7x + 4$
18. $x + 1$
19. $3x - 5$

Example 20

x^2 is not a prime polynomial for it may be written $x \cdot x$.

Example 21

$8x$ is not a prime polynomial for it may be written $4 \cdot 2x$ or $2 \cdot 2 \cdot 2x$.

Example 22

$2x^2 - 4x$ is not a prime polynomial for it may be written $2(x^2 - 2x)$ or $2 \cdot x(x - 2)$.

FACTORING A POLYNOMIAL COMPLETELY

A polynomial is said to be *completely* factored if it is written as a product of its prime factors.

Example 23

Factor the polynomial $6x^2 - 36x$ completely.

$$
\begin{aligned}
6x^2 - 36x &= 6(x^2 - 6x) \qquad &\text{(Distributive law)} \\
&= 6 \cdot x(x - 6) \qquad &\text{(Distributive law)} \\
&= 2 \cdot 3 \cdot x(x - 6)
\end{aligned}
$$

Example 24

Factor the polynomial $8x^3 + 24x^2$ completely.

$$
\begin{aligned}
8x^3 + 24x^2 &= 8(x^3 + 3x^2) \qquad &\text{(Distributive law)} \\
&= 8x^2(x + 3) \qquad &\text{(Distributive law)} \\
&= 2 \cdot 2 \cdot 2 \cdot x \cdot x(x + 3)
\end{aligned}
$$

The procedure to find the L.C.D. of any number of fractions which have polynomials in their denominators is exactly the same as the procedure already given for fractions which do not involve the variable in the denominator. That is,

TO FIND THE L.C.D.

(1) Factor each denominator completely.
(2) The L.C.D. is the product of all the *different* prime factors involved, each with the *highest* exponent that appears in any of the denominators.

Example 25

Find the L.C.D. of the fractions

$$\frac{1}{2x}, \quad \frac{1}{4x^2}, \quad \frac{1}{2x + 6}$$

$2x$ is factored completely for it is already the product of prime factors 2 and x, each with exponent 1.

$4x^2 = 2 \cdot 2 \cdot x \cdot x$. Thus the prime factors here are 2 and x, each with exponent 2. That is,

$$4x^2 = 2^2 \cdot x^2$$

$2x + 6 = 2(x + 3)$. The prime factors here are 2 and $x + 3$, each with exponent 1.

The different prime factors involved are 2, with highest exponent 2; x, with highest exponent 2; and $x + 3$, with highest exponent 1.

Thus the L.C.D. is $2^2 \cdot x^2 \cdot (x + 3) = 4x^2(x + 3)$.

Note

We will not be concerned here with the adding of these fractions.

Example 26

Find the L.C.D. of $\frac{1}{4x - 6}$ and $\frac{1}{6x - 9}$.

$$4x - 6 = 2(2x - 3)$$
$$6x - 9 = 3(2x - 3)$$

The different factors are 2, 3, and $2x - 3$ each with highest exponent 1.

Thus the L.C.D. is $2 \cdot 3(2x - 3) = 6(2x - 3)$.

Exercise Set 4.3B

In exercises 1-6, factor the given polynomial completely.

1. $8x^4$

2. $3x - 9$

3. $3x^2 - 6x$

4. $6x - 24$

5. $x^3 - x^2$

6. $18x^2 - 18x$

In exercises 7-14 find the L.C.D. of the given fractions.

7. $\dfrac{1}{9x^3}, \ \dfrac{1}{3x^2}, \ \dfrac{1}{2x}$

11. $\dfrac{1}{36}, \ \dfrac{1}{9x^2}, \ \dfrac{1}{3x^2 \ - \ 6x}$

8. $\dfrac{1}{6x}, \ \dfrac{1}{5x}, \ \dfrac{1}{30}$

12. $\dfrac{1}{3x \ - \ 12}, \ \dfrac{1}{x \ - \ 2}, \ \dfrac{1}{6x \ - \ 12}$

9. $\dfrac{1}{x \ - \ 3}, \ \dfrac{1}{4x \ - \ 12}$

13. $\dfrac{1}{2x}, \ \dfrac{1}{x^2(x \ - \ 2)}, \ \dfrac{1}{3x(x \ - \ 2)^2}$

10. $\dfrac{1}{3y^2 \ - \ 6y}, \ \dfrac{1}{6(y \ - \ 2)}$

14. $\dfrac{1}{y^3 \ + \ 5y^2}, \ \dfrac{1}{y \ + \ 5}, \ \dfrac{1}{3y^2}$

4.4 SOLVING EQUATIONS CONTAINING FRACTIONS

To solve any equation containing fractions, the first step would be to *clear* the equation of fractions by multiplying both sides of the equation by the *L.C.D. of all the fractions involved.*

Note

If an equation contains fractions where the variable is involved in one or more of the denominators, then we know that it is not a linear equation. However, we will only consider here equations which reduce to linear equations when cleared of the fractions.

Example 1

Clear the fractions in the equation

$$\tfrac{4}{3} + \tfrac{x \ - \ 3}{4} = \tfrac{3x \ - \ 1}{6}$$

The L.C.D. here is 12.

To clear the equation of fractions we now multiply both sides of the equation by 12.

$$12(\tfrac{4}{3} + \tfrac{x \ - \ 3}{4}) = 12\tfrac{(3x \ - \ 1)}{6}$$

Using the distributive law on the left side of the equation, we obtain

$$12(\tfrac{4}{3}) + 12\tfrac{(x \ - \ 3)}{4} = 12\tfrac{(3x \ - \ 1)}{6}$$

Now we use the properties of multiplication of fractions to simplify the fractions and rewrite the equation

$$(\tfrac{12}{3} \cdot \tfrac{4}{1}) + [\tfrac{12}{4} \cdot \tfrac{(x \ - \ 3)}{1}] = \tfrac{12}{6} \cdot \tfrac{(3x \ - \ 1)}{1}$$

or

$$16 + 3(x - 3) = 2(3x - 1)$$

The equation is now cleared of fractions.

Example 2

Clear the following equation of fractions:

$$\frac{x \ + \ 9}{2x} = \frac{15}{x} - \frac{3}{8} \qquad \text{(Here } x \ cannot \ = \ 0. \ \text{Why?)}$$

Here $8 = 2^3$ and thus the different factors involved in the denominators are 2, with highest exponent 3; and x with highest exponent 1. Thus the L.C.D. is $8x$.

We now multiply both sides of the equation by $8x$.

$$8x\frac{(x \ + \ 9)}{2x} = 8x\left(\frac{15}{x} - \frac{3}{8}\right)$$

Using the distributive law on the right side of the equation, we rewrite the equation as

$$8x\frac{(x \ + \ 9)}{2x} = 8x\left(\frac{15}{x}\right) - 8x\left(\frac{3}{8}\right)$$

and now simplifying the fractions, we obtain

$$\frac{2x}{2x} \cdot \frac{4(x \ + \ 9)}{1} = [\frac{x}{x} \cdot \frac{8(15)}{1}] - [\frac{8}{8} \cdot \frac{(x \ . \ 3)}{1}]$$

or

$$4(x + 9) = 120 - 3x$$

Note that although the original equation was not linear, once the equation was cleared of fractions, the resulting equation was linear.

Example 3

Clear the following equation of fractions:

$$\frac{5}{x \ - \ 1} - \frac{2}{x} = \frac{3 + x}{x(x \ - \ 1)} \qquad \text{(Here } x \neq 0, x \neq 1. \ \text{Why?)}$$

It can be seen by inspection that the different factors involved

in the denominators are x and $x - 1$, both with highest exponent 1.
Thus the L.C.D. is $x(x - 1)$.

To clear the equation of fractions, we multiply both sides by
the L.C.D. to obtain

$$x(x - 1)(\frac{5}{x-1} - \frac{2}{x}) = x(x - 1)\frac{(3 + x)}{x(x - 1)}$$

or

$$\frac{5x(x - 1)}{x - 1} - \frac{2x(x - 1)}{x} = \frac{x(x - 1)(3 + x)}{x(x - 1)}$$ (Using distributive law on left side)

or

$$\frac{5x}{1} \cdot \frac{(x - 1)}{(x - 1)} - \frac{2(x - 1)}{1} \cdot \frac{x}{x} = \frac{x(x - 1)}{x(x - 1)} \cdot \frac{3 + x}{1}$$ (Simplifying fractions)

or

$$5x - 2(x - 1) = 3 + x$$

We have now reduced our equation to a *linear equation* in the
variable x.

Once the equation is cleared of fractions, we then can solve
the resulting *linear equation* using the procedure outlined in
Section 4.2.

Example 4

Solve the equation $\frac{4}{3x} - \frac{5}{6x} + \frac{1}{4x} = \frac{3}{4}$ and check the result. (Here x
cannot be 0. Why?)

The L.C.D. is $12x$. Thus we clear fractions by multiplying *both
sides* of the equation by $12x$.

$$12x(\frac{4}{3x} - \frac{5}{6x} + \frac{1}{4x}) = 12x(\frac{3}{4})$$

$$12x(\frac{4}{3x}) - 12x(\frac{5}{6x}) + 12x(\frac{1}{4x}) = 12x(\frac{3}{4})$$ (Distributive law on left side)

$$\frac{3x}{3x} \cdot (\frac{4 \cdot 4}{1}) - \frac{6x}{6x}(\frac{2 \cdot 5}{1}) + \frac{4x}{4x}(\frac{3 \cdot 1}{1}) = \frac{4}{4}(\frac{3x \cdot 3}{1})$$ (Simplifying fractions)

$$16 - 10 + 3 = 9x$$

or

$$9 = 9x$$

$$\tfrac{1}{9}(9) = \tfrac{1}{9} \cdot 9x \qquad \text{(Multiplying both sides by the multiplicative in-}$$
verse of 9 to get the leading coefficient of x to
be 1)

$$1 = x$$

The solution set is therefore $\{1\}$.

    Check: Replace x by 1 wherever it appears in the *original equation*.

$$\tfrac{4}{3} - \tfrac{5}{6} + \tfrac{1}{4} \overset{?}{=} \tfrac{3}{4}$$

Adding $\tfrac{4}{3} - \tfrac{5}{6} + \tfrac{1}{4}$ with L.C.D. 12, we obtain

$$(\tfrac{4}{3} \cdot \tfrac{4}{4}) - (\tfrac{5}{6} \cdot \tfrac{2}{2}) + (\tfrac{1}{4} \cdot \tfrac{3}{3}) \overset{?}{=} \tfrac{3}{4}$$

$$\tfrac{16}{12} - \tfrac{10}{12} + \tfrac{3}{12} \overset{?}{=} \tfrac{3}{4}$$

$$\tfrac{9}{12} \overset{?}{=} \tfrac{3}{4}$$

$$\tfrac{3}{4} = \tfrac{3}{4}$$

Example 5

Solve the equation $\dfrac{3x - 2}{x^2 - x} = \dfrac{7}{2(x - 1)}$, $(x \neq 0, x \neq 1)$ and check the result.

    $x^2 - x$ can be written as the product of x and $x - 1$, which are its prime factors. Thus the different factors involved in the denominators are 2, x, and $x - 1$, each with highest exponent 1. Therefore the L.C.D. is $2x(x - 1)$.

    We now clear fractions by multiplying both sides of the equation by $2x(x - 1)$.

$$2x(x - 1)\frac{(3x - 2)}{x(x - 1)} = 2x(x - 1)\frac{7}{2(x - 1)}$$

or

$$\frac{x(x - 1)}{x(x - 1)} \cdot \frac{2(3x - 2)}{1} = \frac{2(x - 1)}{2(x - 1)} \cdot \frac{7x}{1} \qquad \text{(Simplifying fractions)}$$

or

$$2(3x - 2) = 7x$$

$$6x - 4 = 7x \qquad \text{(Distributive law)}$$

$$-6x + 6x - 4 = -6x + 7x \qquad \text{(Adding } -6x \text{ to both sides)}$$

$$-4 = x \qquad \text{(Combining like terms)}$$

Thus the solution set is $\{-4\}$.

    Check: Replace x by -4 wherever it appears in the *original* equation.

$$\frac{3(-4) - 2}{(-4)^2 - (-4)} \overset{?}{=} \frac{7}{2(-4 - 1)}$$

$$\frac{-12 - 2}{16 + 4} \overset{?}{=} \frac{7}{2(-5)}$$

$$\frac{-14}{20} \overset{?}{=} \frac{7}{-10}$$

$$-\frac{7}{10} = -\frac{7}{10}$$

Note

As we have seen, the clearing of fractions which contain the variable in the denominator results in the multiplication of both sides of the equation by an expression that contains the variable. When this is done, it is possible that the resulting equation *may have solutions that are not solutions of the original equation.* To illustrate this, let us consider the equation:

$$x = 2, \qquad \text{whose only solution is obvious}$$

Multiplying *both sides* of this equation by $x - 1$, we obtain:

$$(x - 1)x = (x - 1)2$$

We can see by inspection that $x = 1$ is a solution of this new equation, for upon replacing x by 1 each side is equal to 0. However, 1 is not a solution of the original equation.

    Thus after the cleared equation is solved, it is extremely important that you *check the solution in the original equation.*

Example 6

Solve the equation $\frac{6}{x - 1} - \frac{3}{x} = \frac{6}{x(x - 1)}$, $(x \neq 1, x \neq 0)$.

Multiplying both sides by the L.C.D., $x(x - 1)$, we obtain:

$$x(x - 1)[(\frac{6}{x - 1}) - \frac{3}{x}] = x(x - 1)\frac{6}{x(x - 1)}$$

$$x(x - 1)(\frac{6}{x - 1}) - x(x - 1)(\frac{3}{x}) = x(x - 1)\frac{6}{x(x - 1}$$

(Distributive law)

$6x - 3(x - 1) = 6$	(Simplifying fractions)
$6x - 3x + 3 = 6$	(Distributive law)
$3x + 3 = 6$	(Combining like terms)
$3x + 3 - 3 = 6 - 3$	(Adding -3 to both sides)
$3x = 3$	
$x = 1$	(Multiplying both sides by $\frac{1}{3}$)

Check: If x is replaced by 1 in the original equation, the fractions $\frac{6}{x - 1}$ and $\frac{6}{x(x - 1)}$ will become $\frac{6}{0}$ and $\frac{6}{1(0)}$ which are *not defined*. Thus 1 cannot be a solution of the original equation.

Since we multiplied *each side* of the original equation by the *same number* to obtain the cleared equation, every solution of the original equation must be a solution of the cleared equation. Therefore, since the only solution of the cleared equation was not a solution of the original equation, the original equation *has no solution.*

Thus the solution is $\emptyset$.

Exercise Set 4.4

In exercises 1-26, find the solution set of the given equation and check the result.

1. $\frac{x}{4} - \frac{x}{3} = \frac{5}{12}$

2. $\frac{5y - 3}{6} = 2$

3. $\frac{3y}{4} - \frac{2y}{7} = 1 + \frac{3y}{14}$

4. $\frac{x + 3}{3} + \frac{x - 3}{6} = 5$

5. $\frac{2x - 3}{3} + \frac{4x - 1}{4} = \frac{5x}{6}$

6. $\frac{y - 4}{3} - \frac{y - 3}{2} = \frac{3 + y}{10} - 2$

7. $\frac{y + 5}{10} - \frac{y}{4} = \frac{2 + y}{4}$

8. $\frac{33}{10} - \frac{2x - 7}{5} = \frac{3x + 5}{4}$

9. $\frac{2(x - 3)}{7} - \frac{3(x - 1)}{14} = \frac{x}{2}$

10. $\frac{3 - 2y}{3} = \frac{9}{5} - \frac{y - 3}{5}$

11. $\frac{15}{x} = 3$

12. $\frac{7}{2x} = -3$

13. $\frac{7}{x} - \frac{3}{x} = 2$

14. $\frac{3}{x} + \frac{5}{3x} = \frac{-7}{6}$

15. $\frac{30}{x} = 7 + \frac{18}{2x}$

16. $\frac{6}{x} + \frac{3}{x} = \frac{9}{x}$

17. $\frac{3y}{y + 2} = 2 + \frac{y}{y + 2}$

18. $\frac{3(x - \frac{5}{3})}{3x + 5} = \frac{1}{2}$

19. $\frac{2}{3x} + \frac{1}{4} = \frac{7}{6x} - \frac{1}{8}$

20. $\frac{3}{2y} - 1 = \frac{y + \frac{3}{2}}{y}$

21. $\frac{x - 5}{2x - 6} = \frac{x + 1}{x - 3}$

22. $\frac{1}{x - 5} + \frac{1}{x + 5} = \frac{4}{x - 5}$

23. $\frac{4}{2y - 3} + \frac{4y}{(2y - 3)(2y + 3)} = \frac{1}{2y + 3}$

24. $\frac{3}{x - 4} = 0$

25. $\frac{4y - 3}{y - 2} - 2 = \frac{5}{y - 2}$

26. $\frac{x}{x^2 + 4x} + \frac{5}{3x} = \frac{4}{9(x + 4)}$

4.5 SIMPLE WORD PROBLEMS

Now that we have seen how to solve linear equations, let us consider some applications of linear equations.

Example 1

Mary's mother is 40 years old. Four years ago, she was 3 times as old as Mary was then. How old is Mary now?

To solve such a problem, we must find an equation that expresses the relationship between their ages. To do this, we will introduce the variable x to represent Mary's age now. Upon *reading the problem carefully*, we can discover the desired relationship.

Let x = Mary's present age.
Four years ago Mary's age was $x - 4$.
Four years ago Mary's mother's age was 36.
From the context of the problem we see that

$36 = 3(x - 4)$ (This is the desired relationship.)

Now, solving this linear equation, we obtain

$36 = 3x - 12$ (Distributive law)

$36 + 12 = 3x - 12 + 12$ (Adding 12 to both sides)

$$48 = 3x$$

$$16 = x \qquad \text{(Multiplying both sides by } \tfrac{1}{3}\text{)}$$

Thus Mary is now 16 years old.

To check this result we look to the context of the problem, *rather than to the equation,* for the equation may not have been set up correctly. Although your solution may then satisfy the equation, it may not satisfy the stated problem.

Check: Four years ago Mary was 12 and her mother was 36 and $36 = 3 \cdot 12$.

Example 2

Mike's sporting goods store sold 25 baseballs last Thursday, some at $3 each and the rest for $2 each. If the store's sales for the baseballs totaled $60, how many of each kind were sold?

Let x denote the number of baseballs sold at $2.
Then $25 - x$ must represent the number sold at $3.

The total amount received from the sale of the $2 baseballs would be $2x$.
The total received from the sale of the $3 baseballs would be $3(25 - x)$.

The desired relationship is then

$$2x + 3(25 - x) = 60 \text{ (total sales received)}$$

Solving this linear equation, we obtain

$$2x + 75 - 3x = 60 \qquad \text{(Distributive law)}$$

$$-x + 75 = 60$$

$$-x + 75 - 75 = 60 - 75$$

$$-x = -15$$

$$(-1)(-x) = (-1)(-15)$$

$$x = 15$$

Thus 15 balls were sold at $2 each and $25 - 15 = 10$ balls were sold at $3 each.

Check: 15 balls at $2 each produces $30 in total sales
          10 balls at $3 each produces $30 in total sales

$30 + $30 = $60 total sales

Example 3

The larger of two numbers is 1 more than twice the smaller. Three times the larger exceeds five times the smaller by 10. Find the numbers.

Let s be the smaller number.
Then the larger number can be represented by $2s + 1$.

From the context of the problem we have that

$$3(2s + 1) = 5s + 10$$
$$6s + 3 = 5s + 10$$
$$-5s + 6s + 3 = -5s + 5s + 10$$
$$s + 3 = 10$$
$$s + 3 - 3 = 10 - 3$$
$$s = 7$$

Thus the smaller number is 7 and the larger is $(2 \cdot 7) + 1 = 14 + 1 = 15$.

Check: 3 times the larger is $3 \cdot 15 = 45$
          5 times the smaller is $5 \cdot 7 = 35$

45 exceeds 35 by 10

Example 4

Martin is 20 years older than John. Three years ago Martin was 3 times as old as John was then. Find the present ages of both Martin and John.

Let x denote John's age now.
Then Martin's age is $x + 20$.

Three years ago John's age was $x - 3$.
Three years ago Martin's age was $x + 20 - 3 = x + 17$.

From the context of the problem we have:

$$x + 17 = 3(x - 3)$$

Solving this equation, we obtain:

$$x + 17 = 3x - 9$$

$$-x + x + 17 = -x + 3x - 9$$

$$17 = 2x - 9$$

$$17 + 9 = 2x - 9 + 9$$

$$26 = 2x$$

$$\tfrac{1}{2}(26) = \tfrac{1}{2}(2x)$$

$$13 = x$$

Thus John is 13 years old and Martin is

$$13 + 20 = 33 \text{ years old.}$$

Check: Three years ago John was 10.
Three years ago Martin was 30.

$$30 = 3 \cdot 10$$

Exercise Set 4.5

1. If x represents a number, then express the following in terms of x:
   (a) The number increased by 7.
   (b) The number decreased by 5.
   (c) Twice the number.
   (d) Three less than twice the number.
   (e) Eight more than four times the number.
   (f) Three times four more than the number.
   (g) Six times eight less than the number.

2. Let y represent Beverly's age now. Express the following in terms of y.
   (a) Beverly's age five years from now.
   (b) Beverly's age three years ago.
   (c) Three times Beverly's age now.
   (d) Four times Beverly's age three years from now.
   (e) Twice Beverly's age three years ago.
   (f) One-half Beverly's age three years ago.

3. Martin was x years old three years ago. Represent Martin's age four years from now.

4. John is 8 years old now. Mary is s years older than John. Represent Mary's age now.

5. If 10 footballs cost a total of x dollars, represent the cost of one football. How much would 15 footballs cost?

6. If x pens cost a total of y dollars, represent the cost of one pen. Represent the cost of z pens.

7. If x represents the least of three consecutive even integers, express the sum of these integers in terms of x.

8. Oscar is y years old now. Willie's age exceeds five times Oscar's age by 2. How old is Willie? (Answer in terms of y.)

9. Christine's grandfather is four years less than four times Christine's age now. If Christine is x years old now, how old is her grandfather? (Answer in terms of x.)

10. The total cost of a shirt and necktie is $16. If the shirt costs three times as much as the necktie, what is the cost of each?

11. The sum of three consecutive integers is 69. Find the three integers.

12. A man distributed $310 among his three friends Tom, Sammy, and Mike. He gave Sammy 3 times as much as Tom and Mike $10 more than Tom. How much money did each receive?

13. The greater of two numbers is two more than three times the smaller. Four times the greater exceeds five times the smaller by 22. Find the numbers.

14. Mrs. Jones bought two kinds of candy for a party, one kind costing 40 cents a pound and the other 70 cents a pound. If she pays $3.40 for 7 pounds of candy, how many pounds of each kind did she buy?

15. Perry is twice as old as Jim. Three years ago Perry was three times as old as Jim was then. What are the present ages of both boys?

16. John sold 500 tickets to a football game and collected a total of $600. If he charged students 75 cents per ticket and nonstudents $1.50 per ticket, how many students did he sell tickets to?

17. Christine is three times as old as Charlotte. Ten years from now, Christine's age will exceed twice Charlotte's age at that time by 1 year. Find their present ages.

18. Harry is now 3 years old and Jerry is 20. In how many years will Jerry be twice as old as Harry?

19. Mary has a coin bank in which the number of dimes exceeds three times the number of quarters by 4. If the bank contains $5.90, how many coins of each kind are there in the bank?

20. Find three consecutive even numbers such that the sum of the first and third exceeds one-sixth of the second by 44.

4.6 INEQUALITIES

In Section 2.2 we defined what is meant by $c < d$, $c > d$, for any real numbers c and d. Let us repeat that definition here.

(1) $c < d$ (c is less than d) if and only if the graph of c lies to the left of the graph of d.

(2) $c > d$ (c is greater than d) if and only if the graph of c lies to the right of the graph of d.

With our increased knowledge of the real number system together with the elementary operations we can restate the above definition in the following manner:

(1) $c < d$ if and only if $c - d < 0$ (that is, $c - d$ is a negative number).

(2) $c > d$ if and only if $c - d > 0$ (that is $c - d$ is a positive number).

AN INEQUALITY

An *inequality* is a mathematical statement that two algebraic expressions are *unequal.* The two expressions are called the *sides or members* of the inequality.

Examples of Inequalities

(1) $3 < 7$ (6) $3x - 5 > -4x + 7$
(2) $5 + 3 \neq 10$ (7) $2x + y < 4$
(3) $7 + 1 < 12$ (8) $x^2 - 9 < 0$
(4) $x + 3 \neq 8$ (9) $x^2 + y^2 > 4$
(5) $2x + 1 < 5$

Before we define the *solution set* of an inequality we will consider some basic properties of an inequality whose members are real numbers.

Note

If two inequalities have their inequality signs pointing in the same direction, we will say that these two inequalities have the *same sense.* For example, $x < 2$ and $3x < 7$ have the *same sense,* whereas $3 < 5$ and $8 > 6$ have *opposite sense.*

PROPERTY I

If $a < b$, where a and b are real numbers, then:

$$a + c < b + c, \quad \text{where } c \text{ is } any \text{ real number}$$

In other words, *if we add the same number to both sides of an inequality, the sense of the inequality remains the same.*

Example 10

We know that $3 < 7$. Adding 5 to both sides, we obtain $3 + 5 < 7 + 5$ or $8 < 12$, which we also know is true.

Example 11

We know that $-3 < 4$. Adding -5 to both sides, we obtain $-3 - 5 < 4 - 5$ or $-8 < -1$, which we also know is true.

PROPERTY II

If $a < b$, where a and b are any real numbers, and c is any *positive* real number, then:

$$ac < bc$$

In other words, if we multiply both sides of an inequality by the *same positive* real number the sense of the inequality *remains the same.*

Example 12

We know that $5 < 9$. Multiplying both sides by 3, we obtain $3 \cdot 5 < 3 \cdot 9$ or $15 < 27$, which we also know is true.

Example 13

We know that $-6 < -2$. Multiplying both sides by 4, we obtain $4(-6) < 4(-2)$ or $-24 < -8$, which we also know is true.

PROPERTY III

If $a < b$, where a and b are any real numbers, and c is any *negative real number*, then:

$$ac > bc$$

In other words, if we multiply both sides of an inequality by the same *negative number*, the sense of the inequality is *reversed.*

Example 14

We know that $3 < 7$. Multiplying both sides by -2, we obtain $(-2)3 > (-2)7$ or $-6 > -14$, which we also know is true.

Example 15

We know that $-5 < -1$. Multiplying both sides by -4, we obtain $(-4)(-5) > (-4)(-1)$ or $20 > 4$, which we also know is true.

Note

Thus we may add *any* real number to both sides of an inequality and the sense will remain the same, but when multiplying, the sense will only remain the same if we multiply by a *positive* real number.

Example 16

We know that $4 > -2$. If we multiply both sides by -2, what would the resulting inequality be?

$$(-2)4 \ ? \ (-2)(-2)$$

If we leave the same sense as the original inequality, we would obtain $-8 > 4$, which is *not true.* However, by Property III we must reverse the sense of the inequality when multiplying by a *negative number,* and thus we obtain $-8 < 4$, which is a true statement.

Let us now define the solution set of an inequality in *one variable.*

SOLUTION SET OF AN INEQUALITY IN ONE VARIABLE

The solution set of an inequality is the set of all values of the variable which make the inequality a true statement.

Note

Finding the solution set of an inequality is referred to as *solving* the inequality.

Example 17

Consider the inequality $x + 1 > 3$.

It is obvious that 1 would *not* be an element of the solution set, for upon replacing x by 1 we get $1 + 1 > 3$ or $2 > 3$, which we know is not a true statement. However, we can easily see that 4 would be an element of the solution set, for upon replacing x by 4 we get $4 + 1 > 3$ or $5 > 3$, which is a true statement. We should also note that there are many elements of the solution set besides 4. In fact, any number greater than 2 would make the inequality a true statement. Thus the solution set would be $\{x \mid x \in R, x > 2\}$.

Exercise Set 4.6

In exercises 1-6 use the symbol "$<$" to order the given numbers.
Example: $-3 < 0 < 4$

1. $4, -12, -1$

2. $-3, -5, -1$

3. $0, -1\frac{1}{2}, -1$

4. $-\frac{1}{2}, -\frac{1}{3}, -\frac{2}{3}$

5. $\frac{5}{6}, \frac{1}{3}, \frac{7}{12}, \frac{8}{15}$

6. $-2\frac{2}{3}, -2\frac{1}{5}, -2\frac{3}{4}, -2\frac{3}{7}$

7. If $x < -4$, which of the following statements are true?
   (a) $x + 3 < -4 + 3$
   (b) $x - 3 > -4 - 3$
   (c) $3x > 3(-4)$
   (d) $-2x > -2(-4)$
   (e) $\frac{1}{3}x > \frac{1}{3}(-4)$
   (f) $-x < 4$
   (g) $-4 < x$
   (h) $-8 > 2x$
   (i) $-\frac{1}{2}x > 2$
   (j) $2x - 3 < -11$

In exercises 8-10 list the elements of the given sets.

8. $A = \{x \mid x \in I, -3 < x < 5\}$ (Recall that I is the set of integers.)

9. $B = \{x \mid 2x - 7 > 0, x$ is a positive integer less than $10\}$

10. $C = \{x \mid -12 < x < 21, x$ is an integral multiple of $3\}$

11. Let $A = \{x \mid x$ is an integer, $-5 < x < 1\}$ and $B = \{x \mid x$ is an integer, $x > -2\}$. List the elements of (a) $A \cap B$, (b) $A \cup B$.

12. Let $A = \{x \mid x \in R, x > 2$ or $x < -3\}$ and $B = \{x \mid x \in R, 0 < x < 2\}$. Find $A \cap B$.

13. Let $A = \{x \mid x \in R, x > 4$ or $x < -1\}$ and $B = \{x \mid x \in R, -3 < x < 0\}$. Find (a) $A \cap B$, (b) $A \cup B$.

4.7   LINEAR INEQUALITIES IN ONE VARIABLE

LINEAR INEQUALITY IN ONE VARIABLE

A linear inequality in one variable is one which contains the first power of the variable, and no higher power, and which contains *no fractions that have the variable in the denominator.*

*Examples of Linear Inequalities in
One Variable*

1. $x + 3 < 7$
2. $3x - 1 > 2x + 5$
3. $\frac{1}{2}x + \frac{3}{2} < 3(x - \frac{1}{3})$

Example 4

$\frac{2}{x} + 1 > 5$ is not a linear inequality. Why?

Example 5

$x^2 - 9 < 0$ is not a linear inequality. Why?

The *procedure* to find the solution set of a linear inequality in one variable is similar to that used in solving a linear equation in one variable, except that we must remember to *reverse the sense of the inequality whenever we multiply both sides by a negative number* (Property III for inequalities).

Example 6

Find the solution set of the inequality $3x + 8 > 11$ and graph the solution set on the real number line.

$$3x + 8 > 11$$
$$3x + 8 - 8 > 11 - 8 \qquad \text{(Adding } -8 \text{ to both sides)}$$
$$3x > 3$$
$$\tfrac{1}{3}(3x) > \tfrac{1}{3}(3) \qquad \text{(Multiplying both sides by } \tfrac{1}{3}\text{)}$$
$$x > 1$$

Thus the solution set is $\{x \mid x \ \epsilon \ R, x > 1\}$.

Recall from Section 2.2 how to graph such a set on the real number line.

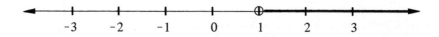

Note that the number 1 is not included in the solution set.

Example 7

Find and graph on the real number line the solution set of the inequality $2x - 3 < 5x + 6$.

$$2x - 3 < 5x + 6$$

$$-5x + 2x - 3 < -5x + 5x + 6 \qquad \text{(Adding } -5x \text{ to both sides)}$$

$$-3x - 3 < 6 \qquad \text{(Combining like terms)}$$

$$-3x - 3 + 3 < 6 + 3 \qquad \text{(Adding 3 to both sides)}$$

$$-3x < 9$$

$$(-\tfrac{1}{3})(-3x) > (-\tfrac{1}{3})9 \qquad \text{(Multiplying both sides by } -\tfrac{1}{3} \text{ } reverses \text{ } the \text{ } sense \text{ of the inequality.)}$$

$$x > -3$$

Thus the solution set is $\{x \mid x \ \epsilon \ R, x > -3\}$.

The graph of this set on the real number line is:

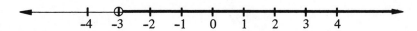

Example 8

Find and graph on the real number line the solution set of the inequality:

$$5(x + 2) < 3(x - \tfrac{4}{3})$$

$$5(x + 2) < 3(x - \tfrac{4}{3})$$

$$5x + 10 < 3x - 4 \qquad \text{(Distributive law)}$$

$$-3x + 5x + 10 < -3x + 3x - 4 \qquad \text{(Adding } -3x \text{ to both sides)}$$

$$2x + 10 < -4 \qquad \text{(Combining like terms)}$$

$$2x + 10 - 10 < -4 - 10 \qquad \text{(Adding } -10 \text{ to both sides)}$$

$$2x < -14$$

$$\tfrac{1}{2}(2x) < \tfrac{1}{2}(-14) \qquad \text{(Multiplying both sides by } \tfrac{1}{2})$$

$$x < -7$$

The solution set is $\{x \mid x \in R, x < -7\}$.

The graph of the solution set is:

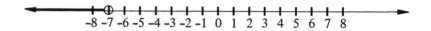

Example 9

Find and graph the solution set of the inequality:

$$\frac{x}{3} + \frac{1}{2} > \frac{3x}{4} - \frac{1}{8}$$

$24(\frac{x}{3} + \frac{1}{2}) > 24(\frac{3x}{4} - \frac{1}{8})$ (Clearing fractions by multiplying both sides by 24, the L.C.D.)

$8x + 12 > 18x - 3$ (Distributive law and multiplying fractions)

$-18x + 8x + 12 > -18x + 18x - 3$ (Why?)

$-10x + 12 > -3$

$-10x + 12 - 12 > -3 - 12$ (Why?)

$-10x > -15$

$(-\frac{1}{10})(-10x) < (-\frac{1}{10})(-15)$ (Why?)

$x < \frac{15}{10}$ or $x < \frac{3}{2}$

The solution set is $\{x \mid x \in R, x < \frac{3}{2}\}$.

The graph is:

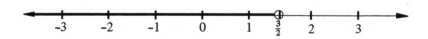

Exercise Set 4.7

In exercises 1-20 find and graph on the real number line the solution set of the given inequality.

1. $x + 3 > 0$

2. $x - 4 < 9$

3. $3 + 2x > 5$

4. $1 - 3x > 7$

5. $4x + 3 > 2x - 5$

6. $2x + 3 < 5x - 12$

7. $11 > 5 - 2x$

8. $3(x + 1) > 3x + 3$

9. $2(x + 5) < 10 - x$

10. $5 + 3x < -5(x + 3)$

11. $\frac{1}{2}x - 1 < 7$

12. $\frac{3x + 6}{3} > 12$

13. $-\frac{1}{2}x + \frac{1}{3}x > \frac{3}{4}$

14. $-2x < 22 + \frac{3}{4}x$

15. $\frac{x}{3} - \frac{3}{8}x > 5 + \frac{3}{4}x$

16. $5(x + 3) - 7(x - 1) < 3(x - 2) - 2$

17. $x > x + 3$

18. $\frac{33}{10} - \frac{2x - 7}{5} > \frac{3x + 5}{4}$

19. $\frac{5x}{12} - \frac{2}{15} < \frac{5x}{6} - \frac{x}{3}$

20. $3y - 33 < 3y$

21. Given $A = \{x | x \in R, x - 3 < 4\}$ and $B = \{x | x \in R, x + 5 > 3\}$. Find $A \cap B$.

22. Let $A = \{x | x \in R, \frac{2 + x}{3} > 2\}$ and $B = \{x | x \in R, -2x > -10\}$. Find $A \cap B$.

23. If $A = \{x | x \in R, \frac{3x + 5}{3} < 0\}$ and $B = \{x | x \in R, x > 2\}$, find $A \cap B$.

24. Let $A = \{x | x$ is an integer, $2x - 3 < 4x - 1\}$ and $B = \{x | x$ is an integer, $\frac{x - 2}{4} < 1\}$. Find $A \cap B$.

REVIEW TEST FOR CHAPTER IV

Note: This test should be completed in 90 minutes.

1. Find the L.C.M. of
   (a) $8, 24, 36, 9$
   (b) $12, 8, 5, 3$

2. If $A = \{x | -5 < x < 4, x$ is an integer$\}$ and $B = \{x | x > 2$ or $x < -1$, x is an integer $\}$, find
   (a) $A \cap B$
   (b) $A \cup B$

3. Perform the indicated addition and simplify the result.

   (a) $-\frac{3}{7} + \frac{1}{2} - \frac{2}{3}$ (b) $-3\frac{1}{6} + 4\frac{1}{5} - 7\frac{1}{3}$

4. Factor the following algebraic expressions completely.

   (a) $8x - 32$ (b) $-6x^3 - 27x^2$

5. If $A = \{x \mid 8 < x < 34, x$ is a prime number $\}$ and $B = \{x \mid 23 < x < 38, x$ is an integral multiple of $3\}$, find

   (a) $A \cap B$ (b) $A \cup B$

6. Using the symbols $<$ and $>$ express the following:

   (a) The graph of x lies to the left of -3 or to the right of 4.

   (b) The graph of x lies between -7 and 4.

7. Find the L.C.M. of $x^2 + 2x, 4x^3, 9(x + 2)^3$.

8. Find the solution set of the following inequalities:

   (a) $\frac{3}{4} - 5x > 6 - 7x$ (b) $5x + 55 > 5x$

9. Find the solution set of the following equations:

   (a) $3(2 + x) = -3(-1 - 4x)$ (b) $\frac{7 - 3x}{3} = \frac{7}{12} - \frac{4 - 7x}{4}$

10. Find the solution set of the equation:

    $$\frac{2}{5x} = \frac{1}{12} - \frac{4}{15x}$$

11. Find the solution set of the equation:

    $$\frac{3}{2(y - 1)} - 1 = \frac{2y + 1}{2y - 2}$$

12. Find the solution set of the equation:

    $$\frac{3}{3x^2 - 6x} - \frac{5}{15x} = \frac{3x}{x(x - 2)}$$

13. Find the solution set of the following inequalities:

    (a) $-\frac{2}{3}x + \frac{1}{4}x > -5$ (b) $-2(x - 1) + 3 > -2x + 7$

14. Marie is now four times as old as her daughter. In four years she will be three times as old as her daughter is then. What are their present ages?

15. Find three consecutive even integers such that three times the sum of the second and third exceeds five times the first by 28.

V EQUATIONS AND INEQUALITIES INVOLVING ABSOLUTE VALUES

5.1 ABSOLUTE VALUE OF A REAL NUMBER

ABSOLUTE VALUE

In Section 2.5 we defined the *absolute value* of a real number as follows:

$$|a| = a \ \text{ if } \ a \geqslant 0$$
$$|a| = -a \ \text{ if } \ a < 0$$

Examples

1. $|7| = 7$

2. $|-21| = -(-21) = 21$

We also saw that the absolute value of a real number a is in essence the distance that the graph of a is from the origin. For example, $|-11| = 11$ since the graph of -11 is 11 units from the origin.

ABSOLUTE VALUE OF A DIFFERENCE

Directly from the above definition of the absolute value of a real number, we have:

175

$$|a - b| = a - b, \quad \text{if } a - b \geqslant 0 \text{ or } a \geqslant b$$
$$|a - b| = -(a - b), \quad \text{if } a - b < 0 \text{ or } a < b$$

Note

Here a and b are real numbers and thus so is $a - b$.

Example 3

By the above definition of the absolute value of a difference, find $|9 - 4|$.

We know that $|9 - 4| = |5| = 5$, but using the above definition, we have a is 9, b is 4, and $9 > 4$. Thus,

$$|9 - 4| = 9 - 4 = 5$$

Example 4

Using the definition of the absolute value of a difference, find $|4 - 9|$.

Here a is 4, b is 9, and $4 < 9$. Thus

$$|4 - 9| = -(4 - 9) = -(-5) = 5$$

Example 5

Using the definition of the absolute value of a difference, find $|11 + 4|$.

$|11 + 4|$ can be written $|11 - (-4)|$, so that here a is 11, b is -4, and $11 > -4$. Thus

$$|11 + 4| = |11 - (-4)| = 11 - (-4) = 15$$

Example 6

Using the definition of the absolute value of a difference, find $|-3 - 7|$.

Here a is -3, b is 7, and $-3 < 7$. Thus

$$|-3 - 7| = -(-3 - 7) = -(-10) = 10$$

Example 7

By the definition of the absolute value of a difference:

$$|x - 3| = x - 3 \quad \text{if} \quad x \geqslant 3$$
$$|x - 3| = -(x - 3) \quad \text{if} \quad x < 3$$

The concept of the absolute value of a number as a distance is a very useful one, for we can now interpret the absolute value of a difference $|a - b|$, where a and b are real numbers, graphically as the *distance from the graph of a to the graph of b*. (See Figure 5.1.)

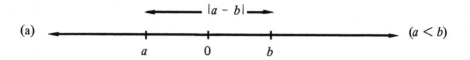

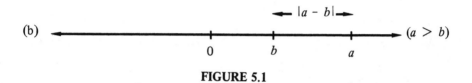

FIGURE 5.1

Note

That $|a|$ is the distance from the graph of a to the origin is consistent with this interpretation can easily be seen, for $|a|$ can be written $|a - 0|$.

Example 8

We know that $|8 - 5| = |3| = 3$. We can also see this graphically, for $|8 - 5|$ is the distance from the graph of 8 to the graph of 5, which is 3 units.

Also $|5 - 8| = |-3| = 3$. Graphically $|5 - 8|$ is the distance from the graph of 5 to the graph of 8, which is again 3 units.

Note

Thus we can see that $|a - b| = |b - a|$, for the distance from the graph of a to the graph of b is the same as the distance from the graph of b to the graph of a.

Example 9

$|8 + 5|$ can be written $|8 - (-5)|$.

Thus, $|8 + 5|$ is the distance from the graph of 8 to the *graph of* -5 which is 13 units.

That is, $|8 + 5| = 13$.

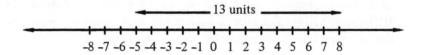

Also $|-5 - 8|$ is the distance from the graph of -5 to the *graph of* 8, which is again 13 units.

Thus $|-5 - 8| = 13$.

Example 10

$|x - 5|$ is the distance from the graph of x to the graph of 5.

Example 11

$|2x + 5| = |2x - (-5)|$, and thus $|2x + 5|$ is the distance from the graph of $2x$ to the graph of -5.

Exercise Set 5.1

In exercises 1-6 determine whether the given statement is true or false.

1. $|x + 5|$ is the distance from the graph of x to the graph of 5.

2. $|a + b| = |a| + |b|$ for all real numbers a and b.

3. $|ab| = |a||b|$ for all real numbers a and b.

4. $|3x - 1|$ is the distance from the graph of $3x$ to the graph of 1.

5. $|a - b| = |a| - |b|$ for all real numbers a and b.

6. If $a > 0$ and $b < 0$, then:
   (a) $b - |a|$ is always a negative number.
   (b) $|a| + b$ is always a negative number.
   (c) $|b - a|$ is a negative number.
   (d) $a - b$ is always a positive number.
   (e) $|a - b|$ is a negative number.

5.2 LINEAR EQUATIONS IN ONE VARIABLE INVOLVING ABSOLUTE VALUES

Suppose we consider the equation $|x| = 4$. Since we know that $|x|$ represents the distance that the graph of x is from the origin, this equation merely states that this distance is 4 units. Thus, we can see by inspection that the solution set must be $\{4, -4\}$. That is, both 4 and -4 have their graphs 4 units from the origin.

We could also solve the equation $|x| = 4$ by using the definition of the absolute value of a number. That is:

$$|x| = x, \quad \text{whenever } x \geqslant 0$$

$$|x| = -x, \quad \text{whenever } x < 0$$

Thus the equation $|x| = 4$ implies:

$$x = 4$$

or

$$-x = 4$$

which produces the root -4 upon multiplying both sides by -1.

Thus we see again that the solution set is $\{4, -4\}$.

Example 1

Solve the equation $|x - 2| = 5$.

Since $|x - 2|$ represents the distance that the graph of x is from the graph of 2 and since this distance is 5 units, we need only look at the real number line and count 5 units to the right of the graph of 2 and 5 units to the left of the graph of 2 to obtain the solutions 7 and -3.

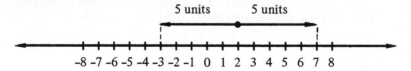

Now to solve this equation directly from the definition of the absolute value of a difference, we have

$$|x - 2| = x - 2, \quad \text{when } x \geqslant 2$$

$$|x - 2| = -(x - 2), \quad \text{when } x < 2$$

Thus the equation $|x - 2| = 5$ implies:

(1) $(x - 2) = 5$

or

(2) $-(x - 2) = 5$

The first of these equations yields the solution 7, whereas the second equation yields the solution -3. Thus the solution set is $\{7, -3\}$.

Example 2

Solve the equation $|x + 4| = 6$.

This equation can be rewritten $|x - (-4)| = 6$, which states that the distance from the graph of x to the graph of -4 is 6. By moving on the real number line 6 units in either direction from -4, we can see that the two solutions are -10 and 2.

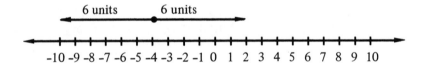

Now directly by the definition of the absolute value of a difference, the equation $|x + 4| = 6$ implies:

(1) $x + 4 = 6$

or

(2) $-(x + 4) = 6$

The first of these equations yields the solution 2 and the second equation yields the solution -10. Thus the solution set is $\{2, -10\}$.

Note

In examples 1 and 2, we solved the given equations both graphically and directly from the definition of an absolute value. It may not always be as easy to solve an equation containing absolute values graphically. However, using the definition directly, no great difficulty should be encountered.

Example 3

Solve the equation $|3x + 5| = 6$.

This equation implies:

(1) $3x + 5 = 6$

or

(2) $-(3x + 5) = 6$

Solving equation (1) we obtain:

$$3x + 5 = 6$$

$$3x = 1 \qquad \text{(Adding } -5 \text{ to both sides)}$$

$$x = \tfrac{1}{3} \qquad \text{(Multiplying both sides by } \tfrac{1}{3})$$

Solving equation (2), we obtain:

$$-(3x + 5) = 6$$

$$-3x - 5 = 6 \qquad \text{(Distributive law)}$$

$$-3x = 11 \qquad \text{(Adding 5 to both sides)}$$

$$x = -\tfrac{11}{3} \qquad \text{(Multiplying both sides by } -\tfrac{1}{3})$$

Thus the solution set is $\{\tfrac{1}{3}, -\tfrac{11}{3}\}$

Exercise Set 5.2

In exercises 1-16, find the solution set of the given equation.

1. $|x| = 0$

2. $|x| = 4$

3. $|2x| = 14$

4. $|x| = -5$

5. $|x - \tfrac{1}{2}| = \tfrac{3}{2}$

6. $|x + 4| = 6$

7. $|2x - 3| = 7$

8. $|x - \tfrac{3}{8}| = \tfrac{1}{4}$

9. $|\tfrac{2}{3}x - 4| = 6$

10. $|\tfrac{3x}{5} + \tfrac{1}{3}| = \tfrac{14}{15}$

11. $|-2x + 1| = 9$

12. $|-3x - 4| = 8$

13. $|-2x - 3| = 3$

14. $|3x + 4| = -\tfrac{1}{2}$

15. $|-3(x + 1)| - |-8| = |-4|$

16. $|-2(x - 3)| + |-7| = 3$

5.3 LINEAR INEQUALITIES IN ONE VARIABLE INVOLVING ABSOLUTE VALUES

Let us now consider the inequality $|x| < 7$. This inequality states that the distance the graph of x is from the origin is less than 7 units. *We can see on the real number line that $-7 < x < 7$* (see Figure 5.2). That is, the graph of x must lie between the graph of -7 and the graph of 7, or to say this still another way, $x < 7$ *and* $x > -7$.

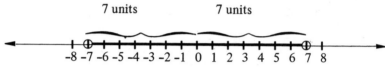

FIGURE 5.2

$|x| < a$

In general we will define $|x| < a$, for any *positive* real number a, as follows:

$$|x| < a \quad \text{means} \quad -a < x < a$$

(See Figure 5.3.)

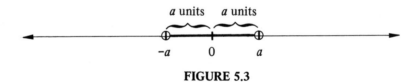

FIGURE 5.3

Recall that the notation $-a < x < a$ means $x > -a$ *and* $x < a$.

Now let us consider the inequality $|x| > 5$. This inequality states that the distance the graph of x is from the origin is greater than 5. We can see on the real number line that this inequality is satisfied by any real number $x > 5$ *or* any real number $x < -5$. (See Figure 5.4.)

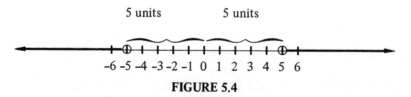

FIGURE 5.4

$|x| > a$

In general we will define $|x| > a$ for any *positive* real number a as follows:

$$|x| > a \quad \text{means} \quad x > a \text{ or } x < -a$$

(See Figure 5.5.)

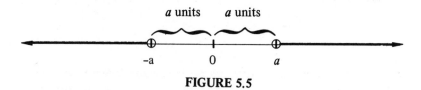

FIGURE 5.5

Note

It is important that you realize that when the word "and" is used, a number must satisfy *both* conditions at the same time to satisfy the original inequality, whereas when the word "or" is used, a number need only satisfy *one* of the conditions to satisfy the original inequality.

Let us now extend the above definitions to any algebraic expression. Recall that an algebraic expression is a representation of a real number.

| algebraic expression | $< a$ means

$$-a < \text{algebraic expression} < a$$

| algebraic expression | $> a$ means

algebraic expression $> a$ or
algebraic expression $< -a$

Example 1

Solve the inequality $|x - 2| < 4$ and graph the solution set on the real number line.

$$|x - 2| < 4 \text{ means}$$

$$-4 < x - 2 < 4$$

If we now add 2 to *each side* of the inequality, we obtain:

$$-4 + 2 < x - 2 + 2 < 4 + 2$$
$$-2 < x < 6$$

Thus the solution set is $\{x \mid x \in R - 2 < x < 6\}$

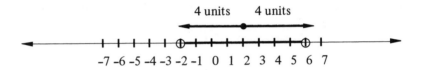

Note

Recall that the inequality $-4 < (x - 2) < 4$ means (a) $(x - 2) < 4$ *and* (b) $(x - 2) > -4$. Thus, we essentially have two inequalities to solve. The first yields the solution set $\{x \mid x \in R, x < 6\}$ and the second yields the solution set $\{x \mid x \in R, x > -2\}$. However, the word "*and*" is used, which means that a number must satisfy *both* conditions to satisfy the original inequality. That is, it must be both greater than -2 *and* less than 6. Thus, the solution set of the original inequality would be, as we've already seen $\{x \mid x \in R, x > -2$ and $x < 6\}$ or written equivalently $\{x \mid x \in R, -2 < x < 6\}$.

Example 2

Solve the inequality $|2x + 1| \leqslant 7$ and graph the solution set on the real number line.

Recall from Section 2.2 that this reads, "$|2x + 1|$ is *less than or equal to* 7." In solving this inequality, we treat it the same as the inequality $|2x + 1| < 7$. However, we maintain the "equal sign" throughout the procedure.

Thus $|2x + 1| \leqslant 7$ means

$$-7 \leqslant 2x + 1 \leqslant 7$$

Adding -1 to each side, we obtain

$$-8 \leqslant 2x \leqslant 6$$

Multiplying each side by $\frac{1}{2}$, we obtain

$$-4 \leqslant x \leqslant 3$$

The solution set is therefore $\{x \mid x \in R, -4 \leqslant x \leqslant 3\}$.

Note that -4 and 3 are included in the solution set.

-5 -4 -3 -2 -1 0 1 2 3 4 5

Example 3

Solve the inequality $|x + 4| > 1$ and graph the solution set on the real number line.

$$|x + 4| > 1 \text{ means}$$

(1) $(x + 4) > 1$ *or*   (2) $(x + 4) < -1$

Upon adding −4 to each side, inequality (1) yields the solution set $\{x \mid x \in R, x > -3\}$ whereas inequality (2) yields the solution set $\{x \mid x \in R, x < -5\}$. (Note that the word *or* is used).

Thus the solution set is $\{x \mid x \in R, x > -3 \text{ or } x < -5\}$

-6 -5 -4 -3 -2 -1 0 1 2 3 4 5 6

Example 4

Solve the inequality $|\frac{1}{2}x + 3| \geqslant 4$ and graph the solution set on the real number line.

$$|\tfrac{1}{2}x + 3| \geqslant 4 \text{ means}$$

(1) $(\frac{1}{2}x + 3) \geqslant 4$ or   (2) $(\frac{1}{2}x + 3) \leqslant -4$

(Again the "equal sign" is maintained throughout the procedure.)

To solve inequality (1):

$$\tfrac{1}{2}x + 3 \geqslant 4$$
$$\tfrac{1}{2}x \quad\;\; \geqslant 1 \qquad \text{(Adding −3 to both sides)}$$
$$x \quad\;\; \geqslant 2 \qquad \text{(Multiplying both sides by 2)}$$

To solve inequality (2):

$$\tfrac{1}{2}x + 3 \leqslant -4$$
$$\tfrac{1}{2}x \quad\;\; \leqslant -7 \qquad \text{(Adding −3 to both sides)}$$
$$x \quad\;\; \leqslant -14 \qquad \text{(Multiplying both sides by 2)}$$

Again note the use of the word "*or*."

Thus the solution set is

$$\{x \mid x \in R, x \geqslant 2 \text{ or } x \leqslant -14\}$$

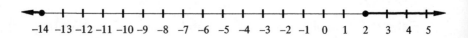

Exercise Set 5.3

In exercises 1-20 find and graph the solution set of the given inequality.

1. $-6 < 2x - 4 < 4$
2. $10 < -2x < 20$
3. $|x| < 6$
4. $|x| \geqslant 3$
5. $|x| \leqslant -2$
6. $|2x| \leqslant 10$
7. $|x - 4| < 3$
8. $|x| > -2$
9. $|x + 5| \geqslant 9$
10. $|2x - 1| \leqslant 5$

11. $|x + 3| < -5$
12. $|\frac{3}{2}x| \leqslant 1$
13. $|x - \frac{3}{8}| < \frac{1}{2}$
14. $|3x + 6| \leqslant 0$
15. $|\frac{1}{2}x + 3| > 4$
16. $|\frac{x - 3}{4}| \geqslant \frac{1}{2}$
17. $|-2x - 4| < -1$
18. $|2 - 3x| \geqslant 8$
19. $|1 - 2x| < 4$
20. $|2 - x| > 0$

21. If $A = \{x \mid x \in R, |x + 3| \leqslant 9\}$ and $B = \{x \mid x \in R, |2x + 1| < 15\}$, find $A \cap B$.

22. If $A = \{x \mid x \in R, |x - 2| < 7\}$ and $B = \{x \mid x \in R, |2x - 1| > 5\}$, find $A \cap B$.

REVIEW TEST FOR CHAPTER V

Note: This test should be completed in 70 minutes.

Find the solution set of the following:

1. $|x + 3| \geqslant 6$
2. $|\frac{x + 4}{3}| = 1$

3. $|\frac{4y - 8}{4}| \leqslant -2$
4. $|3x - 1| < 8$

5. $\left|\frac{1}{x}\right| = 4$

6. $\left|2 - 3x\right| = 7$

7. $\left|\frac{2y - 1}{4}\right| \geqslant 3$

8. $\left|\frac{3y + 1}{5}\right| > -5$

9. $-10 < 3x - 1 < 8$

10. $\left|\frac{3}{x}\right| + 4 = 7$

11. $\left|-5(-x - 2)\right| - 6 = -1$

12. $\left|-4x - 4\right| < 8$

13. $\left|2x - 4\right| > 0$

14. $\left|\frac{1}{2}x - \frac{1}{6}\right| < \frac{5}{12}$

VI GRAPHING THE SOLUTION SETS OF LINEAR EQUATIONS AND INEQUALITIES IN TWO VARIABLES

6.1 CARTESIAN PRODUCT OF TWO SETS

In Chapter II we established a one-to-one correspondence between the set of all real numbers R and the set of all points on a line (referred to as the real number line). That is, to each point on the number line corresponds one and only one real number, and to each real number corresponds one and only one point on the line. The real number is referred to as the *coordinate* of the point to which it corresponds, and the point is called the *graph* of the number to which it corresponds. In this chapter we would like to extend the above idea from one dimension (the line) to two dimensions (the plane). Before we can consider this extension however, we must first see what is meant by an *ordered pair*, and in particular an *ordered pair of real numbers*.

ORDERED PAIR

When we consider the order in which a pair of objects is named, that pair is referred to as an ordered pair. For example, if object a is to be named before object b, we denote the ordered pair as (a, b), where a is referred to as the *first component* and b as the *second component* of the ordered pair (a, b).

Note

It is important to distinguish between the ordered pair (a, b), where parentheses are used, and the set $\{a, b\}$, where braces are used. If you recall, the set $\{a, b\} = \{b, a\}$, that is, the ordering of the elements of a set does not affect their membership. However the ordered pair $(a, b) \neq (b, a)$.

Examples of Ordered Pairs

1. *A* teacher may want to consider ordered pairs where the first component is the midterm examination grade and the second component is the final examination grade. Thus the ordered pair (65, 75) would represent a 65 on the midterm exam and a 75 on the final exam. This is quite different from the ordered pair (75, 65), which represents a 75 on the midterm exam and a 65 on the final exam.
2. A table which lists a baseball player's number of official times at bat as the first component and number of hits as the second component may contain the ordered pair (60, 20), meaning a player was up to bat officially 60 times and had 20 hits.

Now that we have established what is meant by an ordered pair, we will define a set operation involving ordered pairs.

CARTESIAN PRODUCT

The *cartesian product* of two sets A and B, denoted by $A \times B$ (read "*A* cross *B*"), is the *set* of *all ordered pairs* (a, b) where $a \in A$ and $b \in B$.

Example 3

Let $A = \{2, 4, 6\}$ and $B = \{1, 3\}$.

Then:

$$A \times B = \{(2, 1), (2, 3), (4, 1), (4, 3), (6, 1), (6, 3)\}$$

Note that the first component of each ordered pair is an element of A and the second component of each ordered pair is an element of B.

$$B \times A = \{(1, 2), (1, 4), (1, 6), (3, 2), (3, 4), (3, 6)\}$$

Here the first components are the elements of B and the second components are the elements of A.

Note that although $A \times B \neq B \times A$, both sets have six elements.

Example 4

Let $A = \{a, c, e\}$ and $B = \{a, e, i, o\}$.

Then:

$A \times B = \{(a, a), (a, e), (a, i), (a, o), (c, a), (c, e), (c, i), (c, o),$

$(e, a), (e, e), (e, i), (e, o)\}$

and

$B \times A = \{(a, a), (a, c), (a, e), (e, a), (e, c), (e, e), (i, a), (i, c),$

$(i, e), (o, a), (o, c), (o, e)\}$

Note that although $A \times B \neq B \times A$, they both have twelve elements.

Let us now consider an example where A and B are equal sets. That is, given a set A, we wish to find the cartesian product $A \times A$. This set consists of *all* ordered pairs, both components of which are elements of A.

Example 5

If $A = \{2, 4, 6\}$, then

$A \times A = \{(2, 2), (2, 4), (2, 6), (4, 2), (4, 4), (4, 6),$

$(6, 2), (6, 4), (6, 6)\}$

Here $A \times A$ has nine elements.

NUMBER OF ELEMENTS IN $A \times B$

In general, the number of ordered pairs in $A \times B$ is equal to the *product* of the number of elements in A and the number of elements in B. Also the number of elements in $A \times B$ equals the number of elements in $B \times A$.

R X R

The cartesian product that we will make use of in the remainder of the book is $R \times R$, where R is the set of all real numbers. That is, $R \times R$ *is the set of all possible ordered pairs of real numbers.* Since the set R is an infinite set, it is obvious that $R \times R$ is an infinite set.

Note

If the sets A and B are subsets of R, that is, if each set consists of real numbers, then $A \times B$ is a subset of $R \times R$.

Exercise Set 6.1

In exercises 1-8 find the cartesian product $A \times B$.

1. $A = \{1\}, B = \{1, 2\}$

2. $A = \{-2, -1, 0\}, B = \{3\}$

3. $A = \{c, d\}, B = \{b, e\}$

4. $A = \{-1, 1\}, B = \{1, 2, 3\}$

5. $A = B = \{0\}$

6. $A = \{x_1, x_2, x_3, x_4\}, B = \{y_1, y_2\}$

7. $A = B = \{-5, -1, 0, 3\}$

8. $A = \{0, 1\}, B = \{-2, -1, 0, 1, 2\}$

9. If $A = \{1, 2, 3, \ldots, 10\}$ and $B = \{2, 4, 6, \ldots, 20\}$, how many elements are in $B \times A$? $A \times B$?

10. If a house has four windows and one door, how many ways can a burglar enter and leave the house if he makes use of the door and windows only?

11. If there are eight horses in the first race and nine horses in the second race, how many *different* daily double tickets can one purchase?

6.2 THE CARTESIAN COORDINATE SYSTEM

THE GRAPH OF AN ORDERED PAIR, AND
THE COORDINATES OF A POINT

The plane (two-dimensional space), like the line, can be considered as an infinite set of points. The extension from the one-dimensional line to the two-dimensional plane is that there exists a one-to-one correspondence between the set of all points in the plane and the set of all ordered pairs of real numbers, $R \times R$. Each point in the plane is called the *graph* of the ordered pair to which it corresponds, and the *components* of each ordered pair are called the *coordinates* of the point to which it corresponds. The first component is called the *first coordinate* and the second component is called the *second coordinate*. We will now exhibit this one-to-one correspondence. That is, given any ordered pair of real numbers, we will see how to locate the graph of this ordered pair, and given any point in the plane, we will see how to determine the coordinates of this point.

To locate the graph of an ordered pair, we will start with two real number lines, one drawn horizontally and the other drawn vertically (the two number lines are perpendicular to each other). We will intersect these two lines at the point *O*, which is the origin of both lines. Thus this point *O* will correspond to the ordered pair (0, 0). (See Figure 6.1.)

As we've already seen, on the horizontal number line *positive* real numbers are represented to the *right* of the origin and *negative* real numbers to the *left* of the origin. On the vertical number line we will represent *positive* real numbers *above* the origin and *negative* real numbers *below* the origin. (See Figure 6.1.)

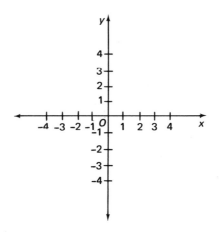

FIGURE 6.1

x-AND-*y*-AXES

The horizontal real number line is called the *x-axis* and the vertical real number line is called the *y-axis*. These two axes are referred to as the *cartesian coordinate axes*. The two axes divide the plane on which they are drawn into four sections called *quadrants*. These quadrants will be labeled in a counterclockwise direction, as seen in Figure 6.2.

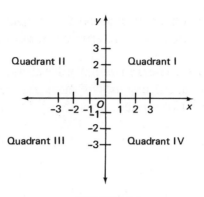

FIGURE 6.2

The two axes and the four quadrants together constitute what is known as the *cartesian coordinate system*. The point *O* at which the *x*- and *y*-axes intersect is called the *origin* of this coordinate system.

GRAPHING AN ORDERED PAIR; *x*- AND *y*-COORDINATES

Let us now examine the procedure to locate the graph of any given ordered pair. As an example, we will locate the graph of the ordered pair (2, 4). In the *cartesian coordinate system the first coordinate* is called the *x-coordinate* and the *second coordinate* is called the *y-coordinate*. We first locate the point *P on the x-axis* whose coordinate is 2 (the *x*-coordinate). (See Figure 6.3.) Through this

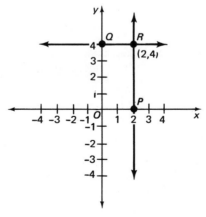

FIGURE 6.3

point we draw a vertical line. Then we locate the point Q on the y-axis whose coordinate is 4 (y-coordinate). Through this point we draw a horizontal line. The point R, in the first quadrant, where the two lines intersect (see Figure 6.3) is the point whose x-coordinate is 2 and whose y-coordinate is 4. That is, the point R is the *graph* of the ordered pair (2, 4).

Example 1

Locate the graph of (−3, 2).

(1) Locate the point on the x-axis whose coordinate is −3 (x-coordinate) and draw a vertical line through this point.

(2) Locate the point on the y-axis whose coordinate is 2 (y-coordinate) and draw a horizontal line through this point.

(3) The point R of intersection of these two lines, located in the second quadrant is the graph of (−3, 2).

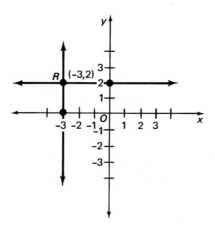

Example 2

Locate the graphs of the points $A(−2, −4)$ and $B(3, −2)$.

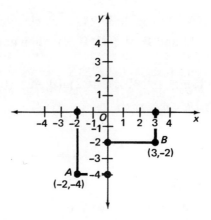

Note that the point A is in the third quadrant and B is in the fourth quadrant.

Example 3

Locate the graphs of the points $A(3, 0)$, $B(-2, 0)$, $C(0, 4)$, and $D(0, -1)$.

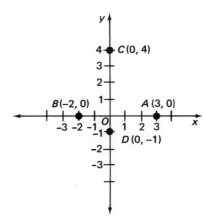

Note

The graph of any ordered pair whose y-coordinate is 0 will lie on the x-axis. Also the graph of any ordered pair whose x-coordinate is 0 will lie on the y-axis.

Example 4

If A = {$-1, 0, 1$} and B = {$-2, 0, 2$}, then graph the cartesian product $A \times B$.

$A \times B$ = {$(-1, -2), (-1, 0), (-1, 2), (0, -2), (0, 0),$

$(0, 2), (1, -2), (1, 0), (1, 2)$}

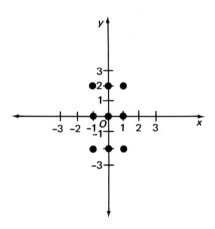

Example 5

Let A = {$-2, 1$} and B = {$0, 1$}. Graph the set $(A \times B) \cap (B \times A)$.

$A \times B$ = {$(-2, 0), (-2, 1), (1, 0), (1, 1)$}

$B \times A$ = {$(0, -2), (0, 1), (1, -2), (1, 1)$}

$(A \times B) \cap (B \times A)$ = {$(1, 1)$}

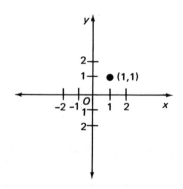

It still remains to show how to determine the coordinates of any given point in the plane. To do this we will start with an arbitrary point P in the plane in which the axes have already been placed (see Figure 6.4). We first draw a vertical line through P and read the x-coordinate of the point Q where this line crosses the x-axis. In Figure 6.4 we see that this coordinate is -6. We then draw a horizontal line through P and read the y-coordinate of the point R, where this line crosses the y-axis. In Figure 6.4 this coordinate is seen to be 5. Thus the ordered pair corresponding to the point P is $(-6, 5)$.

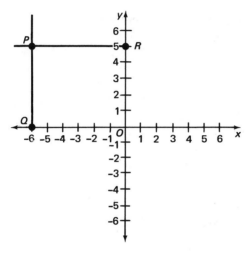

FIGURE 6.4

SUMMARY

We would find it most valuable here to summarize the important ideas of this section.

(1) There exists a one-to-one correspondence between the set of all points in the plane and the set of all ordered pairs of real numbers.
(2) The origin O corresponds to the ordered pair $(0, 0)$.
(3) All points on the x-axis correspond to ordered pairs whose y-coordinate is 0.
(4) All points on the y-axis correspond to ordered pairs whose x-coordinate is 0.

(5) All points in quadrant I correspond to ordered pairs with positive x and y coordinates.

(6) All points in quadrant II correspond to ordered pairs with negative x-coordinates and positive y-coordinates.

(7) All points in quadrant III correspond to ordered pairs with negative x- and y-coordinates.

(8) All points in quadrant IV correspond to ordered pairs with positive x-coordinates and negative y-coordinates.

Exercise Set 6.2

1. Locate the graph of each of the following ordered pairs on the same set of coordinate axes. Label each point.

(a) $(0,0)$ (d) $(-3,-5)$ (g) $(-5,0)$ (j) $(-5,-3)$

(b) $(3,5)$ (e) $(5,-2)$ (h) $(-2,\frac{7}{2})$ (k) $(0,-3)$

(c) $(-1,4)$ (f) $(0,5)$ (i) $(-\frac{3}{2},-\frac{5}{2})$ (l) $(6,0)$

2. If $A = \{-2,-3\}$ and $B = \{3,0,-1\}$, graph the cartesian product $A \times B$, and list its ordered pairs.

3. If $A = \{-4,-1,0\}$, graph the cartesian product $A \times A$, and list its ordered pairs.

4. If $A = \{0,1,2\}$ and $B = \{1,2,3,4\}$:
   (a) List the ordered pairs in $(A \times B) \cap (B \times A)$ and graph the resulting set.
   (b) List the ordered pairs in $(A \times B) \cup (B \times A)$ and graph the resulting set.

5. Let $A = \{x \mid x$ is an integer, $-2 < x \leqslant 2\}$ and
   $B = \{x \mid x$ is an integer, $-3 \leqslant x < 1\}$.
   List the elements of and graph the set $A \times B$.

6. Let $A = \{x \mid x$ is an integer, $x > -1\}$
   $B = \{x \mid x$ is an integer, $-4 < x < 2\}$
   $C = \{x \mid x$ is an integer, $x < 1\}$.
   List the elements of and graph the set $(A \cap B) \times (B \cap C)$.

6.3 GRAPHING THE SOLUTION SETS OF LINEAR EQUATIONS AS SUBSETS OF $R \times R$

In Section 4.2 we defined a linear equation in one variable as an equation which contains the first power of the variable, and no higher power, and which contains no fractions that have the variable in the denominator. Let us now define a linear equation in two variables.

LINEAR EQUATION IN TWO VARIABLES

An equation in two variables which contains the first power of each variable, and no higher power, and which contains no fractions that have either variable in the denominator, and which contains *no product of the two variables* is called a linear equation in two variables.

Examples of Linear Equations in Two Variables

1. $3x + 4y = 7$
2. $\frac{3}{2}x + 2(y + 3) = 4x$

Examples of Equations which are not Linear

3. $x^2 + 3x + 2y = 5$ (Contains the second power of x)

4. $x + \frac{3}{y} - 4 = 0$ (The variable y is involved in a denominator.)

5. $3x + 5xy + 6y - 3 = 0$ (Contains the product xy)

6. $3x^{-1} + 5y = 0$ (Recall that $x^{-1} = \frac{1}{x}$.)

The equation $3x + 4y = 7$ (example 1 above) may be rewritten in the form $3x + 4y - 7 = 0$ (adding -7 to both sides).

The equation $\frac{3}{2}x + 2(y + 3) = 4x$ (example 2 above) may be rewritten as follows:

$$\frac{3}{2}x - 4x + 2y + 6 = 0 \qquad \text{(Why?)}$$

or

$$-\frac{5}{2}x + 2y + 6 = 0$$

GENERAL LINEAR EQUATION IN TWO VARIABLES

In general any linear equation in two variables can be written in the form:

$$Ax + By + C = 0,$$

where A, B, and C are any real numbers and A and B are *not both* 0.

Example 7

In example 1 above, $A = 3$, $B = 4$, $C = -7$.
In example 2 above, $A = -\frac{5}{2}$, $B = 2$, $C = 6$.

Example 8

The equation $3x + 6 = 0$ may be written

$$3x + 0y + 6 = 0$$

and thus can be considered a linear equation in two variables, where the coefficient of y is 0, that is, $B = 0$.

Example 9

Similarly the equation $y = 7$ can be considered as a linear equation in two variables, where the coefficient of x is 0, that is, $A = 0$.

Let us now define the *solution set* of a linear equation in two variables.

SOLUTION SET OF A LINEAR EQUATION IN TWO VARIABLES

The solution set of a linear equation in two variables, $Ax + By + C = 0$, is the set of all ordered pairs of real numbers, (a, b), which satisfy the equation. That is, when x is replaced by a and y is replaced by b the equation becomes a true statement.

Suppose we are given the linear equation $-x + y - 5 = 0$ (here $A = -1$, $B = 1$, $C = -5$). To find the solution set of this equation we would:

(1) Select an arbitrary value for *one* of the two variables. For example, let $x = 0$.
(2) Replace that variable in the given equation by the value selected. Replacing x by 0 in the given equation above, we obtain the linear equation in the variable y,

$$y - 5 = 0$$

(3) Solve the remaining equation, $y - 5 = 0$. Thus we obtain

$y = 5$. Therefore, ordered pair $(0, 5)$ will satisfy the given equation.

(4) Continuing this process, we can obtain as many ordered pairs that satisfy the given equation as we might desire. For example, if we let $x = -1$, then $y = 4$ (why?); if we let $x = 1$, then $y = 6$; if we let $y = 0$, then $x = -5$; if we let $y = 7$, then $x = 2$, etc. Thus the ordered pairs $(-1, 4)$, $(1, 6)$, $(-5, 0)$, and $(2, 7)$ are also elements of the solution set.

Note

You may have realized by now that the solution set will be an *infinite* subset of $R \times R$.

Let us now graph the solution set of the above given equation $-x + y - 5 = 0$. The elements of the solution set that we have found can be seen in the following table and the graph of these ordered pairs can be seen in Figure 6.5.

x	0	-1	1	-5	2
y	5	4	6	0	7

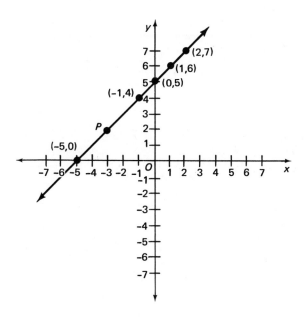

FIGURE 6.5

It appears that the five points graphed lie in a straight line. If we select a point $P(-3, 2)$ which appears to lie on this line, we find that its coordinates do satisfy the equation, for

$$-(-3) + 2 - 5 = 3 + 2 - 5 = 0$$

We are actually saying two things when we say that the *line in Figure 6.5 is the graph of the solution set of the equation* $-x + y - 5 = 0.$

(1) Every point whose coordinates satisfy the equation $-x + y - 5 = 0$ must lie on this line.
(2) Every point which lies on this line has coordinates which satisfy the equation $-x + y - 5 = 0.$

Although we will not prove it here, it can be shown that the *graph of the solution set of any equation that can be written in the form* $Ax + By + C = 0,$ *where A and B are not both 0, is a straight line.* Since any two distinct points determine a straight line, we would only have to find *two different ordered pairs* that satisfy such an equation to determine the graph of the solution set.

Example 10

Graph the solution set of the equation $3x + 2y + 6 = 0.$

Since we now know that the graph of the solution set is a straight line, we need only find two different ordered pairs that

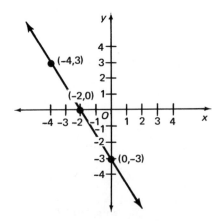

satisfy this equation. However, a third ordered pair would be helpful, for if the graph of the three ordered pairs do not lie on the same straight line, we can determine that an error was made. (See figure at the bottom of page 202.)

(1) If we let $x = 0$, then $y = -3$, giving us the ordered pair $(0, -3)$.
(2) If we let $y = 0$, then $x = -2$, giving us the ordered pair $(-2, 0)$.
(3) If $x = -4$, then $y = 3$, giving us the ordered pair $(-4, 3)$.

We still have two special cases to consider:

Case I: $A = 0, B \neq 0$, giving the equation $By + C = 0$
Case II: $B = 0, A \neq 0$, giving the equation $Ax + C = 0$

For Case I, let us consider the equation $y - 2 = 0$ as an equation in two variables.

$$0x + y - 2 = 0$$

No matter what value we choose for the *variable x*, this equation yields $y = 2$. For example, the ordered pairs $(0, 2)$, $(1, 2)$, $(-2, 2)$ all satisfy this equation. Upon graphing these points and connecting them with a straight line, we see that this line is parallel to the *x*-axis (that is, horizontal). (See Figure 6.6.)

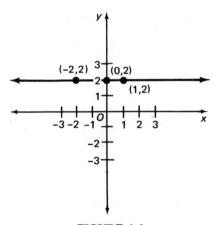

FIGURE 6.6

For Case II let us consider the equation $2x - 5 = 0$ as an equation in two variables.

$$2x + 0y - 5 = 0$$

Here no matter what value we choose for the *variable y*, this equation yields $2x = 5$ or $x = \frac{5}{2}$. For example, the ordered pairs $(\frac{5}{2}, 0)$, $(\frac{5}{2}, 2)$, $(\frac{5}{2}, -2)$ all satisfy this equation. The graph of the solution set of this equation will be a straight line parallel to the y-axis (that is, vertical). (See Figure 6.7.)

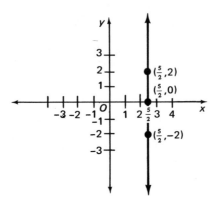

FIGURE 6.7

Exercise Set 6.3

In exercises 1-3 determine the missing coordinate so that each ordered pair satisfies the given equation.

1. $3x - 2y + 7 = 0$:
   (a) $(0, \ )$ (b) $(\ , 0)$ (c) $(\ , 2)$ (d) $(\ , -4)$

2. $y = 4$:
   (a) $(0, \ )$ (b) $(-4, \ )$ (c) $(-3, \ )$ (d) $(\ , 4)$

3. $-2x + 5y = 0$:
   (a) $(0, \ )$ (b) $(-3, \ )$ (c) $(\frac{4}{3}, \ )$ (d) $(\ , \frac{2}{7})$

In exercises 4-8 state whether the graph of the given equation passes through the point with given coordinates.

4. $4x - 2y = 6; (1, 2)$

5. $x - y = 2; (6, -4)$

6. $2x + 3y + 2 = 0; (5, -4)$

7. $y = 7; (-8, 7)$

8. $x = -3; (0, -3)$

In exercises 9-12 find the value of c so that the graph of the given equation will pass through the point with given coordinates.

9. $2x + y = c; (1, 2)$

10. $-3x - 2y = c; (-1, 2)$

11. $3x + cy = 5; (-1, -2)$

12. $cx - 4y = 9; (5, 3)$

In exercises 13-26 graph the solution set of the given equation.

13. $y = 2x$

14. $y = 3x - 2$

15. $x - y + 6 = 0$

16. $-3x + 4y + 1 = 0$

17. $x + 3y - 9 = 0$

18. $y = -7$

19. $x = 4$

20. $4y = 5x$

21. $y = 3$

22. $8x + 5y + 10 = 0$

23. $\frac{1}{2}x - \frac{1}{3}y - \frac{1}{6} = 0$

24. $x = -1$

25. $y - \frac{2}{3}x + 3 = 0$

26. $\frac{1}{2}y + \frac{2}{5}x - \frac{5}{2} = 0$

6.4 SLOPE OF A LINE

The concept of the *slope* of a straight line is one that we will now consider.

Let us consider a straight line, *not vertical*, passing through any two points P_1, with coordinates (x_1, y_1), and P_2, with coordinates (x_2, y_2). (See Figure 6.8.)

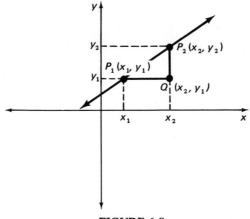

FIGURE 6.8

Through either point, say P_1, draw a line parallel to the x-axis (horizontal); and through the other point, which is now P_2, draw a line parallel to the y-axis (vertical). The coordinates of the point Q where these two lines intersect would be (x_2, y_1). We will now define the slope of a line as follows:

SLOPE OF A NONVERTICAL LINE

The *slope* of a nonvertical line, denoted by the letter m, passing through *any two points* $P_1(x_1, y_1)$ and $P_2(x_2, y_2)$ is the quotient:

$$m = \frac{y_2 - y_1}{x_2 - x_1}$$

Essentially the slope of a line passing through $P_1(x_1, y_1)$ and $P_2(x_2, y_2)$ is the quotient:

$$m = \frac{\text{change in } y}{\text{change in } x}$$

in going from P_1 to P_2.

Note

If we take the quotient, $\frac{\text{change in } y}{\text{change in } x}$ in going from P_2 to P_1, we would obtain the same slope. This will be observed in the following example.

Example 1

Find the slope of the line passing through the points $P(2, 4)$ and $Q(5, 8)$.

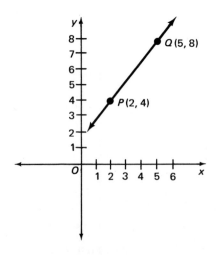

If we let P be our first point, so that $x_1 = 2$, $y_1 = 4$, and Q our second point, so that $x_2 = 5$, $y_2 = 8$, we obtain

$$m = \frac{8 - 4}{5 - 2} = \frac{4}{3}$$

If we had let P be our second point, so that $x_2 = 2$, $y_2 = 4$, and Q our first point, so that $x_1 = 5$, $y_1 = 8$, then we obtain

$$m = \frac{4 - 8}{2 - 5} = \frac{-4}{-3} = \frac{4}{3}$$

which is the same slope as previously obtained.

Note

It can be shown (although this will not be done here) that the same slope will be obtained regardless of which two points on the line are chosen. This will be observed in the following example.

Example 2

Given the linear equation $x + 2y - 6 = 0$, find the slope of the line which is the graph of the solution set of this equation.

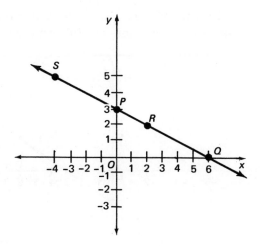

Two points whose coordinates satisfy the above equation are $P(0, 3)$ and $Q(6, 0)$(check this!).

Letting P be the first point and Q the second, we would obtain

$$m = \frac{0 - 3}{6 - 0} = \frac{-3}{6} = -\frac{1}{2}$$

You may have found two other points which would lie on the line, that is, whose coordinates satisfy the given equation. For example $R(2, 2)$ and $S(-4, 5)$ (check this!). Letting R be the first point and S the second, we would obtain for the slope

$$m = \frac{5 - 2}{-4 - 2} = \frac{3}{-6} = -\frac{1}{2}$$

which is the same as previously obtained.

Example 3

Show that the points $A(0, -2)$, $B(6, 2)$, and $C(9, 4)$ lie on the same straight line.

If we take the slope of the line segment from A to B, we obtain

$$m = \frac{2 - (-2)}{6 - 0} = \frac{4}{6} = \frac{2}{3}$$

Now if we take the slope of the line segment from B to C, we obtain

$$m = \frac{4 - 2}{9 - 6} = \frac{2}{3}$$

Since the two segments, *with the point B in common to both*, have the same slope, the three points must lie on the same straight line.

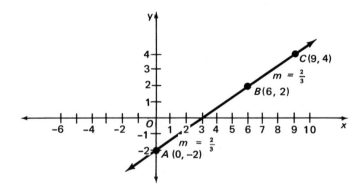

Observe that in example 1 above we obtained a *positive slope* $(+\frac{4}{3})$ and the graph of the resulting line *rises when moving from left to right*. This will be the case for any line with positive slope. In example 2 above we obtained a *negative slope* $(-\frac{1}{2})$ and the graph of the resulting line *falls as we move from left to right*. This will be the case for any line with negative slope.

We will now consider the special cases:

Case I: Line parallel to the x-axis (horizontal)
Case II: Line parallel to the y-axis (vertical)

In Case I (see Figure 6.9) any two points on the line will have the same y-coordinate, that is $y_1 = y_2$.

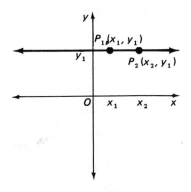

FIGURE 6.9

Thus the slope would be

$$m = \frac{y_2 - y_1}{x_2 - x_1} = \frac{y_1 - y_1}{x_2 - x_1} = \frac{0}{x_2 - x_1}$$

$$m = 0$$

Therefore we can conclude:

The slope of any horizontal line is 0.

In Case II (see Figure 6.10) any two points will have the same x-coordinate, that is, $x_1 = x_2$.

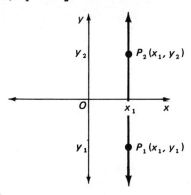

FIGURE 6.10

We can now see why the definition of the slope of a line *excluded the vertical line*, for in the case of the vertical line the slope would be

$$m = \frac{y_2 - y_1}{x_2 - x_1} = \frac{y_2 - y_1}{x_1 - x_1} = \frac{y_2 - y_1}{0}$$

which is undefined.

Therefore we can conclude:

<blockquote>The slope of any vertical line is undefined.</blockquote>

Let us once again examine the general linear equation in two variables $Ax + By + C = 0$. Here we will assume that *neither A nor B is* 0.

(1) We will now locate two points on the line which is the graph of the solution set of the above general equation.

If $x = 0$, then we obtain

$$By + C = 0$$

or

$$By = -C$$

or

$$y = -\frac{C}{B} \qquad \text{(Recall, we assumed } B \neq 0.\text{)}$$

y-INTERCEPT

Thus the point P whose coordinates are $(0, -\frac{C}{B})$ is one point on the desired line. *This is the point where the line intersects the y-axis.* This point is referred to as the *y-intercept*.

If $y = 0$, then we obtain

$$Ax + C = 0$$

or

$$Ax = -C$$

$$x = -\frac{C}{A} \qquad \text{(Recall, we assumed } A \neq 0.\text{)}$$

x-INTERCEPT

The point Q whose coordinates are $(-\frac{C}{A}, 0)$ is the *point where the line intersects the x-axis.* This point is referred to as the *x-intercept.*

(2) Now that we have located the two points $P(0, -\frac{C}{B})$ and $Q(-\frac{C}{A}, 0)$ we can determine the slope of the line. If we take Q as our first point, so that $x_1 = -\frac{C}{A}, y_1 = 0$, and P as our second point, so that $x_2 = 0, y_2 = -\frac{C}{B}$, then

$$m = \frac{-\frac{C}{B} - 0}{0 - (-\frac{C}{A})} = \frac{\frac{C}{B}}{+\frac{C}{A}}$$

$$m = -\frac{A}{B}$$

(3) If we now solve the general equation $Ax + By + C = 0$ for y in terms of x, we will observe some interesting results.

$$Ax + By + C = 0$$

or

$$By = -Ax - C$$

or

$$y = -\frac{A}{B}x - \frac{C}{B}$$

We can now see that when the equation *is solved for y in terms of x, the coefficient of x,* $-\frac{A}{B}$, *is the slope* and the constant term, $-\frac{C}{B}$, is the *y-intercept.*

SLOPE-INTERCEPT FORM OF A LINEAR EQUATION

Thus we can write the general linear equation, $Ax + By + C = 0$ in the form:

$$y = mx + k$$

where m is the slope and the point with coordinates $(0, k)$ is the *y*-intercept of the line determined by the given equation. This form of the linear equation is referred to as the *slope-intercept form.*

Example 4

Given the equation $y = -3x + 4$, find the slope and y-intercept of the line determined by this equation.

This equation is already in slope-intercept form. Thus the slope $m = -3$ and the y-intercept is the point with coordinates $(0, 4)$.

Example 5

Given the linear equation $4x + 5y - 7 = 0$, find the slope and y-intercept of the line determined by this equation.

Here $A = 4$, $B = 5$, $C = -7$. We know that $m = -\frac{A}{B}$ and the y-intercept has coordinates $(0, -\frac{C}{B})$.
But

$$-\frac{A}{B} = -\frac{4}{5}$$

and

$$-\frac{C}{B} = -\frac{-7}{5} = \frac{7}{5}$$

Thus $m = -\frac{4}{5}$ and the y-intercept is the point with coordinates $(0, \frac{7}{5})$.

This result may also be obtained by rewriting the equation in slope-intercept form.

$$4x + 5y - 7 = 0$$
$$5y = -4x + 7$$
$$y = -\frac{4}{5}x + \frac{7}{5}$$

Example 6

Write the equation whose graph is the line with slope $\frac{3}{4}$ and which passes through the point whose coordinates are $(4, 5)$.

If we use the slope-intercept form of a linear equation

$$y = mx + k$$

we can replace m by $\frac{3}{4}$ and write

$$y = \frac{3}{4}x + k$$

Knowing that the line passes through the point with coordinates
(4, 5) tells us that these coordinates must satisfy our equation. Thus
upon replacing x by 4 and y by 5, we obtain

$$5 = (\tfrac{3}{4})4 + k$$

or

$$5 = 3 + k$$

$$2 = k$$

Therefore the desired equation is

$$y = \tfrac{3}{4}x + 2$$

This equation may also be written in general form as

$$3x - 4y + 8 = 0 \qquad \text{(How?)}$$

PARALLEL LINES

Two lines are said to be *parallel* if they are *distinct*, and have the
same slope.

Example 7

Show that the lines l_1 and l_2 determined by the equations

$$l_1: \quad 2x - 5y + 3 = 0$$
$$l_2: \quad 6x - 15y - 2 = 0$$

are parallel.

If we write the given equations in slope-intercept form, we
obtain

$$l_1: \quad 2x - 5y + 3 = 0$$
$$-5y = -2x - 3$$
$$y = \tfrac{2}{5}x + \tfrac{3}{5}$$

$$l_2: \quad 6x - 15y - 2 = 0$$
$$-15y = -6x + 2$$
$$y = \tfrac{6}{15}x - \tfrac{2}{15}$$

or

$$y = \tfrac{2}{5}x - \tfrac{2}{15}$$

Thus we see that l_1 and l_2 are not the same line, but do have the same slope ($\frac{2}{5}$), and thus are parallel.

Exercise Set 6.4

In exercises 1-8 find the slope of the line which passes through the points whose coordinates are given.

1. $(-2, 10), (4, 8)$ **5.** $(3, 2), (-3, -2)$

2. $(-3, 0), (0, -4)$ **6.** $(8, 10), (1, 2)$

3. $(3, -6), (7, -6)$ **7.** $(-3, \frac{3}{2}), (\frac{5}{2}, 2)$

4. $(4, 2), (4, -2)$ **8.** $(0, \frac{-7}{4}), (\frac{7}{8}, \frac{1}{2})$

9. Given the point $O(0, 0)$ locate a point B so that the line segment OB will have slope:

    (a) $\frac{5}{2}$ (c) 5   (e) 0

    (b) $-\frac{3}{4}$ (d) -2 (f) $-\frac{2}{5}$

10. Given the point $A(3, 4)$ locate a point B so that the line segment AB will have slope:

    (a) $\frac{1}{3}$ (c) 0   (e) $-\frac{2}{7}$

    (b) 4   (d) -3 (f) -1

In exercises 11-15 determine whether the points whose coordinates are given lie on the same straight line.

11. $A(7, 0), B(1, 3), C(3, 2)$

12. $A(0, 2), B(1, 5), C(-2, 3)$

13. $A(2, 3), B(-4, 3), C(3, 0)$

14. $A(2, 3), B(2, -4), C(2, -7)$

15. $A(-3, -10), B(5, -2), C(-2, -9)$

In exercises 16-25 find the slope and y-intercept, and graph the line determined by the given equation.

16. $4x + y - 3 = 0$ **21.** $3x + 8y - 24 = 0$

17. $2x + 4y = 0$ **22.** $5y - 2x = 15$

18. $y + 4 = 0$ **23.** $x = 6 + 3y$

19. $-2y + 3x = 6$ **24.** $\frac{1}{15}y + \frac{1}{5}x = \frac{4}{3}$

20. $4x - 8 = 0$ **25.** $\frac{3}{4}x + \frac{2}{3} - \frac{1}{6}y = 0$

In exercises 26-33 write the equation whose graph is the line whose slope is given and which passes through the point whose coordinates are given.

26. $m = \frac{1}{2}; (0, -2)$ **30.** $m = \frac{3}{2}; (2, 2)$

27. $m = 0; (5, -6)$ **31.** $m = \frac{5}{2}; (4, 0)$

28. $m = -\frac{2}{3}; (0, 0)$ **32.** $m = 1; (0, 0)$

29. $m = -\frac{2}{3}; (1, 1)$ **33.** $m = -\frac{3}{2}; (-2, -4)$

In exercises 34-41 write the linear equation whose graph passes through the points whose coordinates are given.

34. $(0, 0)$ and $(5, 4)$ **38.** $(-3, -5)$ and $(2, 5)$

35. $(2, 0)$ and $(0, 4)$ **39.** $(0, -3)$ and $(-2, -4)$

36. $(4, -2)$ and $(4, 2)$ **40.** $(7, -4)$ and $(1, 6)$

37. $(3, 4)$ and $(-6, 4)$ **41.** $(-3, 6)$ and $(3, -2)$

In exercises 42-47 determine whether or not the given pair of lines are parallel.

42. $l_1: \quad -3x + 4y - 2 = 0$ **45.** $l_1: \quad 3x - 8y = 5$

$\quad\; l_2: \quad 9x - 12y - 1 = 0$ $\quad\; l_2: \quad \frac{3}{2}x + 4y = 1$

43. $l_1: \quad 2x - y - 7 = 0$ **46.** $l_1: \quad \frac{1}{2}x + 2y = 5$

$\quad\; l_2: \quad -x + 2y - 4 = 0$ $\quad\; l_2: \quad \frac{1}{4}x + y = \frac{1}{10}$

44. $l_1: \quad 3x + 2y = 7$ **47.** $l_1: \quad 3x + 2y - 4 = 0$

$\quad\; l_2: \quad -6x - 4y = -14$ $\quad\; l_2: \quad 6x + 3y - 8 = 0$

In exercises 48-53 find the equation of the line passing through the point whose coordinates are given and parallel to the line determined by the given equation.

48. $(5, 1); y = 3$ **51.** $(6, 1); 2x + 3y - 2 = 0$

49. $(0, 3); 5x - 2y = 0$ **52.** $(-4, 0); 7x - 3y = 5$

50. $(1, 2); 3x - y - 5 = 0$ **53.** $(-2, -2); -4x - 9y + 4 = 0$

6.5 LINEAR INEQUALITIES IN TWO VARIABLES

In this section we will be considering inequalities of the form

$$Ax + By + C < 0$$

and

$$Ax + By + C > 0$$

where A, B, C are any real numbers and A and B are not both 0. We will start by considering the special cases

Case I: $A = 0, B \neq 0$
Case II: $B = 0, A \neq 0$

We will illustrate Case I in the following example.

Example 1

Graph the solution set of the inequality

$$y < 3$$

This inequality may be written $0x + y - 3 < 0$, so that here $A = 0$, $B = 1$, $C = -3$. The solution set of the given inequality consists of all ordered pairs whose y-coordinate is less than 3, and whose x-coordinate can take on any real value.

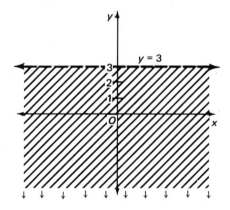

For example, $(0, 2)$, $(19, 1)$, $(-5, 0)$ are three ordered pairs which satisfy the given inequality.

(1) To graph the solution set of the inequality $y < 3$, we first graph the solution set of the equation $y = 3$, which we know to be a horizontal line. This straight line is not part of the graph of the

solution set of the inequality, which is indicated by using a *broken line*.

(2) Every point *below* the line obtained in step (1) will have *y-coordinate less than* 3. To illustrate the graph of the desired solution set, we then shade the entire region below the line $y = 3$.

To illustrate Case II let us consider the following example:

Example 2

Graph the solution set of the inequality $x \geqslant -2$.

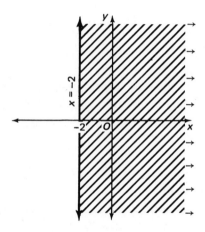

Here this inequality could have been written in the form $x + 0y + 2 \geqslant 0$.

(1) We first graph the solution set of the equation $x = -2$ (vertical line). Here this line is included in the graph of the solution set of the given inequality. (Recall $\geqslant$ reads "greater than or equal to.") This is indicated by using a *solid line*.

(2) We then shade the entire region *to the right* of the line obtained in step (1), for all points to the right of this line have *x*-coordinate greater than -2.

Example 3

Graph the solution of the inequality $x - y < 0$.

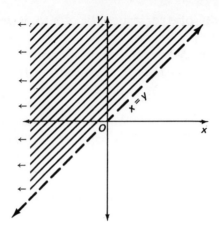

(1) We first solve for one of the variables in terms of the other. Here we will solve for x in terms of y to obtain $x < y$.

(2) We now graph the solution set of the equation $x = y$. (All points will have their x-coordinate equal to their y-coordinate.) The straight line thus obtained is *not* part of the graph of the solution set of the inequality, which is again indicated by using a *broken line*.

(3) We are looking for all points whose *x-coordinate is less than the y-coordinate*, and thus we shade the entire region to the *left* of the line obtained in step (2).

Example 4

Graph the solution set of the inequality

$$3x + 2y - 6 \geqslant 0$$

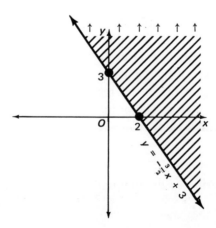

(1) Here we will solve for y in terms of x to obtain

$$2y \geqslant -3x + 6$$

or

$$y \geqslant \tfrac{-3}{2} x + 3$$

(2) We now graph the solution set of the equation $y = \tfrac{-3}{2}x + 3$. The straight line obtained, which *is included* in the graph of the solution set of the given inequality, has slope $\tfrac{-3}{2}$ and y-intercept $(0, 3)$.

(3) Since we are looking for all points whose *y-coordinate is greater than or equal to* $\tfrac{-3}{2}x + 3$, we shade the entire region above the line obtained in step (2) (which is drawn as a *solid line* to indicate its inclusion in the graph of the desired solution set).

Exercise Set 6.5

In exercises 1-12 graph the solution set of the given inequality.

1. $y > 3$

2. $y > 2x$

3. $x < -5$

4. $x \leqslant -2y$

5. $x \geqslant 4$

6. $y + 2x > 0$

7. $y + 4 \leqslant 0$

8. $y + 4 \geqslant x$

9. $2y - 3x - 6 > 0$

10. $x - y + 6 < 0$

11. $4y - 8 > 16x$

12. $y \leqslant \tfrac{3}{4}x - 1$

REVIEW TEST FOR CHAPTER VI

Note: This test should be completed in 70 minutes.

1. Given $A = \{-1, 1, 3\}$, graph $A \times A$ and list its ordered pairs.

2. If $A = \{-1, 0\}$ and $B = \{-2, -1, 0, 1, 2\}$, find $(A \times B) \cap (B \times A)$.

3. (a) What is the slope of the line passing through the points with coordinates $(0, 4)$ and $(0, 2)$?
   (b) What is the slope of the line passing through the points with coordinates $(6, -4)$ and $(5, -5)$?

4. Find the slope and y-intercept of the line determined by each of the following equations:

  (a) $3x + 2y = 7$

  (b) $y + 3 = 0$

  (c) $4x + 9y = 0$

5. Determine the number of elements in $A \times B$ if
  (a) $A = \{0, 1, 2, 3, 4, 5\}$ and $B = \{-2, 0, 2, 4, 7, 9\}$
  (b) $A = \{x \mid x$ is an integer, $-7 \leqslant x < -1\}$ and
     $B = \{x \mid x$ is an integer, $x \geqslant 4$ and $x < 7\}$

6. Find the x-intercept of the line determined by each of the following equations:
  (a) $2x + 3y - 8 = 0$
  (b) $2x - 5 = 0$
  (c) $3y - 7 = 0$

7. Find k so that the point with coordinates $(3, k)$ lies on the line determined by the equation $5x - 3y + 6 = 0$.

8. If the graph of the solution set of the linear equation $2Ax + 3By = 12$ passes through the point with coordinates $(2, 0)$, what is the value of A?

9. (a) Determine the slope and y-intercept of the graph of the linear equation $-3x + 4y - 8 = 0$.
  (b) Graph the solution set of the inequality $-3x + 4y - 8 < 0$.

10. Determine whether or not the points $A(0, 2)$, $B(4, 0)$, and $C(-2, 3)$ lie on the same straight line. State the reason for your answer.

11. (a) Graph the solution set of the equation $2x - 2y - 3 = 0$.
   (b) Graph the solution set of the inequality $3 \geqslant 2x - 2y$.

12. Graph the solution set of each of the following equations:
   (a) $\frac{2}{3}y - 4 = 0$
   (b) $\frac{x}{3} - \frac{y}{2} = 2$

13. Graph the solution set of the following inequalities
   (a) $\frac{x}{3} - \frac{5}{3} > 0$
   (b) $x + \frac{5}{2}y \leqslant 0$

14. Write the linear equation whose graph passes through the points whose coordinates are:
   (a) $(3, 4)$ and $(-4, -3)$
   (b) $(-1, -6)$ and $(-4, 3)$

15. Write the equation of the line passing through the point with coordinates $(3, -4)$ and parallel to the line determined by the equation $-x - 2y - 7 = 0$.

VII

SYSTEMS OF LINEAR EQUATIONS

7.1 INTRODUCTION

Frequently it is desired to find ordered pairs (x, y) which satisfy two linear equations at the same time:

$$\left.\begin{array}{l} A_1 x + B_1 y + C_1 = 0 \\ A_2 x + B_2 y + C_2 = 0 \end{array}\right\} \text{ I}$$

The set of equations (I) is referred to as a *system of simultaneous linear equations,* and the solution set of such a system of equations is the set of all ordered pairs which satisfy *both* equations. In other words, if S_1 is the solution set of the equation

$$A_1 x + B_1 y + C_1 = 0$$

and if S_2 is the solution set of the equation

$$A_2 x + B_2 y + C_2 = 0$$

then the solution set of the system (I) would be $S_1 \cap S_2$.

For example, let us consider the system of equations

$$3x - 4y - 11 = 0$$

$$2x + 5y + 8 = 0$$

The ordered pair $(1, -2)$ would be an element of the solution set of this system of equations, for if we replace x by 1 and y by -2 in the first equation we obtain

$$3(1) - 4(-2) - 11 = 3 + 8 - 11 = 0$$

and if we replace x by 1 and y by -2 in the second equation we obtain

$$2(1) + 5(-2) + 8 = 2 - 10 + 8 = 0$$

Thus we can see that the ordered pair $(1, -2)$ satisfies both equations. The problem we wish to consider is how to find the solution set of any pair of simultaneous linear equations.

7.2 GRAPHICAL INTERPRETATION OF A SYSTEM OF TWO SIMULTANEOUS LINEAR EQUATIONS

As we have seen in Chapter VI, the graph of the solution set of a linear equation in two variables is a straight line. Thus a system of two simultaneous linear equations in two variables determines a pair of straight lines in the plane. The *graph of the solution set of such a system of equations is represented by the set of all points which lie on both lines.*

Note

Essentially we are saying that an ordered pair satisfies both equations if and only if the point represented by that ordered pair lies on both lines.

There are three cases that arise when considering the graphical interpretation of the solution set of a system of two linear equations.

CASE A

The lines determined by the two equations intersect at a single point P (see Figure 7.1). In this case the solution set will consist of one ordered pair, that which corresponds to the point of intersection of the two lines.

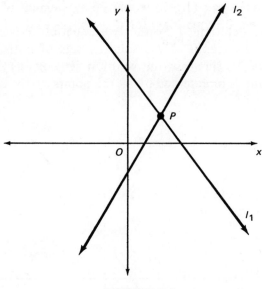

FIGURE 7.1

CASE B

The lines determined by the two equations are parallel (two distinct lines with the same slope) (see Figure 7.2). In this case there are no points which lie on both lines and therefore the solution set is the null set, 0.

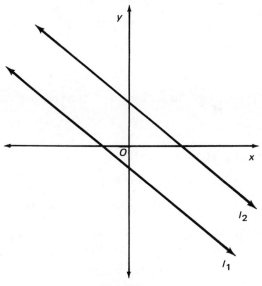

FIGURE 7.2

CASE C

The lines determined by the two equations coincide (see Fig. 7.3). That is, the graphs of the solution sets of both equations are the *same line*. In this case the solution set consists of infinitely many points, and is represented by all the points on the common line.

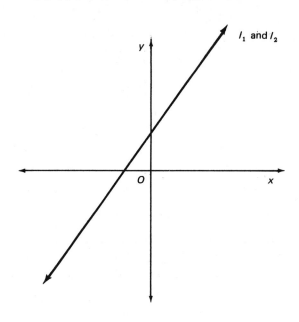

FIGURE 7.3

Let us illustrate these cases with the following examples.

Example 1

Consider the system of equations

$$(1) \ 3x + 2y - 6 = 0$$

$$(2) \quad x + 2y - 4 = 0$$

If we graph the solution set of each of these equations, we will see that the two straight lines intersect at one point.

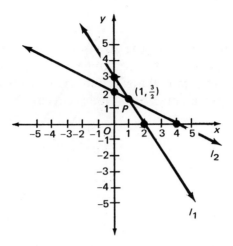

The point of intersection seems to correspond to the ordered pair $(1, \frac{3}{2})$. Upon replacing x by 1 and y by $\frac{3}{2}$ in equations (1) and (2), we obtain

$$(1) \quad 3(1) + 2(\tfrac{3}{2}) - 6 = 3 + 3 - 6 = 0$$

and

$$(2) \quad 1 + 2(\tfrac{3}{2}) - 4 = 1 + 3 - 4 = 0$$

Therefore the solution set is $\{(1, \frac{3}{2})\}$.

Note

It might be rather difficult to locate on the graph the exact point of intersection of the two lines if the coordinates of this point were not integers. For this reason we should establish other methods of finding the solution set of a system of two linear equations.

Example 2

Let l_1 and l_2 be the lines determined by the equations of the following system:

$$l_1 : \ 3x + 2y - 6 = 0$$
$$l_2 : \ 3x + 2y - 12 = 0$$

If we graph these two lines, they seem to be parallel.

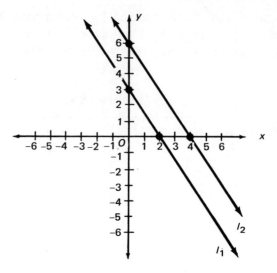

Calculating the slopes of these lines we obtain

$$m_1 = -\tfrac{3}{2} = m_2$$

which confirms the fact that they are parallel. Therefore the solution set is $\emptyset$.

Example 3

Let

$$l_1: \; 3x + 2y - 6 = 00$$

$$l_2: \; \tfrac{3}{2}x + y - 3 = 0$$

If we graph lines l_1 and l_2, we notice that the two lines coincide (that is, they are the same line).

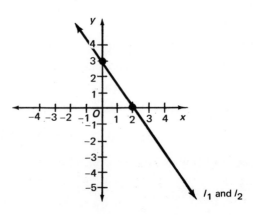

This could have been realized by multiplying both sides of the second equation above by 2 (which does not change the solution set of that equation) and noticing that the first equation is obtained.

Exercise Set 7.2

In exercises 1-10 graph the lines determined by the equations of the given system and obtain the solution set from the graph. Check your results in the given system.

1. $x + 4 = 0$
   $y - 3 = 0$

2. $y = 7$
   $2x - y = 9$

3. $3y - 4x + 2 = 0$
   $y - 2x = 0$

4. $6y + 9x = 1$
   $2y + 3x = 5$

5. $2x - 3y + 5 = 0$
   $3x + y - 9 = 0$

6. $y = x - 1$
   $3x + 2y = -2$

7. $2x + y - 6 = 0$
   $-x + y - 3 = 0$

8. $3x - y = 1$
   $-6x + 2y = 4$

9. $3x - 4y = 6$
   $2x - y = -1$

10. $x + 2y + 6 = 0$
    $2y - x = 0$

7.3 SOLVING TWO SIMULTANEOUS EQUATIONS BY SUBSTITUTION

To find the solution set of a system of two simultaneous equations in two variables we can

(1) First solve one of the equations for y in terms of x.
(2) Substitute the expression obtained in the other equation, thus producing a linear equation in x, for which we can find the solution set by previous methods.
(3) Substitute the value of x obtained in step (2) in either equation of the given system to obtain the corresponding value of y.
(4) Check your result by replacing the variables in each equation of the given system by the values obtained.

Note

We could also have started the above procedure by solving one of the equations for x in terms of y and then making the appropriate substitutions.

Example 1

Find the solution set of the system of equations.

$$(1) \quad x - y + 1 = 0$$
$$(2) \quad x + 2y - 5 = 0$$

Solving equation (1) for x in terms of y, we obtain

$$x = y - 1$$

Substituting this expression for x in equation (2), we obtain

$$(y - 1) + 2y - 5 = 0$$

or

$$3y - 6 = 0 \qquad \text{(Collecting like terms)}$$

Solving this equation for y, we obtain

$$3y = 6$$
$$y = 2$$

Substituting this value for y in equation (1) of the given system, we obtain

$$x - 2 + 1 = 0$$
$$x - 1 = 0$$
$$x = 1$$

Check: $(1) \quad x - y + 1 = 0 \qquad (2) \quad x + 2y - 5 = 0$

$\qquad\qquad 1 - 2 + 1 = 0 \qquad\qquad\quad 1 + 4 - 5 = 0$

Thus the solution set is $\{(1, 2)\}$.

Example 2

Find the solution set of the system

$(1) \quad y = 7$

$(2) \quad 2x + 3y - 3 = 0$

We can see from equation (1) that for an ordered pair to satisfy both equations the y value must be 7.

Thus we merely substitute this value of y in equation (2) to find the corresponding value of x.

$$2x + 3(7) - 3 = 0$$
$$2x + 21 - 3 = 0$$
$$2x + 18 = 0$$
$$2x = -18$$
$$x = -9$$

Therefore the solution set is $\{(-9, 7)\}$.

Check this result by replacing x by -9 and y by 7 in equation (2).

Example 3

Find the solution set of the system

(1) $3x - y = 6$

(2) $6x - 2y = 9$

Solving for y in terms of x in equation (1), we obtain

$$y = 3x - 6$$

Substituting this expression for y in equation (2), we obtain

(3) $6x - 2(3x - 6) = 9$

     $6x - 6x + 12 = 9$ (Distributive law)

     $12 = 9$

Since this is a false statement, there must be no value of x that satisfies equation (3) and thus we must conclude that there are no ordered pairs that satisfy both given linear equations. Therefore the solution set is $\emptyset$.

Note

The entire procedure in example 3 could have been avoided if we would have *first found the slopes of the lines* determined by the two equations.

In this case we would have obtained $m_1 = m_2 = 3$, and since the lines are not the same, they must be parallel, and therefore the solution set is $\emptyset$.

Example 4

Find the solution set of the system of equations

(1) $3x + 2y - 6 = 0$

(2) $5x + 2y - 4 = 0$

Solving equation (1) for y in terms of x,

$$2y = -3x + 6$$

$$y = -\tfrac{3}{2}x + 3$$

Substituting this expression for y in equation (2),

$$5x + 2(-\tfrac{3}{2}x + 3) - 4 = 0$$

$$5x - 3x + 6 - 4 = 0 \qquad \text{(Distributive law)}$$

$$2x + 2 = 0$$

$$2x = -2$$

$$x = -1$$

Substituting this value in equation (1),

$$3(-1) + 2y - 6 = 0$$

$$-3 + 2y - 6 = 0$$

$$2y - 9 = 0$$

$$2y = 9$$

$$y = \tfrac{9}{2}$$

Therefore the solution set is $\{(-1, \tfrac{9}{2})\}$. Check this result.

Exercise Set 7.3

In exercises 1-14 find the solution set of the given system by substitution. Check your result.

1. $y = 5$
    $x + y = 7$

2. $y = 4x$
    $x + 2y = 18$

3. $5x + 2y = 20$
   $y = 1 + 2x$

4. $y = \frac{1}{2}x + 2$
   $y = 2 - 2x$

5. $-x + 2y = 7$
   $4x - 8y = 1$

6. $4x - y - 2 = 0$
   $3x - 4y + 18 = 0$

7. $2x + y + 2 = 0$
   $x - 2y - 6 = 0$

8. $x + y = -8$
   $-2x + y = 7$

9. $-9x + y = 0$
   $2x - \frac{1}{3}y + \frac{1}{3} = 0$

10. $-x + 2y = 9$
    $-x + y = 3$

11. $x - 5y + 3 = 0$
    $3x + 7y - 9 = 0$

12. $-x + 2y = 7$
    $-x + 3y = 9$

13. $2x + 3y = -3$
    $5x + 6y = -4$

14. $4x + 5y - 7 = 0$
    $3x + 4y - 6 = 0$

7.4 SOLVING A SYSTEM OF LINEAR EQUATIONS BY ELIMINATION OF A VARIABLE

Another procedure to find the solution set of a system of two linear equations in two variables is to eliminate one of the variables as will be seen in the following examples:

Example 1

Find the solution set of the system

(1) $2x + y - 3 = 0$

(2) $3x + 2y + 4 = 0$

We will first multiply both sides of equation (1) by 2 to obtain

(1') $4x + 2y - 6 = 0$

which has the same solution set as equation (1) and where now the coefficient of y is the same as that in equation (2).
We can now rewrite the system as follows

(1') $4x + 2y - 6 = 0$

(2) $3x + 2y + 4 = 0$

If we subtract the corresponding sides of these equations, the y variable will be eliminated and we will obtain

$$x - 10 = 0$$

or

$$x = 10$$

We now substitute this value for x in either of the equations of the original system [here we will use equation (1)] to obtain the corresponding value of y.

$$2x + y - 3 = 0$$
$$2(10) + y - 3 = 0$$
$$20 + y - 3 = 0$$
$$y + 17 = 0$$
$$y = -17$$

Therefore the solution set is $\{(10, -17)\}$. Check this result by replacing x by 10 and y by -17 in both equations of the given system.

Example 2

Find the solution set of the system

(1) $2x + 3y = 4$

(2) $-3x + 7y = 17$

We will multiply both sides of equation (1) by 3, and both sides of equation (2) by 2, to rewrite the system as

(1′) $6x + 9y = 12$

(2′) $-6x + 14y = 34$

where now we can eliminate the x variable by *adding* corresponding sides of these equations.

$$23y = 46$$
$$y = 2$$

Upon substituting this value in equation (1) of the original system, we obtain the corresponding value of x.

$$2x + 3y = 4$$
$$2x + 3(2) = 4$$
$$2x + 6 = 4$$
$$2x = -2$$
$$x = -1$$

Therefore the solution set is $\{(-1, 2)\}$. Check this result in the original system.

Example 3

Find the solution set of the system

(1) $2x - y - 6 = 0$

(2) $10x - 5y - 30 = 0$

Upon multiplying equation (1) by 5 we see that equation (2) is obtained. Thus there is no need to eliminate one of the variables, for we know that *every ordered pair* which satisfies equation (1) also satisfies equation (2), and every ordered pair which satisfies equation (2) will also satisfy equation (1). Therefore the solution set consists of *infinitely many ordered pairs*.

Note

Graphically this means that the lines determined by the two equations coincide.

Exercise Set 7.4

In exercises 1-14 find the solution set of the given system by elimination of a variable, using addition or subtraction. Check your result.

1. $x + y = 7$
   $x - y = 3$

2. $-2x + y = 5$
   $2x + 2y = 7$

3. $2x + 4y = 3$
   $2x - 8y = -3$

4. $4x - 3y = 8$
   $2x - 3y = 2$

5. $-x + 2y = 7$
   $-x + 3y = 9$

6. $5x + 2y = 4$
   $-10x - 4y = -2$

7. $2x - 5y - 8 = 0$
   $-x - 3y - 7 = 0$

8. $4x - y - 24 = 0$
   $3x - 5y - 1 = 0$

9. $2x + 3y = 9$
   $3x + 5y = 11$

10. $-4x + 3y = -1$
    $8x + 9y = 12$

11. $5x + 2y - 38 = 0$
    $-6x + 5y + 16 = 0$

12. $3y - 4x - 14 = 0$
    $4y - 3x - 14 = 0$

13. $3x - 4y = 7$
    $-6x - 5y = 12$

14. $6x - 2y = -5$
    $-4x + \frac{1}{2}y = 0$

7.5 DETERMINANTS OF SECOND ORDER

Let us now find the solution set of a system of two general linear
equations in two variables by elimination of one of the variables.

(1) $A_1x + B_1y = C_1$

(2) $A_2x + B_2y = C_2$

We will eliminate the y variable by first multiplying equation (1) by
B_2 and equation (2) by B_1 and rewriting the system as

(1') $A_1B_2x + B_1B_2y = C_1B_2$

(2') $B_1A_2x + B_1B_2y = B_1C_2$

where the coefficient of y is the same in each equation. Upon subtracting the corresponding sides of these equations, we obtain

$$A_1B_2x - B_1A_2x = C_1B_2 - B_1C_2$$

or

$$(A_1B_2 - B_1A_2)x = C_1B_2 - B_1C_2$$

Upon solving this equation for x, we obtain

$$x = \frac{C_1B_2 - B_1C_2}{A_1B_2 - B_1A_2}, \quad \text{provided } A_1B_2 - B_1A_2 \neq 0$$

A SECOND ORDER DETERMINANT

We will now define the symbol $\begin{vmatrix} a & b \\ c & d \end{vmatrix}$, where $a, b, c,$ and d are real
numbers, to mean the *real number ad* $-$ *bc*. Such a square array of
numbers is called a *determinant*. The numbers $a, b, c,$ and d are
called the *elements* of the determinant. The sets of numbers arranged
vertically are called the *columns* of the determinant and the sets of

numbers arranged horizontally are called the *rows* of the determinant. Thus the numbers a and c constitute the first column, the numbers b and d the second column; the numbers a and b constitute the first row, and the numbers c and d the second row. Moreover, a determinant consisting of two rows and two columns is called a *second order determinant*.

Example 1

Evaluate the determinant $\begin{vmatrix} 3 & 2 \\ 5 & 9 \end{vmatrix}$.

$$\begin{vmatrix} 3 & 2 \\ 5 & 9 \end{vmatrix} = (3 \cdot 9) - (2 \cdot 5) = 27 - 10 = 17$$

Example 2

Evaluate the determinant $\begin{vmatrix} 1 & 2 \\ 7 & 5 \end{vmatrix}$.

$$\begin{vmatrix} 1 & 2 \\ 7 & 5 \end{vmatrix} = (1 \cdot 5) - (2 \cdot 7) = 5 - 14 = -9$$

Example 3

Evaluate the determinant $\begin{vmatrix} 2 & -4 \\ 7 & -3 \end{vmatrix}$.

$$\begin{vmatrix} 2 & -4 \\ 7 & -3 \end{vmatrix} = 2(-3) - (-4)(7) = -6 - (-28)$$
$$= -6 + 28$$
$$= 22$$

Returning now to the problem we've been considering, we recall that we found

$$x = \frac{C_1 B_2 - B_1 C_2}{A_1 B_2 - B_1 A_2}$$

Now we can replace

$$C_1 B_2 - B_1 C_2 \quad \text{by} \quad \begin{vmatrix} C_1 & B_1 \\ C_2 & B_2 \end{vmatrix}$$

and

$$A_1 B_2 - B_1 A_2 \quad \text{by} \quad \begin{vmatrix} A_1 & B_1 \\ A_2 & B_2 \end{vmatrix}$$

and thus we can write

$$x = \frac{\begin{vmatrix} C_1 & B_1 \\ C_2 & B_2 \end{vmatrix}}{\begin{vmatrix} A_1 & B_1 \\ A_2 & B_2 \end{vmatrix}}$$

In a similar manner we could have eliminated the x variable and obtained

$$y = \frac{A_1 C_2 - C_1 A_2}{A_1 B_2 - B_1 A_2}$$

which can be written in determinant form as

$$y = \frac{\begin{vmatrix} A_1 & C_1 \\ A_2 & C_2 \end{vmatrix}}{\begin{vmatrix} A_1 & B_1 \\ A_2 & B_2 \end{vmatrix}}$$

Let us now return to the given system of general linear equations in two variables,

(1) $A_1 x + B_1 y = C_1$

(2) $A_2 x + B_2 y = C_2$

and establish a general procedure to find the solution set by determinants.

THE DETERMINANT OF COEFFICIENTS

(1) In solving for x and y, *the denominators are the same determinant*, consisting of the coefficients of x and y *exactly in the order that they appear in the given system*. Such a determinant is known as the *determinant of coefficients*.

$$\begin{vmatrix} A_1 & B_1 \\ A_2 & B_2 \end{vmatrix}$$

(2) In solving for x, the determinant in the numerator is obtained by *replacing the coefficients of x* in the determinant of coefficients *by the constant terms* in the same order that they appear (where we should also note that the constant terms should be on the *right-hand side* of the original equations).

$$\begin{vmatrix} C_1 & B_1 \\ C_2 & B_2 \end{vmatrix}$$

(3) In solving for y, the determinant in the numerator is obtained by replacing the *coefficients of y* in the determinant of coefficients by the constant terms, again in the order that they appear.

$$\begin{vmatrix} A_1 & C_1 \\ A_2 & C_2 \end{vmatrix}$$

Example 4

Using determinants, find the solution set of the system

$$3x - 4y = 11$$
$$2x + 5y = -8$$

(1) The determinant of coefficients is

$$\begin{vmatrix} 3 & -4 \\ 2 & 5 \end{vmatrix} = 3(5) - (-4)2 = 15 - (-8)$$

$$= 15 + 8$$

$$= 23$$

(2)
$$x = \frac{\begin{vmatrix} 11 & -4 \\ -8 & 5 \end{vmatrix}}{23} = \frac{11(5) - (-4)(-8)}{23}$$

$$= \frac{55 - 32}{23}$$

$$= \frac{23}{23} = 1$$

Note: To obtain the determinant in the numerator we replaced the first column (coefficients of x) in the determinant of coefficients by $\begin{pmatrix} 11 \\ -8 \end{pmatrix}$ (the constant terms).

(3)

$$y = \dfrac{\begin{vmatrix} 3 & 11 \\ 2 & -8 \end{vmatrix}}{23} = \dfrac{3(-8) - 11(2)}{23}$$

$$= \dfrac{-24 - 22}{23}$$

$$= \dfrac{-46}{23} = -2$$

Note: To obtain the determinant in the numerator we replaced the second column (coefficients of y) in the determinant of coefficients by $\begin{pmatrix} 11 \\ -8 \end{pmatrix}$.

Thus the solution set is $\{(1, -2)\}$.

Example 5

Using determinants, find the solution set of the system

$$-3x + 2y - 6 = 0$$
$$x - 4y - 4 = 0$$

Before we use determinants, the constant terms, if you recall, should be on the right-hand side of the equations:

$$-3x + 2y = 6$$
$$x - 4y = 4$$

$$x = \dfrac{\begin{vmatrix} 6 & 2 \\ 4 & -4 \end{vmatrix}}{\begin{vmatrix} -3 & 2 \\ 1 & -4 \end{vmatrix}} = \dfrac{6(-4) - 2(4)}{(-3)(-4) - 2(1)}$$

$$= \dfrac{-24 - 8}{12 - 2}$$

$$= \dfrac{-32}{10}$$

$$= \dfrac{-16}{5}$$

$$y = \frac{\begin{vmatrix} -3 & 6 \\ 1 & 4 \end{vmatrix}}{\begin{vmatrix} -3 & 2 \\ 1 & -4 \end{vmatrix}} = \frac{-3(4) - 6(1)}{10}$$

$$= \frac{-12 - 6}{10}$$

$$= \frac{-18}{10}$$

$$= \frac{-9}{5}$$

Thus the solution set is $\{(\frac{-16}{5}, \frac{-9}{5})\}$.

Exercise Set 7.5

In exercises 1-6 evaluate the given second order determinant.

1. $\begin{vmatrix} 4 & 3 \\ 9 & 8 \end{vmatrix}$

2. $\begin{vmatrix} -4 & 0 \\ 2 & 5 \end{vmatrix}$

3. $\begin{vmatrix} 2 & 4 \\ 4 & 8 \end{vmatrix}$

4. $\begin{vmatrix} -3 & 4 \\ 6 & -4 \end{vmatrix}$

5. $\begin{vmatrix} -2 & -7 \\ 1 & -5 \end{vmatrix}$

6. $\begin{vmatrix} -5 & -3 \\ -6 & -7 \end{vmatrix}$

In exercises 7-20 use determinants to find the solution set of the given system.

7. $y = 8$
   $3x + 2y = 1$

8. $x + 4y = 4$
   $3x - 2y = -2$

9. $2x + 3y = 4$
   $5x - 2y = 10$

10. $2x - 3y = 0$
    $2x + y = 16$

11. $3x - y = 7$
    $12x - 4y = 3$

12. $3x + 5y = 0$
    $5x - 3y = 0$

13. $3x - 4y = -1$
    $9x + 8y = 12$

14. $6x - 4y = 5$
    $-3x + 2y = -1$

15. $3x - y = 13$
    $5x + y = 5$

16. $-5x + 12y = 8$
    $10x + 6y = 9$

17. $5x - y = -7$
    $2x + 3y = -9$

18. $-4x + 3y = -3$
    $2x - 2y = 5$

19. $x + 2y = -6$
    $x - 4y = 0$

20. $3x + 4y = -3$
    $\frac{1}{2}x + \frac{2}{3}y = 1$

7.6 DETERMINANTS OF THIRD ORDER

We can extend the method of Section 7.5 to find the solution set of a system of three linear equations in three variables. Before this can be done, however, we must consider a number of definitions.

A LINEAR EQUATION IN THREE VARIABLES

Any equation of the form $Ax + By + Cz = D$, where A, B, C, D are real numbers and $A, B,$ and C are not all 0 is called a *linear equation in three variables.*

A SYSTEM OF THREE LINEAR EQUATIONS IN THREE VARIABLES

A system of three linear equations in three variables is a set of three equations of the form

$$A_1 x + B_1 y + C_1 z = D_1$$

$$A_2 x + B_2 y + C_2 z = D_2$$

$$A_3 x + B_3 y + C_3 z = D_3$$

THE SOLUTION SET

The solution set of a system of three linear equations in three variables is the set of all values of x, y, and z which satisfy all three equations at the same time.

DETERMINANT OF THIRD ORDER

In order to now extend the method of Section 7.5, we must introduce a square array of real numbers,

$$\begin{vmatrix} A_1 & B_1 & C_1 \\ A_2 & B_2 & C_2 \\ A_3 & B_3 & C_3 \end{vmatrix}$$

consisting of three rows (sets of numbers arranged horizontally) and three columns (sets of numbers arranged vertically), and known as a *determinant of third order*.

A THIRD ORDER DETERMINANT

The third order determinant given above is defined as the *real number* obtained as follows:

$$
\begin{vmatrix} A_1 & B_1 & C_1 \\ A_2 & B_2 & C_2 \\ A_3 & B_3 & C_3 \end{vmatrix} = A_1 \begin{vmatrix} B_2 & C_2 \\ B_3 & C_3 \end{vmatrix} - A_2 \begin{vmatrix} B_1 & C_1 \\ B_3 & C_3 \end{vmatrix} + A_3 \begin{vmatrix} B_1 & C_1 \\ B_2 & C_2 \end{vmatrix}
$$

OBSERVE

(1) The second order determinant which is multiplied by A_1 in the expansion on the right side of the above definition is the determinant that remains after *crossing out the row and column in which A_1 appears in the original determinant* (on left side of the above).

$$
\begin{vmatrix} A_1 & B_1 & C_1 \\ A_2 & B_2 & C_2 \\ A_3 & B_3 & C_3 \end{vmatrix}
$$

(2) The determinant multiplied by A_2 is that which remains after crossing out the row and column in which A_2 appears.

$$
\begin{vmatrix} A_1 & B_1 & C_1 \\ A_2 & B_2 & C_2 \\ A_3 & B_3 & C_3 \end{vmatrix}
$$

(3) The determinant multiplied by A_3 is that which remains after crossing out the row and column in which A_3 appears.

$$
\begin{vmatrix} A_1 & B_1 & C_1 \\ A_2 & B_2 & C_2 \\ A_3 & B_3 & C_3 \end{vmatrix}
$$

A MINOR

The second order determinant that remains after crossing out the row and column in which an element appears in a third order determinant is called the minor of that element.

Example 1

The minor of C_2 in the determinant

$$\begin{vmatrix} A_1 & B_1 & C_1 \\ A_2 & B_2 & C_2 \\ A_3 & B_3 & C_3 \end{vmatrix} \quad \text{is}$$

$$\begin{vmatrix} A_1 & B_1 \\ A_3 & B_3 \end{vmatrix}$$

Example 2

What is the minor of 3 in the determinant

$$\begin{vmatrix} 1 & -4 & 2 \\ 5 & -1 & -3 \\ 7 & 3 & 6 \end{vmatrix}$$

Crossing out the 3rd *row* and 2nd *column* in which 3 appears, the determinant that remains is

$$\begin{vmatrix} 1 & 2 \\ 5 & -3 \end{vmatrix}$$

EVEN AND ODD ORDER OF AN ELEMENT

An element of a determinant is said to be of *even order* if the sum of the number of the row and the number of the column in which the element appears is an even number. An element is said to be of *odd order* if the sum of the number of the row and the number of the column in which the element appears is an odd number. Thus in the third order determinant

$$\begin{vmatrix} A_1 & B_1 & C_1 \\ A_2 & B_2 & C_2 \\ A_3 & B_3 & C_3 \end{vmatrix}$$

the element C_1 is of even order, for it is in the 1st row and 3rd column, and $1 + 3 = 4$. The element B_3 is of odd order, for it is in row 3 and column 2, and $3 + 2 = 5$.

   With our definition of the minor of an element and the order of an element we can say that the value of a third order determinant may be obtained as follows:

(1) Write the product of each element of the first column and its minor.
(2) Prefix the product with a + *sign* if the element is of *even order* and a – *sign* if the element is of *odd order*.
(3) Take the sum of these three products with the appropriate sign.

Finding the value of a determinant by such a process is called *expanding the determinant by minors,* and in particular, in the above process, expanding by minors of the first column.

Example 3

Expand by minors of the first column to evaluate the determinant

$$\begin{vmatrix} 3 & 2 & 6 \\ 1 & 4 & 3 \\ 5 & 1 & 7 \end{vmatrix}$$

$$\begin{vmatrix} 3 & 2 & 6 \\ 1 & 4 & 3 \\ 5 & 1 & 7 \end{vmatrix} = +3 \begin{vmatrix} 4 & 3 \\ 1 & 7 \end{vmatrix} - 1 \begin{vmatrix} 2 & 6 \\ 1 & 7 \end{vmatrix} + 5 \begin{vmatrix} 2 & 6 \\ 4 & 3 \end{vmatrix}$$

Note: 3 is of even order (row 1, column 1) and thus the sign prefixing the first product is + ; 1 is of odd order (row 2, column 1) and thus the sign prefixing the second product is – ; 5 is of even order (row 3, column 1) and thus the sign prefixing the third product is +. Now continuing our evaluation we obtain

$$3[4(7) - 3(1)] - 1[2(7) - 6(1)] + 5[2(3) - 6(4)]$$
$$= 3(25) - 1(8) + 5(-18)$$
$$= 75 - 8 - 90$$
$$= -23$$

Example 4

Expand by minors of the first column to evaluate the determinant

$$\begin{vmatrix} 2 & 5 & 0 \\ -3 & -2 & 3 \\ 1 & 7 & -4 \end{vmatrix}$$

$$\begin{vmatrix} 2 & 5 & 0 \\ -3 & -2 & 3 \\ 1 & 7 & -4 \end{vmatrix} = 2 \begin{vmatrix} -2 & 3 \\ 7 & -4 \end{vmatrix} - (-3) \begin{vmatrix} 5 & 0 \\ 7 & -4 \end{vmatrix} + 1 \begin{vmatrix} 5 & 0 \\ -2 & 3 \end{vmatrix}$$

$$= 2[(-2)(-4) - 3(7)] + 3[5(-4) - 0(7)]$$
$$+ 1[5(3) - 0(-2)]$$
$$= 2(-13) + 3(-20) + 1(15)$$
$$= -26 - 60 + 15$$
$$= -71$$

Note

A third order determinant can be expanded by minors of *any row* or *any column*, using a process analogous to the one outlined above; in *each case the same numerical value is obtained.*

Example 5

Expand the determinant of example 3 by minors of the *second column*.

$$\begin{vmatrix} 3 & 2 & 6 \\ 1 & 4 & 3 \\ 5 & 1 & 7 \end{vmatrix} = -2 \begin{vmatrix} 1 & 3 \\ 5 & 7 \end{vmatrix} + 4 \begin{vmatrix} 3 & 6 \\ 5 & 7 \end{vmatrix} - 1 \begin{vmatrix} 3 & 6 \\ 1 & 3 \end{vmatrix}$$

Here the element 2 is of odd order (row 1, column 2) and thus the sign prefixing the first product is – ; the element 4 is of even order (row 2, column 2) and thus the sign prefixing the second product is + ; the element 1 is of odd order (row 3, column 2) and thus the sign prefixing the third product is – . Now continuing our evaluation we obtain

$$- 2[1(7) - 3(5)] + 4[3(7) - 6(5)] - 1[3(3) - 6(1)]$$

$$= -2(-8) + 4(-9) - 1(3)$$

$$= 16 - 36 - 3$$

$$= -23$$

Example 6

Expand the determinant of example 4 by minors of the *first row*.

$$\begin{vmatrix} 2 & 5 & 0 \\ -3 & -2 & 3 \\ 1 & 7 & -4 \end{vmatrix} = 2\begin{vmatrix} -2 & 3 \\ 7 & -4 \end{vmatrix} - 5\begin{vmatrix} -3 & 3 \\ 1 & -4 \end{vmatrix} + 0\begin{vmatrix} -3 & -2 \\ 1 & 7 \end{vmatrix}$$

$$= 2[8 - 21] - 5[12 - 3] + 0[-21 - (-2)]$$

$$= -26 - 45 + 0$$

$$= -71$$

Note here that the element 2 is of even order, 5 is of odd order, and 0 is of even order.

We should also notice that if 0 is an element of a determinant, expanding that determinant by the row or column in which 0 appears will reduce the number of calculations, for we need not evaluate the minor of 0.

Example 7

Expand the determinant

$$\begin{vmatrix} 5 & -1 & 4 \\ -3 & 6 & 7 \\ 0 & -2 & 0 \end{vmatrix}$$

Since there are two 0's in the *third row*, it will be advantageous to expand by minors of that row.

$$\begin{vmatrix} 5 & -1 & 4 \\ -3 & 6 & 7 \\ 0 & -2 & 0 \end{vmatrix} = +0\begin{vmatrix} -1 & 4 \\ 6 & 7 \end{vmatrix} - (-2)\begin{vmatrix} 5 & 4 \\ -3 & 7 \end{vmatrix} + 0\begin{vmatrix} 5 & -1 \\ -3 & 6 \end{vmatrix}$$

$$= 0 + 2[35 - (-12)] + 0$$

$$= 2(47) = 94$$

Note

It should be evident at this point that the order of the elements in a third order determinant *alternates*. Thus we can set up the following scheme which indicates the signs to be used before each product in the expansion of a third order determinant by minors.

$$+ \quad - \quad +$$
$$- \quad + \quad -$$
$$+ \quad - \quad +$$

This says, for example, that in expanding a third order determinant by minors of the second column the signs to be used are − + − ; and using minors of the third row the signs would be + − +.

Exercise Set 7.6

1. State the minor of each of the following elements in the determinant

$$\begin{vmatrix} 3 & -5 & 2 \\ -1 & 4 & 0 \\ 6 & -2 & 7 \end{vmatrix}$$

(a) 3   (b) −5   (c) 4   (d) 0   (e) 6   (f) −2

2. State and evaluate the minor of each of the following elements in the determinant

$$\begin{vmatrix} -7 & 5 & 0 \\ -2 & -1 & 9 \\ 4 & -8 & -3 \end{vmatrix}$$

(a) −2   (b) −7   (c) 4   (d) 9

3. Given the determinant

$$\begin{vmatrix} -1 & 2 & 4 \\ 6 & -4 & 3 \\ 1 & 5 & -3 \end{vmatrix}$$

complete the following expansion of this determinant by minors of the second column.

$$-2\begin{vmatrix} & \\ & \end{vmatrix} + (-4)\begin{vmatrix} & \\ & \end{vmatrix} - 5\begin{vmatrix} & \\ & \end{vmatrix}$$

$$= -2(\qquad) - 4(\qquad) - 5(\qquad) = ?$$

4. Given the determinant

$$\begin{vmatrix} 4 & 1 & 2 \\ -1 & -2 & -3 \\ -4 & 5 & 0 \end{vmatrix}$$

complete the following expansion of this determinant by minors of the third row.

$$+(-4)\begin{vmatrix} & & \end{vmatrix} \quad \begin{vmatrix} & & \end{vmatrix}-5 \quad \begin{vmatrix} & +0 \end{vmatrix} \quad \begin{vmatrix} & & \end{vmatrix}$$

$$= -4(\qquad) - 5(\qquad) + 0(\qquad) = \ ?$$

In exercises 5-10 expand the given determinant in terms of the minors of the row or column indicated and find the value of the determinant.

5. $\begin{vmatrix} 3 & -1 & 5 \\ 0 & 4 & 6 \\ 0 & 7 & 1 \end{vmatrix}$

First column

8. $\begin{vmatrix} 0 & -5 & 4 \\ -1 & 0 & 8 \\ -2 & 3 & 0 \end{vmatrix}$

Third column

6. $\begin{vmatrix} 1 & 7 & -2 \\ 2 & 1 & 5 \\ 3 & -4 & 1 \end{vmatrix}$

Third row

9. $\begin{vmatrix} 1 & 2 & 3 \\ 4 & 5 & 6 \\ 7 & 8 & 9 \end{vmatrix}$

Second column

7. $\begin{vmatrix} 1 & -1 & 3 \\ -5 & -3 & 4 \\ 2 & -4 & 1 \end{vmatrix}$

First row

10. $\begin{vmatrix} 1 & 2 & 3 \\ -3 & -1 & 5 \\ -1 & 4 & 7 \end{vmatrix}$

Second row

In exercises 11-14 find the value of the given determinant.

11. $\begin{vmatrix} -1 & 4 & 9 \\ 3 & 0 & 0 \\ 5 & -2 & 6 \end{vmatrix}$

13. $\begin{vmatrix} 4 & 1 & 7 \\ -3 & -8 & -6 \\ -1 & 3 & -4 \end{vmatrix}$

12. $\begin{vmatrix} 5 & -3 & 0 \\ -4 & 0 & 8 \\ 3 & 2 & -1 \end{vmatrix}$

14. $\begin{vmatrix} -2 & 3 & -5 \\ 6 & -3 & 4 \\ 1 & -9 & 1 \end{vmatrix}$

7.7 USING DETERMINANTS TO FIND THE SOLUTION SET OF A SYSTEM OF THREE LINEAR EQUATIONS IN THREE VARIABLES

Now that we know how to evaluate a third order determinant we are ready to write a general procedure to find the solution set of the system of three linear equations in three variables

$$A_1 x + B_1 y + C_1 z = D_1$$

$$A_2 x + B_2 y + C_2 z = D_2$$

$$A_3 x + B_3 y + C_3 z = D_3$$

$$x = \frac{\begin{vmatrix} D_1 & B_1 & C_1 \\ D_2 & B_2 & C_2 \\ D_3 & B_3 & C_3 \end{vmatrix}}{\begin{vmatrix} A_1 & B_1 & C_1 \\ A_2 & B_2 & C_2 \\ A_3 & B_3 & C_3 \end{vmatrix}} \qquad y = \frac{\begin{vmatrix} A_1 & D_1 & C_1 \\ A_2 & D_2 & C_2 \\ A_3 & D_3 & C_3 \end{vmatrix}}{\begin{vmatrix} A_1 & B_1 & C_1 \\ A_2 & B_2 & C_2 \\ A_3 & B_3 & C_3 \end{vmatrix}}$$

$$z = \frac{\begin{vmatrix} A_1 & B_1 & D_1 \\ A_2 & B_2 & D_2 \\ A_3 & B_3 & D_3 \end{vmatrix}}{\begin{vmatrix} A_1 & B_1 & C_1 \\ A_2 & B_2 & C_2 \\ A_3 & B_3 & C_3 \end{vmatrix}}$$

The above formulas are obtained in the following manner:

(1) In solving for x, y, and z, the denominators are the same determinant, that is, the determinant of coefficients.

$$\begin{vmatrix} A_1 & B_1 & C_1 \\ A_2 & B_2 & C_2 \\ A_3 & B_3 & C_3 \end{vmatrix}$$

(2) In solving for x, the determinant in the numerator is obtained by *replacing the column of coefficients of x* in the determinant of coefficients by a column consisting of the constant terms, in the same order that they appear in the given system.

$$\begin{vmatrix} D_1 & B_1 & C_1 \\ D_2 & B_2 & C_2 \\ D_3 & B_3 & C_3 \end{vmatrix}$$

(3) In solving for y, the determinant in the numerator is obtained by *replacing the column of coefficients of y* in the determinant of coefficients by the column consisting of the constant terms, in the same order that they appear in the given system.

$$\begin{vmatrix} A_1 & D_1 & C_1 \\ A_2 & D_2 & C_2 \\ A_3 & D_3 & C_3 \end{vmatrix}$$

(4) In solving for z, the determinant in the numerator is obtained by *replacing the column of coefficients of z* in the determinant of coefficients by the constant terms.

$$\begin{vmatrix} A_1 & B_1 & D_1 \\ A_2 & B_2 & D_2 \\ A_3 & B_3 & D_3 \end{vmatrix}$$

Example 1

Find the solution set of the system

$$2x - 4y + 2z = 16$$
$$3x + y - 5z = -14$$
$$2x - 3y + 3z = 17$$

The determinant of coefficients is

$$\begin{vmatrix} 2 & -4 & 2 \\ 3 & 1 & -5 \\ 2 & -3 & 3 \end{vmatrix}$$

and upon expanding by minors of the *first column*, we obtain

$$2\begin{vmatrix} 1 & -5 \\ -3 & 3 \end{vmatrix} - 3\begin{vmatrix} -4 & 2 \\ -3 & 3 \end{vmatrix} + 2\begin{vmatrix} -4 & 2 \\ 1 & -5 \end{vmatrix}$$

$$= 2[3 - 15] - 3[-12 - (-6)] + 2[20 - 2]$$

$$= 2(-12) - 3(-6) + 2(18)$$

$$= -24 + 18 + 36$$

$$= 30$$

Now

$$x = \frac{\begin{vmatrix} 16 & -4 & 2 \\ -14 & 1 & -5 \\ 17 & -3 & 3 \end{vmatrix}}{30}$$

Expanding the determinant in the numerator by minors of the *3rd column* we obtain

$$2\begin{vmatrix} -14 & 1 \\ 17 & -3 \end{vmatrix} - (-5)\begin{vmatrix} 16 & -4 \\ 17 & -3 \end{vmatrix} + 3\begin{vmatrix} 16 & -4 \\ -14 & 1 \end{vmatrix}$$

$$= 2[42 - 17] + 5[-48 - (-68)] + 3[16 - 56]$$

$$= 2(25) + 5(20) + 3(-40)$$

$$= 50 + 100 - 120$$

$$= 30$$

Thus $x = \frac{30}{30} = 1$.

$$y = \frac{\begin{vmatrix} 2 & 16 & 2 \\ 3 & -14 & -5 \\ 2 & 17 & 3 \end{vmatrix}}{30}$$

Expanding the determinant in the numerator by minors of the *1st row* we obtain

$$2 \begin{vmatrix} -14 & -5 \\ 17 & 3 \end{vmatrix} - 16 \begin{vmatrix} 3 & -5 \\ 2 & 3 \end{vmatrix} + 2 \begin{vmatrix} 3 & -14 \\ 2 & 17 \end{vmatrix}$$

$= 2[-42 - (-85)] - 16[9 - (-10)] + 2[51 - (-28)]$

$= 2(43) - 16(19) + 2(79)$

$= 86 - 304 + 158$

$= -60$

Thus $y = \frac{-60}{30} = -2$.

$$z = \frac{\begin{vmatrix} 2 & -4 & 16 \\ 3 & 1 & -14 \\ 2 & -3 & 17 \end{vmatrix}}{30}$$

Expanding the determinant in the numerator by minors of the *2nd column* we obtain

$$-(-4) \begin{vmatrix} 3 & -14 \\ 2 & 17 \end{vmatrix} + 1 \begin{vmatrix} 2 & 16 \\ 2 & 17 \end{vmatrix} - (-3) \begin{vmatrix} 2 & 16 \\ 3 & -14 \end{vmatrix}$$

$= 4[51 - (-28)] + 1[34 - 32] + 3[-28 - 48]$

$= 4(79) + 1(2) + 3(-76)$

$= 316 + 2 - 228$

$= 90$

Thus $z = \frac{90}{30} = 3$.

Thus $x = 1, y = -2, z = 3$

Example 2

Find the solution set of the system

$2x + 3z = 4$

$x + y = 3$

$-3x - 2y + 5z = 0$

We first rewrite this system as follows:

$2x + 0y + 3z = 4$

$x + y + 0z = 3$

$-3x - 2y + 5z = 0$

The determinant of coefficients is

$$\begin{vmatrix} 2 & 0 & 3 \\ 1 & 1 & 0 \\ -3 & -2 & 5 \end{vmatrix}$$

and upon expanding by minors of the *1st row* we obtain

$$2 \begin{vmatrix} 1 & 0 \\ -2 & 5 \end{vmatrix} - 0 \begin{vmatrix} 1 & 0 \\ -3 & 5 \end{vmatrix} + 3 \begin{vmatrix} 1 & 1 \\ -3 & -2 \end{vmatrix}$$

$= 2[5 - 0] - 0 + 3[-2 - (-3)]$

$= 10 - 0 + 3$

$= 13$

Now

$$x = \cfrac{\begin{vmatrix} 4 & 0 & 3 \\ 3 & 1 & 0 \\ 0 & -2 & 5 \end{vmatrix}}{13}$$

Expanding the determinant in the numerator by minors of the *1st row* we obtain

$$4 \begin{vmatrix} 1 & 0 \\ -2 & 5 \end{vmatrix} - 0 \begin{vmatrix} 3 & 0 \\ 0 & 5 \end{vmatrix} + 3 \begin{vmatrix} 3 & 1 \\ 0 & -2 \end{vmatrix}$$

$= 4[5 - 0] - 0 + 3[-6 - 0]$

$= 20 - 18$

$= 2$

Thus $x = \frac{2}{13}$.

$$y = \frac{\begin{vmatrix} 2 & 4 & 3 \\ 1 & 3 & 0 \\ -3 & 0 & 5 \end{vmatrix}}{13}$$

Expanding the determinant in the numerator by minors of the *3rd row* we obtain

$$-3 \begin{vmatrix} 4 & 3 \\ 3 & 0 \end{vmatrix} - 0 \begin{vmatrix} 2 & 3 \\ 1 & 0 \end{vmatrix} + 5 \begin{vmatrix} 2 & 4 \\ 1 & 3 \end{vmatrix}$$

$= -3(0 - 9) - 0 + 5(6 - 4)$

$= 27 + 10$

$= 37$

Thus $y = \frac{37}{13}$.

$$z = \frac{\begin{vmatrix} 2 & 0 & 4 \\ 1 & 1 & 3 \\ -3 & -2 & 0 \end{vmatrix}}{13}$$

Expanding the determinant in the numerator by minors of the *3rd column* we obtain

$$4 \begin{vmatrix} 1 & 1 \\ -3 & -2 \end{vmatrix} - 3 \begin{vmatrix} 2 & 0 \\ -3 & -2 \end{vmatrix} + 0 \begin{vmatrix} 2 & 0 \\ 1 & 1 \end{vmatrix}$$

$= 4[-2 - (-3)] - 3[-4 - 0] + 0$

$= 4 + 12$

$= 16$

Thus $z = \frac{16}{13}$.

Thus $x = \frac{2}{13}, y = \frac{37}{13}, z = \frac{16}{13}$

Exercise Set 7.7

In exercises 1 and 2 find the solution set of the given system by first filling in the empty columns and then evaluating the determinants involved.

1. $3x - y + 2z = 4$
$\quad 2x + y + 5z = 1$
$\quad -x - 3y + z = -2$

$$x = \cfrac{\begin{vmatrix} & -1 & 2 \\ & 1 & 5 \\ & -3 & 1 \end{vmatrix}}{\begin{vmatrix} 3 & & 2 \\ 2 & & 5 \\ -1 & & 1 \end{vmatrix}}, \quad y = \cfrac{\begin{vmatrix} & 4 & \\ & 1 & \\ & -2 & \end{vmatrix}}{\begin{vmatrix} -1 & 2 \\ 1 & 5 \\ -3 & 1 \end{vmatrix}}$$

$$z = \cfrac{\begin{vmatrix} 3 & -1 & \\ 2 & 1 & \\ -1 & -3 & \end{vmatrix}}{\begin{vmatrix} 3 & -1 \\ 2 & 1 \\ -1 & -3 \end{vmatrix}}$$

2. $x - 2y = -4$
$\quad 3x + 2y - 5z = 7$
$\quad 4x - z = 2$

$$x = \cfrac{\begin{vmatrix} -2 & 0 & \\ 2 & -5 & \\ 0 & -1 & \end{vmatrix}}{\begin{vmatrix} 1 & & \\ 3 & & \\ 4 & & \end{vmatrix}}, \quad y = \cfrac{\begin{vmatrix} 1 & & \\ 3 & & \\ 4 & & \end{vmatrix}}{\begin{vmatrix} 1 & & 0 \\ 3 & & -5 \\ 4 & & -1 \end{vmatrix}}$$

$$z = \cfrac{\begin{vmatrix} 1 & -2 & \\ 3 & 2 & \\ 4 & 0 & \end{vmatrix}}{\begin{vmatrix} 1 & & \\ 3 & & \\ 4 & & \end{vmatrix}}$$

In exercises 3-12 use determinants to find the solution set of the given system of equations

3. $4x - 8y = -16$
   $3y + 2z = 1$
   $5x + 3z = -5$

4. $2x + 3y = 0$
   $-3x + y - 2z = -1$
   $2x - y = 5$

5. $-y + z = 1$
   $3x - 2z + y = 4$
   $x + y - 2z = -1$

6. $3y - 4z = -13$
   $8x + 6y = -2$
   $2x + 5z = 9$

7. $2x + y - 2z = 3$
   $x - y = 0$
   $-3x - 2y + 4z = 0$

8. $x + y + z = 4$
   $-x + 2y + z = 1$
   $-2x + y + 4z = 1$

9. $3x - 4y + z = -2$
   $5x + y - 2z = 1$
   $7x + 3y + 2z = 19$

10. $3x - 2y + z = 5$
    $2x - 2y + 4z = 8$
    $x + y - 2z = -2$

11. $2x + 3y - z = 3$
    $3x - 2y + 3z = -2$
    $x - y - 4z = -1$

12. $2x - y - 3z = 7$
    $x + 2y - z = 10$
    $3x - 3y + 2z = -7$

REVIEW TEST FOR CHAPTER VII

Note: This test should be completed in 1 hour and 45 minutes.

1. For each of the following systems of equations, find the solution set graphically and check your result.
   (a) $2x + 3y = 5$
       $-3x + 5y = 21$
   (b) $3x + 2y = 8$
       $6x = 13 - 4y$

2. For each of the following systems of equations, find the solution set by substitution and check your result.
   (a) $-x + 3y - 7 = 0$
       $3x + 2y - 12 = 0$
   (b) $-3x + 2y = 12$
       $2x + 5y + 8 = 0$

3. For each of the following systems of equations, find the solution set by elimination of a variable, using addition or subtraction.
   (a) $6x + 9y = -14$
       $3x - 6y = 14$
   (b) $6x + 4y = -9$
       $4x + 6y = -1$

4. Evaluate each of the following determinants
   (a) $\begin{vmatrix} 1 & 2 \\ -3 & 4 \end{vmatrix}$
   (b) $\begin{vmatrix} -1 & 2 \\ 0 & 1 \end{vmatrix}$
   (c) $\begin{vmatrix} 5 & 0 \\ 0 & 5 \end{vmatrix}$
   (d) $\begin{vmatrix} 3 & -4 \\ -2 & 3 \end{vmatrix}$

5. Expand each of the following determinants by minors of the row or column indicated. Evaluate each determinant.

(a) $\begin{vmatrix} 1 & 3 & 2 \\ 2 & -5 & 0 \\ 3 & 1 & -3 \end{vmatrix}$ (b) $\begin{vmatrix} 1 & -3 & 2 \\ 1 & -3 & 2 \\ -1 & 3 & 5 \end{vmatrix}$ (c) $\begin{vmatrix} 3 & 4 & -1 \\ -1 & 2 & 3 \\ 2 & 6 & 5 \end{vmatrix}$

    First row   Second column   Second row

6. Evaluate each of the following determinants:

(a) $\begin{vmatrix} 2 & 0 & 0 \\ 0 & 2 & 0 \\ 0 & 0 & 2 \end{vmatrix}$ (b) $\begin{vmatrix} 3 & -1 & 5 \\ 0 & 0 & 0 \\ 4 & 2 & -1 \end{vmatrix}$ (c) $\begin{vmatrix} -1 & -7 & -2 \\ -3 & -1 & -2 \\ -5 & -3 & -4 \end{vmatrix}$

7. Find the solution set of each of the following systems:

(a) $-2x - y = 7$
    $4x + 2y = -5$

(b) $-3x - 2y = 4$
    $2x - 3y = 6$

8. Find the solution set of each of the following systems:

(a) $3y - 5z = 1$
    $3x + z = 1$
    $z + 2y = 2$

(b) $3x - 2z = -1$
    $5y + 4z = 2$
    $9x + 10y = -1$

9. Find the solution set of the following systems:

(a) $-5x - 9y + 4z = 7$
    $3x + 6y - 2z = -3$
    $2x - 3y + z = -2$

(b) $3x - 2y + 5z = 0$
    $6x + 4y - 5z = 7$
    $3x - 4y - 10z = 2$

10. Find the solution set of the system

$2x - 3z + y = 4$
$2y + 3x - 2z = 3$
$-5z - y + 4x = -6$

VIII QUADRATIC EQUATIONS

8.1 DEFINITION OF FACTORING

In Section 4.3 we said that if a polynomial can be expressed as the product of two or more algebraic expressions, then each expression of the product is called a *factor* of the given polynomial.

FACTORING A POLYNOMIAL

Thus to *factor a polynomial is to find two or more algebraic expressions whose product is the given polynomial.*

Note

As in Section 4.3 we will restrict our discussion to polynomials with integral coefficients, and *seek only the factors which are monomials or polynomials with integral coefficients.* Again we will also *exclude factors which are negative integers.*

Example 1

Find the factors of $2x^2 + 4x$.

$2x^2 + 4x$ can be written as a product of two or more expressions as follows:

$$2x^2 + 4x = 1(2x^2 + 4x)$$

$$2x^2 + 4x = 2(x^2 + 2x) \qquad \text{(Distributive law)}$$

$$2x^2 + 4x = x(2x + 4) \qquad \text{(Distributive law)}$$

$$2x^2 + 4x = 2x(x + 2) \qquad \text{(Distributive law)}$$

$2x^2 + 4x$ may also be written as a product of two or more expressions in many other ways. However, in each of these other ways the expressions of the product are either not polynomials or do not have integral coefficients or are negative integers. For example:

$$2x^2 + 4x = \tfrac{1}{2}(4x^2 + 8x) \qquad (\tfrac{1}{2} \text{ is an expression with}$$
$$\text{nonintegral coefficients)}$$

$$2x^2 + 4x = x^{1/2}(2x^{3/2} + 4x^{1/2}) \qquad \text{(Neither expression is a}$$
$$\text{polynomial.)}$$

$$2x^2 + 4x = -1(-2x^2 - 4x) \qquad (-1 \text{ is a negative integral}$$
$$\text{factor.)}$$

But since we are seeking only those factors which are monomials or polynomials with integral coefficients, and are not negative integers, the factors of $2x^2 + 4x$ are: $1, 2, x, 2x, x + 2, 2x + 4, x^2 + 2x,$ $2x^2 + 4x$.

A PRIME POLYNOMIAL

In Section 4.3 we also defined a *prime polynomial* as being any polynomial with no other factor but itself and 1.

Example 2

x and $3x + 4$ are prime polynomials.

FACTORING COMPLETELY

A polynomial is said to be *completely factored* if it is written as a product of its prime factors.

Example 3

Factor the polynomial $12x^2 + 6x$ completely.

$$12x^2 + 6x = x(12x + 6) \qquad \text{(Distributive law)}$$

$$= 6x(2x + 1) \qquad \text{(Distributive law)}$$

$$= 2 \cdot 3 \cdot x(2x + 1)$$

Since the factors 2, 3, x, and $2x + 1$ are all prime, the polynomial $12x^2 + 6x$ has been factored completely.

Exercise Set 8.1

In exercises 1-10 fill in the blank to complete the factorization.

1. $5x - 25 = 5($)
2. $6x^2 + 42 = 6($)
3. $3x^2 + 7x = x($)
4. $7x^2 - 21 = ($ $)(x - 3)$
5. $8x^2 + 12x = ($ $)(2x + 3)$
6. $x^3 + 3x^2 + 6x = x($)
7. $16x^4 + 8x^3 - 4x^2 = ($ $)(4x^2 + 2x - 1)$
8. $15x^2y - 3xy^2 = 3xy($)
9. $21a^3b^2 + 24a^3b = ($ $)(7b + 8)$
10. $4a^2bc + 8abc^2 + 20ab^2c^3 = 4abc($)

In exercises 11-15 replace the ? by that term which will make the statement true.

11. $x^2 - 16 = (x + 4)(x - ?)$
12. $x^2 - 81 = (x + ?)(x - ?)$
13. $3x^2 - 27 = 3(x^2 - 9) = 3(x + ?)(x - ?)$
14. $x^2 - 5x + 6 = (x - 2)(x - ?)$
15. $x^2 + 6x + 8 = (x + 4)(x + ?)$

8.2 FINDING A COMMON MONOMIAL FACTOR

A COMMON MONOMIAL FACTOR

A monomial which is a factor of *each term* of a polynomial is called a *common monomial factor* of the terms of the polynomial.

Let us consider the polynomial $3x + 7xy + xy^2$. Since x is a factor of each term of this polynomial, x would be a common monomial factor.

By the distributive law the polynomial $3x + 7xy + xy^2$ can be written:

$$3x + 7xy + xy^2 = x(3 + 7y + y^2)$$

where the factor $3 + 7y + y^2$ is obtained by dividing each term of the given polynomial by x (the common factor).

FACTORING A POLYNOMIAL WITH A COMMON MONOMIAL FACTOR

In general, to factor a polynomial which contains a common monomial factor, use the *distributive law* to express the given polynomial as the product of the common factor and the factor obtained by dividing each term of the given polynomial by this common factor.

Note

Our aim here is to have the factor which is *not a monomial* contain *no further common factor*.

Example 1

Factor the polynomial $4x^2 + 16$.

$$4x^2 + 16 = 4(x^2 + 4) \qquad \text{(Distributive law)}$$

To obtain the second factor we divided each term of the given polynomial by 4.

Example 2

Factor the polynomial $3a + 5ab + 6a^2$.

Here the only common monomial factor is a. Thus upon dividing each term of the given polynomial by a to find the second factor, we obtain

$$3a + 5ab + 6a^2 = a(3 + 5b + 6a) \qquad \text{(Distributive law)}$$

Example 3

Factor the polynomial $3x^3 y^3 + 6x^2 y^2 + 27xy^3$.

$$3x^3 y^3 + 6x^2 y^2 + 27xy^3 = 3xy^2 (x^2 y + 2x + 9y)$$

To obtain the second factor above we divided each term of the given polynomial by $3xy^2$.

Note: Had we removed only $3xy$, for example, we would have obtained

$$3x^3y^3 + 6x^2y^2 + 27xy^3 = 3xy(x^2y^2 + 2xy + 9y^2)$$

But here the monomial y is still a common factor of the terms of the polynomial $x^2y^2 + 2xy + 9y^2$. Thus upon removing this remaining common factor, namely y, we would obtain the result above.

The procedure for removing a common monomial factor can also be applied to such expressions as

$$5(x + y) + 7x(x + y) + 3xy(x + y)$$

Here we have three products, each having the factor $x + y$. Thus, using the distributive law, we obtain

$$5(x + y) + 7x(x + y) + 3xy(x + y) = (x + y)(5 + 7x + 3xy)$$

Example 4

Factor the expression $3(x + 4) + 6x(x + 4) + 18x^2(x + 4)$.

Here $3(x + 4)$ is a common factor in each of the three products in the given expression. Therefore upon using the distributive law we obtain

$$3(x + 4) + 6x(x + 4) + 18x^2(x + 4) = 3(x + 4)(1 + 2x + 6x^2)$$

where the second factor is obtained by dividing each product of the given expression by $3(x + 4)$.

Exercise Set 8.2

In exercises 1-26 factor the given expression, if possible.

1. $6x - 9y$
2. $4a + 8b$
3. $3x + 7y$
4. $4x^2 + 4$
5. $4ax - 8ay$
6. $bx^2 + 4b$
7. $2ax + 3by$
8. $7x^2 + 21x$

9. $6x^4 - 18x^2$

10. $4y^3x^2 - 12y^2x^3$

11. $7x^2y^2z - 14xy^2z^2$

12. $5x - 15y + 25w$

13. $24y^3 + 16y^2 - 12y$

14. $6a^5 - 8a^7 + 3a^9$

15. $x^2 + y^2 + z^2$

16. $4x^2yz + 5xy^2z + 6xy$

17. $5a^2b^2c^2 - 10a^2c - 15a^2bc^2$

18. $3x^{125} - 9x^{128}$

19. $7a^2 + 8ab - 14ab^2 - 3a^2b^2$

20. $3x^2yz - 6xy^2z + 9xyz^2 - 18xyz$

21. $3(x - 1) - 5(x - 1)$

22. $6(x - y) + 18x(x - y)$

23. $(x + y)^2 + (x + y)(x - y)$

24. $5(x - 3) + 10(x + 1)(x - 3)$

25. $y(x + 2)^3 + 2y(x + 2)^2$

26. $(x + y)(x - 2y) + (x + y)(2x + y)$

8.3   DIFFERENCE OF TWO SQUARES

Let a and b be any real numbers. Suppose we compute the product of the sum and difference of these two numbers. That is,

$$(a + b)(a - b) = (a + b)a - (a + b)b \qquad \text{(Distributive law)}$$
$$= a^2 + ba - ab - b^2 \qquad \text{(Distributive law)}$$
$$= a^2 - b^2 \qquad \text{(Recall that } ba = ab.)$$

What this essentially says is: The product of the sum and difference of any two real numbers is equal to the difference of their squares, or

$$(a + b)(a - b) = a^2 - b^2$$

Example 1

$$\underbrace{(9 + 4)}\underbrace{(9 - 4)} = 9^2 - 4^2$$
$$13 \quad \cdot \quad 5 \quad\ = 81 - 16$$
$$65 \qquad\quad = 65$$

Example 2

$$(2x + 5y)(2x - 5y) = (2x)^2 - (5y)^2$$
$$= 4x^2 - 25y^2$$

This product of the sum and difference of two real numbers is very useful in factoring a polynomial which is the *difference of two squares.* For example, knowing that $(x + y)(x - y) = x^2 - y^2$, if we are given the polynomial $x^2 - y^2$, we could write it as the product $(x + y)(x - y)$, thus obtaining its two factors.

Example 3

Factor the polynomial $x^2 - 9$.

$$x^2 - 9 = x^2 - 3^2$$
$$= (x + 3)(x - 3)$$

Example 4

Factor the polynomial $9x^2 - 225y^2$.

$$9x^2 - 225y^2 = (3x)^2 - (15y)^2$$
$$= (3x + 15y)(3x - 15y)$$

Example 5

Factor the polynomial $x^4 - y^4$.

This polynomial can be written as the difference of two squares as follows:

$$x^4 - y^4 = (x^2)^2 - (y^2)^2$$
$$= (x^2 + y^2)(x^2 - y^2)$$

The second factor above, $x^2 - y^2$, being the difference of two squares, may be factored further as $(x + y)(x - y)$. Thus

$$x^4 - y^4 = (x^2 + y^2)(x + y)(x - y)$$

Why can't $x^2 + y^2$ be factored using the method of this section?

Example 6

Factor the polynomial $4x^6 - 9y^4$.

$$4x^6 - 9y^4 = (2x^3)^2 - (3y^2)^2$$
$$= (2x^3 + 3y^2)(2x^3 - 3y^2)$$

Exercise Set 8.3

In exercises 1-8 find the given products.

1. $(x + 5)(x - 5)$

5. $(x^3 + 2)(x^3 - 2)$

2. $(2x + 6)(2x - 6)$

6. $(3 + x^2)(3 - x^2)$

3. $(a^2 + 4)(a^2 - 4)$

7. $(a^2 + b^2)(a^2 - b^2)$

4. $(5y + 2x)(5y - 2x)$

8. $(a^3 + b^3)(a^3 - b^3)$

In exercises 9-30 factor the given expression *if possible*. Factor completely. (Allow only monomial or polynomial factors with integral coefficients.)

9. $x^2 - 81$

20. $48x^4 - 243$

10. $100 - x^2$

21. $x^2y^2 - 9$

11. $a^2 + 16$

22. $a^6 - 49$

12. $2x^2 - 50$

23. $a^5 - 9$

13. $9x^2 - 64y^2$

24. $x^6 - y^6$

14. $25x^2 - 4$

25. $a^8 - b^6$

15. $4x^2 - 5$

26. $x^8 - y^8$

16. $4a^2 - 9b^2$

27. $32x^6 - 18x^2$

17. $b^4 - c^2$

28. $144 - 4x^8$

18. $x^4 - 36$

29. $a^3b^3 - ab$

19. $x^4 - 16$

30. $x^6 - 9x^3$

8.4 FACTORING QUADRATIC TRINOMIALS IN ONE VARIABLE

A QUADRATIC POLYNOMIAL IN ONE VARIABLE

A *quadratic* polynomial in one variable is a polynomial which contains the second power of the variable and no higher power. A quadratic polynomial of three terms is referred to as a quadratic trinomial.

Examples of Quadratic Polynomials

1. x^2

4. $3x^2 - 5x + 7$

2. $x^2 + 1$

5. $3 - 5x^2 + 6x$

3. $x^2 + 4x$

Examples 4 and 5 are quadratic trinomials.

Note

Any quadratic trinomial can be written in the form:

$$ax^2 + bx + c,$$

where a, b, and c are *any real numbers, except 0*. However, in this section, as was previously stated, we will deal only with quadratic trinomials with *integral coefficients*.

Before we see how to factor a quadratic trinomial, let us first examine some products that produce quadratic trinomials.

Example 6

Find the product of the binomials $x + 4$ and $x + 1$.

$$
\begin{aligned}
(x + 4)(x + 1) &= x(x + 1) + 4(x + 1) && \text{(Distributive law)} \\
&= x^2 + x + 4x + 4 && \text{(Distributive law)} \\
&= x^2 + 5x + 4 && \text{(Combining like terms)}
\end{aligned}
$$

This result could have been obtained by the following three steps :
(1) The product of the first terms of the binomials produces the first term of the resulting trinomial. That is, $x \cdot x = x^2$.
(2) The product of the last terms of the binomials produces the last term of the trinomial. That is, $1 \cdot 4 = 4$.
(3) The sum of the "inner" and "outer" products indicated below produces the middle term of the trinomial.

"inner" product

$(x + 4)(x + 1)$: $4x + 1x = 5x$ (middle term)

"outer" product

Example 7

Compute the product of the binomials $3x - 4$ and $2x + 3$.

$$
\begin{aligned}
(3x - 4)(2x + 3) &= 3x(2x + 3) - 4(2x + 3) \\
&\qquad\qquad \text{(Distributive law)} \\
&= 6x^2 + 9x - 8x - 12 \\
&\qquad\qquad \text{(Distributive law)}
\end{aligned}
$$

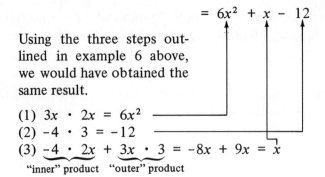

$$= 6x^2 + x - 12$$

Using the three steps outlined in example 6 above,
we would have obtained the
same result.

(1) $3x \cdot 2x = 6x^2$

(2) $-4 \cdot 3 = -12$

(3) $\underbrace{-4 \cdot 2x} + \underbrace{3x \cdot 3} = -8x + 9x = x$

   "inner" product   "outer" product

Example 8

Using the method outlined in example 6, compute the product:

   "inner" product

$(5x \overbrace{-8)(4x} - 7)$

   "outer" product

(1) $5x \cdot 4x = 20x^2$ (first term of product)

(2) $-8 \cdot -7 = 56$ (last term of product)

(3) $-8 \cdot 4x + (5x)(-7) = -32x - 35x = -67x$ (middle term)

Thus $(5x - 8)(4x - 7) = 20x^2 - 67x + 56$.

Now let us seek the factors of the quadratic trinomial

$$ax^2 + bx + c, \qquad a, b, c$$

are integers

$$a \neq 0, b \neq 0, c \neq 0$$

The method used in the previous examples of this section for
multiplying binomials leads us to look for two binomial factors of
the form

$$dx + e \text{ and } jx + k$$

where d, e, j and k are integers such that:

(1) The product of the first terms of the binomials is equal to the
first term of the trinomial. That is, $djx^2 = ax^2$

(2) The product of the last terms of the binomials is equal to the last
term of the trinomial, that is $ek = c$

(3) The sum of the "inner" and "outer" products of the binomials is equal to the middle term of the trinomial. That is, $dkx + ejx = (dk + ej)x = bx$

Note

Finding these binomial factors is usually done by trial and error.

Example 9

Factor the trinomial $x^2 + 4x + 3$.

We are looking for two binomials of the form $dx + e$ and $jx + k$.

(1) The product of the first terms must be x^2, so that the first terms must be x and x (that is, $d = 1, j = 1$). Thus we can write

"inner" product

$$x^2 + 4x + 3 = (x + e)(x + k)$$

"outer" product

where e and k are still to be found.

(2) We must now have

$ek = 3$ (the last term of the trinomial)

$(e + k)x = 4x$ (the middle term of the trinomial)

$3 \cdot 1 = 3$

and $(3 + 1)x = 4x$. Thus the last terms of the binomials are 3 and 1 and, therefore,

$$x^2 + 4x + 3 = (x + 3)(x + 1)$$

Note

You should check your result by multiplying the two factors to see that the product is the given trinomial.

Example 10

Factor $x^2 - 7x - 30$.

(1) The first terms of the binomials that we seek are x and x. (Why?) Thus we can write

"inner"

$$x^2 - 7x - 3 = (x + e)(x + k)$$

"outer"

(2) We must now have

$$ek = -30$$

and

$$(e + k)x = -7x$$

The different possibilities for e, k are: $(-1)(30)$; $(-2)(15)$; $(-3)(10)$; $(-5)(6)$; $(-6)(5)$; $(-10)(3)$; $(-15)(2)$; $(-30)(1)$. Of these we must use the pair -10 and 3, for

$$(-10 + 3)x = -7x$$

Thus we obtain:

$$x^2 - 7x - 30 = (x - 10)(x + 3)$$

Check your result by multiplying the two factors $(x - 10)$ and $(x + 3)$.

Example 11

Factor the trinomial $2x^2 - 11x + 15$.

We are again seeking two binomials of the form $dx + e$ and $jx + k$.

(1) The product of the first terms must be $2x^2$, so that here the first terms must be x and $2x$. Thus we can write $2x^2 - 11x + 15 = (x + e)(2x + k)$.

(2) We must now have

$$ek = 15$$

and

$$(2e + k)x = -11x.$$

The different possibilities for e and k can be seen in the following table:

e	1	3	15	5	-1	-3	-15	-5
k	15	5	1	3	-15	-5	-1	-3

Since the middle term is $-11x$, we should only try the pairs where both e and k are negative. (Why?) The pair which satisfies the condition $(2e + k)x = -11x$ is $e = -3$, $k = -5$, for $[2 \cdot (-3) + (-5)]x = (-6 - 5)x = -11x$.

Thus $2x^2 - 11x + 15 = (x - 3)(2x - 5)$.

Check the result by multiplying the above two factors.

Example 12

Factor $6x^2 + 13x - 5$.

(1) Here the first terms of the binomials which we seek can be either $6x$ and x or $3x$ and $2x$.
(2) The last terms of the binomials can be either -1 and 5 or 1 and -5.

Thus the possible products which can yield the given trinomial are

$(2x - 1)(3x + 5)$

$(2x + 1)(3x - 5)$

$(2x + 5)(3x - 1)$

$(2x - 5)(3x + 1)$

$(6x - 1)(x + 5)$

$(6x + 1)(x - 5)$

$(6x + 5)(x - 1)$

$(6x - 5)(x + 1)$

If we now proceed to compute each of the above products, we will discover that

$$(2x + 5)(3x - 1) = 6x^2 + 13x - 5$$

Let us now summarize all the methods of factoring discussed in this chapter by means of the following examples.

Example 13

Factor the polynomial $3x^5 - 48xy^4$ completely.

Recall that to factor a polynomial completely is to write it as the product of its prime factors.

(1) We first look for a common factor. Here $3x$ is a common factor. Thus

$$3x^5 - 48xy^4 = 3x(x^4 - 16y^4)$$

(2) The second factor above is the difference of two squares. That is,

$$x^4 - 16y^4 = (x^2 + 4y^2)(x^2 - 4y^2)$$

(3) Now $x^2 - 4y^2$, also being the difference of two squares, can be written as the product:

$$x^2 - 4y^2 = (x + 2y)(x - 2y)$$

Therefore $3x^5 - 48xy^4 = 3x(x^2 + 4y^2)(x + 2y)(x - 2y)$.

Example 14

Factor completely: $2x^3y - 4x^2y - 16xy$.

(1) We first note that $2xy$ is a common factor. Thus $2x^3y - 4x^2y - 16xy = 2xy(x^2 - 2x - 8)$.
(2) Now the trinomial $x^2 - 2x - 8$ can be factored as the product $(x - 4)(x + 2)$.

Therefore $2x^3y - 4x^2y - 16xy = 2xy(x - 4)(x + 2)$.

Note

Not all trinomials can be factored with integral coefficients. Consider for example, $x^2 + x + 1$.

Exercise Set 8.4

In exercises 1-16 find the given product.

1. $(x + 5)(x + 7)$
2. $(x + 7)(x - 5)$
3. $(x - 4)(x - 3)$
4. $(x + 3)(x - 4)$
5. $(x + 7)(x - 7)$
6. $(3 - x)(5 - x)$
7. $(4x + 5)(2x + 3)$
8. $(5x - 2)(6x + 1)$
9. $(6x - 2)(3x - 5)$
10. $(4x + 3)(4x - 3)$

11. $(3x + 7)(5 - x)$ 14. $(4x + 5y)(4x - 5y)$

12. $(x + y)(x + 2y)$ 15. $(6xy - 2a)(4xy + a)$

13. $(3x + y)(2x - 3y)$ 16. $(7xy - 3)(5 - 6x)$

In exercises 17-24 fill in the blank spaces to complete the given factorization.

17. $x^2 + 7x + 10 = (x + 5)(\underline{\ \ ?\ \ } + \underline{\ \ ?\ \ })$

18. $x^2 - 6x - 40 = (x + 4)(x\underline{\ \ ?\ \ })$

19. $x^2 - 11x + 10 = (\underline{\ \ ?\ \ } - 10)(x\underline{\ \ ?\ \ })$

20. $x^2 + 6x - 27 = (\underline{\ \ ?\ \ })(x - 3)$

21. $2y^2 + 5y - 12 = (y + 4)(\underline{\ \ ?\ \ } - \underline{\ \ ?\ \ })$

22. $8x^2 - 26x - 7 = (4x\underline{\ \ ?\ \ })(2x\underline{\ \ ?\ \ })$

23. $6x^2 - 17x + 12 = (2x\underline{\ \ ?\ \ })(\underline{\ \ ?\ \ } - 4)$

24. $6x^2 - 7xy - 3y^2 = (\underline{\ \ ?\ \ })(2x - 3y)$

In exercises 25-56 factor the given trinomial as a product of two binomials with integral coefficients, if possible.

25. $x^2 - 3x - 10$ 41. $3x^2 - 37x - 12$

26. $x^2 - 7x + 10$ 42. $2x^2 - x - 2$

27. $x^2 + 9x + 5$ 43. $8x^2 - 2x - 3$

28. $x^2 + 9x + 8$ 44. $15x^2 - 23x + 4$

29. $x^2 - 2x - 8$ 45. $6x^2 + 11x - 35$

30. $x^2 - 4x - 32$ 46. $8x^2 + 11x + 3$

31. $y^2 + 3y - 54$ 47. $3x^2 - 10x + 3$

32. $y^2 - 21y + 54$ 48. $6x^2 + 41x - 7$

33. $a^2 - a - 30$ 49. $7y^2 - 40y - 12$

34. $b^2 + 13b - 30$ 50. $22x^2 + 5x - 3$

35. $36 - 16y - y^2$ 51. $12x^2 - 11x + 2$

36. $36 - 15x + x^2$ 52. $6x^2 - 7x + 3$

37. $x^2 + 15xy + 36y^2$ 53. $6a^2 - 7a + 6$

38. $x^2 + 3xy - 28y^2$ 54. $10x^2 - x - 9$

39. $2x^2 + 11x + 15$ 55. $6a^2 - 13ab + 5b^2$

40. $2x^2 - x - 15$ 56. $24x^2 + xy - 3y^2$

In exercises 57-70 factor each polynomial completely. (*Hint:* First look for common monomial factors.)

57. $9x^2 - 49$

58. $8x^2 - 72$

59. $4x^3 - x$

60. $3y^3 - 12y^2 + 9y$

61. $x^2 + 10x + 25$

62. $100x^2 - 16y^2$

63. $x - xy^2$

64. $8x^2 + 6x^3 + x^4$

65. $2x^5 - 12x^4 + 18x^3$

66. $3x^3 - 12xy^2$

67. $4x^2y^2 - 16xy^2$

68. $6a^3b - 3a^2b^2 - 3ab^3$

69. $x^3 + 4x^2y + 4xy^2$

70. $x^5 - x$

8.5 QUADRATIC EQUATIONS

A quadratic equation in one variable is any equation which can be written in the form:

$$ax^2 + bx + c = 0$$

where a, b, c are any real numbers and $a \neq 0$.

Examples of Quadratic Equations

1. $2x^2 + 4x - 5 = 0$
2. $x^2 - \frac{3}{2}x = 0$
3. $3x^2 - \frac{3}{5} = 0$
4. $4x^2 = 0$
5. $3x^2 - 2x = 8$
6. $x^2 = 3x - 7$

Note 1

Example 5 can be written in the form $3x^2 - 2x - 8 = 0$.
Example 6 can be written in the form $x^2 - 3x + 7 = 0$.

Note 2

From this point on in this chapter we will *no longer exclude polynomials and factors with nonintegral coefficients.*

8.6 FINDING THE SOLUTION SET OF A QUADRATIC EQUATION BY FACTORING

Let us begin by attempting to find the solution set of the quadratic equation

$$x^2 - 5x = -6$$

We will first write this equation in the form

$$x^2 - 5x + 6 = 0$$

We now notice that the quadratic polynomial $x^2 - 5x + 6$ can be factored as the product $(x - 2)(x - 3)$. Thus we can now write the equation in the form

$$(x - 2)(x - 3) = 0$$

When written in this form we must now make use of the following property of the real numbers (stated in Section 2.6).

> $ab = 0$ *if and only if* $a = 0$ *or* $b = 0$, *that is, the product* $ab = 0$ *if and only if one or the other or both factors are* 0.

Thus $(x - 2)(x - 3) = 0$ if and only if

$$x - 2 = 0 \quad \text{or} \quad x - 3 = 0$$

That is, if and only if $x = 2$ or $x = 3$. Therefore the solution set would be $\{2, 3\}$.

We can now set up a general procedure to solve a quadratic equation by factoring.

PROCEDURE FOR SOLVING A QUADRATIC EQUATION BY FACTORING

(1) First write the equation in the form

$$ax^2 + bx + c = 0, \quad a \neq 0$$

(2) Factor the quadratic polynomial $ax^2 + bx + c$, if possible. We now have the product of two factors equal to 0.

(3) Set each factor equal to 0 and find the solution set of each of the two resulting equations.

(4) The solution set of the given quadratic equation will be the *union* of the two solution sets obtained in step (3).

Example 1

Find the solution set of the equation $2x^2 + 3x - 5 = 0$.

This is already in the form $ax^2 + bx + c = 0$.

$$2x^2 + 3x - 5 = (2x + 5)(x - 1)$$

Thus we now have $(2x + 5)(x - 1) = 0$
Setting both factors equal to 0, we obtain

$$2x + 5 = 0 \qquad\qquad x - 1 = 0$$
$$2x = -5 \qquad\qquad\quad x = 1$$
$$x = -\tfrac{5}{2}$$

The solution set is $\{-\tfrac{5}{2}, 1\}$.

Note

The solution set should be checked by showing that each element satisfies the original quadratic equation.

Example 2

Find the solution set of the equation $8y^2 = -14y - 3$.

We first write the equation in the form

$$8y^2 + 14y + 3 = 0$$
$$8y^2 + 14y + 3 = (4y + 1)(2y + 3)$$

Thus we write $(4y + 1)(2y + 3) = 0$.
Setting each factor equal to 0, we obtain

$$4y + 1 = 0 \qquad\qquad 2y + 3 = 0$$
$$4y = -1 \qquad\qquad\quad 2y = -3$$
$$y = -\tfrac{1}{4} \qquad\qquad\quad y = -\tfrac{3}{2}$$

Therefore the solution set is $\{-\tfrac{1}{4}, -\tfrac{3}{2}\}$.

Example 3

Find the solution set of the equation $4x^2 = 8x$.

We first write the equation in the form

$$4x^2 - 8x = 0 \qquad \text{(Note here that the constant term is 0,}$$
$$\text{that is, } c = 0.)$$

Here $4x$ is a common factor of the terms of $4x^2 - 8x$, so that

$$4x^2 - 8x = 4x(x - 2)$$

Thus we now have $4x(x - 2) = 0$.

Setting each factor equal to 0, we obtain

$$
\begin{array}{c|c}
4x = 0 & x - 2 = 0 \\
x = 0 & x = 2
\end{array}
$$

Therefore the solution set is $\{0, 2\}$.

Example 4

Find the solution set of the equation $2x^2 = 9 + x^2$.

This can be written in the form

$$2x^2 - 9 - x^2 = 0$$

or

$$x^2 - 9 = 0 \qquad \text{(Combining like terms)}$$

(Note here that the middle term is missing, that is, $b = 0$.) Here $x^2 - 9$ is the difference of two squares, so that $x^2 - 9 = (x + 3)(x - 3)$

Thus we can write $(x + 3)(x - 3) = 0$.

$$
\begin{array}{c|c}
x + 3 = 0 & x - 3 = 0 \\
x = -3 & x = 3
\end{array}
$$

Therefore the solution set is $\{-3, 3\}$.

We could have also approached this problem by writing the equation in the form

$$x^2 = 9$$

Then the values of x that would make $x^2 = 9$ are the two square roots of 9, $+3$ and -3.

Example 5

Find the solution set of the equation

$$2y^2 - 35 = -5y^2$$

This equation can be written

$$7y^2 - 35 = 0 \qquad \text{(Note again that } b = 0.)$$

or

$$7y^2 = 35$$

Multiplying both sides by $\frac{1}{7}$ (the multiplicative inverse of 7), we obtain

$$y^2 = 5$$

The values of y that satisfy this equation are the two square roots of 5, $\sqrt{5}$ and $-\sqrt{5}$. Therefore the solution set is

$$\{\sqrt{5}, -\sqrt{5}\}$$

Example 6

Find the solution set of the equation

$$(x - 3)^2 = 16$$

If we were to square $(x - 3)$ and subtract 16 from both sides, we could write this equation in the form of $ax^2 + bx + c = 0$. However, if we leave the equation in the form above, we could find the solution set by making use of the method of examples 4 and 5 of this section. That is, this equation says that $x - 3$ represents some number which when squared is equal to 16. Thus $(x - 3)$ must equal 4 or -4, the two square roots of 16. Thus

$$
\begin{array}{c|c}
x - 3 = 4 & x - 3 = -4 \\
x = 7 & x = -1
\end{array}
$$

Therefore the solution set is $\{7, -1\}$.

Exercise Set 8.6

In exercises 1-28 find the solution set of the given equation.

1. $x^2 - 25 = 0$

2. $9x^2 - 36 = 0$

3. $x^2 - 7x = 0$

4. $4x^2 + 5x = 0$

5. $x^2 - 4x - 21 = 0$

6. $2x^2 - 9x + 10 = 0$

7. $3x^2 = 21$

8. $3x^2 + 24x = 0$

9. $x^2 + 8x = -15$

10. $40 + 3x = x^2$

11. $0 = 6x^2 + 21x - 12$

12. $3x^2 = 5 - 2x$

13. $8y^2 + 15 = 26y$

14. $2(x^2 + 2) = 9x$

15. $(y + 5)^2 = 25$

16. $3(x - 2)^2 - 12 = 0$

17. $36x - 12x^2 = 0$

18. $27y^2 + 15y - 2 = 0$

19. $x^2 - 4x + 4 = 0$

20. $7x^2 - 42 = 0$

21. $(x - 2)^2 + 8x = 0$

22. $(x + 3)^2 - x - 23 = 0$

*23. $\frac{y^2}{3} - \frac{2y}{3} - 8 = 0$

*24. $\frac{2x^2}{3} - \frac{1}{18}x - \frac{1}{18} = 0$

*25. $\frac{x^2}{3} + \frac{13x}{6} = \frac{-5}{2}$

*26. $\frac{x^2}{4} = \frac{-7x}{12} - \frac{1}{6}$

27. $(x - 1)^2 + (2x - 1)(3x - 1) + x - 2 = 0$

28. $(2x - 1)(2x + 1) + 1 = 6(x^2 - 3)$

*Clear fractions first.

8.7 COMPLETING THE SQUARE

Let us examine the quadratic equation

$$x^2 - 6x + 9 = 16$$

If we observe that $x^2 - 6x + 9$ can be written as $(x - 3)(x - 3)$, or simply $(x - 3)^2$, then this equation can take on the form

$$(x - 3)^2 = 16$$

The equation in this form is now seen to be the equation that we considered in example 6 of the previous section, whose solution set was found by setting $x - 3$ equal to the two square roots of 16 (+4 and −4).

Using the above example, we can see that it would be a great help in finding the solution set of any quadratic equation if we could write it in the form

$$(x + d)^2 = e$$

for then we would set $x + d$ equal to the two square roots of e *(provided e is a nonnegative number).* It can be shown that every quadratic equation can be written in this form. Before we do this, however, we must consider what is meant by a perfect square trinomial, and how to construct one.

A PERFECT SQUARE TRINOMIAL

A *perfect square trinomial* is one which can be expressed as the square of some binomial (that is, as the product of two identical factors).

How can we tell if a trinomial is a perfect square, without actually going through a trial and error process to find its factor? To do this let us compute the product $(a + b)^2$, where a and b are any real numbers.

"inner" product

$$(a + b)^2 = (a + b)(a + b)$$

"outer" product

$$= a^2 + ba + ab + b^2$$
$$= a^2 + 2ab + b^2$$

In essence this states that the form of the square of any binomial is as follows:

$$(\text{Any binomial})^2 = (\text{first term})^2 + 2(\text{first term})(\text{second term})$$
$$+ (\text{second term})^2$$

Example 1

Square $x + 3$.

$$(x + 3)^2 = x^2 + 2 \cdot x \cdot 3 + 3^2$$
$$= x^2 + 6x + 9$$

Example 2

Square $2x - 5$.

Here the first term is $2x$ and the second term is -5.

$$(2x - 5)^2 = (2x)^2 + 2(2x)(-5) + (-5)^2$$
$$= 4x^2 - 20x + 25$$

To help us recognize perfect square trinomials let us consider the following example.

Example 3

Fill in the blank space to make each trinomial a perfect square.

(a) $x^2 + 10x +$ _____

(b) $x^2 +$ _____ $+ 36$

(c) $x^2 - 24x +$ _____

For each of the above trinomials to be a perfect square it must have the form

(First term)^2 + 2(first term) (second term) + (second term)^2

(a) $x^2 + 10x +$ _____ $= x^2 + 2 \cdot x \cdot \underline{5} + 5^2$

                         ↓   ↓   ↓   ↓
        (first)^2 (first) (second) (second)^2

Thus the number in the blank space is 5^2 or 25. At the same time we have found the second term of the binomial factor to be 5. Therefore $x^2 + 10x + 25 = (x + 5)^2$.

(b) $x^2 +$ _____ $+ 36 = x^2 + 2(x)(?) + (?)^2$

                        ↓   ↓ ↓   ↓
        (first)^2 (first) (second) (second)^2

Since $36 =$ (second term)^2, the second term can be either +6 or -6. Thus we can replace the (?) above by either +6 or -6, and the term in the blank space can be either

$$2(x)(+6) = 12x \quad \text{or} \quad 2(x)(-6) = -12x$$

(c) $x^2 - 24x +$ _____ $= x^2 + 2x \underline{(-12)} + \underline{(-12)^2}$

                       ↓   ↓   ↓   ↓
        (first)^2 (first) (second)   (second)^2

Therefore the term in the blank space is $(-12)^2 = 144$. Also note that the second term of the binomial factor must be -12. Therefore

$$x^2 - 24x + 144 = (x - 12)^2$$

COMPLETING THE SQUARE

The process used in examples 3(a) and 3(c) above, that of *finding the constant term* that will make the trinomial $x^2 + bx +$ __?__ a perfect square, is known as *completing the square*.

If you examine examples 3(a) and 3(c), you will observe that *the constant term is the square of one-half the coefficient of x*. In 3(a) this was $(\frac{1}{2}(10)]^2 = 5^2 = 25$. In 3(b) this was $[\frac{1}{2}(-24)]^2 = (-12)^2 = 144$. We also know that the constant term of the trinomial must be the square of the second term of the binomial factor. Therefore *the second term of the binomial factor must be one-half the coefficient of x*.

TO COMPLETE THE SQUARE

In general from any polynomial of the form $x^2 + bx$ we can construct a perfect square trinomial by *adding* to that polynomial the square of *one-half* the coefficient of x, that is, $(\frac{1}{2}b)^2$.

Example 4

Given the polynomial $x^2 - 5x$, construct from this polynomial a perfect square trinomial.
    Following the above procedure we simply add to this polynomial

$$[\frac{1}{2}(-5)]^2 = (-\frac{5}{2})^2 = +\frac{25}{4}$$

Thus the perfect square trinomial is

$$x^2 - 5x + \frac{25}{4} = (x - \frac{5}{2})^2$$

Note

To complete the square by the above procedure, the *coefficient of x^2 must be 1*. If it is not 1, the procedure would be more involved.

Completing the square will make it possible to write any quadratic equation in one variable in the form

$$(x + d)^2 = e$$

Let us illustrate this in the following examples.

Example 5

Find the solution set of the equation $x^2 + 6x - 5 = 0$ by completing the square.

(1) Add 5 to both sides to write the equation in the form

$$x^2 + 6x = 5$$

(2) We now add that constant *to both sides* which will *make the left side a perfect square.* This constant is

$$[\tfrac{1}{2}(6)]^2 = 3^2 = 9$$

Thus we obtain

$$x^2 + 6x + 9 = 5 + 9$$

or

$$(x + 3)^2 = 14$$

(3) Using the procedure of the previous section, we now set $x + 3$ equal to the two square roots of 14:

$$x + 3 = +\sqrt{14} \qquad\qquad x + 3 = -\sqrt{14}$$

$$x = -3 + \sqrt{14} \qquad\qquad x = -3 - \sqrt{14}$$

Therefore the solution set is $\{-3 + \sqrt{14}, -3 - \sqrt{14}\}$.

Example 6

Find the solution set of the equation $2x^2 + 5x + 2 = 0$ by completing the square.

(1) We first write the equation in the form

$$2x^2 + 5x = -2$$

(2) Noticing that the coefficient of x^2 is 2, we now multiply *both sides* of the equation by $\tfrac{1}{2}$, thus obtaining

$$x^2 + \tfrac{5}{2}x = -1 \qquad \text{(where the coefficient of } x^2 \text{ is now 1)}$$

(3) We now add $[\tfrac{1}{2}(\tfrac{5}{2})]^2 = (\tfrac{5}{4})^2 = \tfrac{25}{16}$ to both sides of the equation to obtain

$$x^2 + \tfrac{5}{2}x + \tfrac{25}{16} = -1 + \tfrac{25}{16}$$

or

$$\left(x + \tfrac{5}{4}\right)^2 = \tfrac{9}{16}$$

(4) Setting $x + \tfrac{5}{4}$ equal to the two square roots of $\tfrac{9}{16}$, we obtain

$x + \tfrac{5}{4} = +\sqrt{\tfrac{9}{16}}$	$x + \tfrac{5}{4} = -\sqrt{\tfrac{9}{16}}$
$x + \tfrac{5}{4} = \tfrac{3}{4}$	$x + \tfrac{5}{4} = -\tfrac{3}{4}$
$x = \tfrac{3}{4} - \tfrac{5}{4}$	$x = -\tfrac{3}{4} - \tfrac{5}{4}$
$x = \tfrac{-2}{4} = -\tfrac{1}{2}$	$x = -\tfrac{8}{4} = -2$

Therefore the solution set is $\{-\tfrac{1}{2}, -2\}$.

Example 7

Find the solution set of the equation $3x^2 - 12x - 1 = 0$

(1) $3x^2 - 12x = 1$ (Why?)
(2) $x^2 - 4x = 1/3$ (Why?)
(3) $x^2 - 4x \lceil +4 \rceil = \tfrac{1}{3} \lceil +4 \rceil$ (Why?)

or

$$(x - 2)^2 = \tfrac{13}{3}$$

(4) $x - 2 = +\sqrt{\tfrac{13}{3}}$ $x - 2 = -\sqrt{\tfrac{13}{3}}$

    $x = 2 + \sqrt{\tfrac{13}{3}}$ $x = 2 - \sqrt{\tfrac{13}{3}}$

Therefore the solution set is $\{2 + \sqrt{\tfrac{13}{3}}, 2 - \sqrt{\tfrac{13}{3}}\}$.

Exercise Set 8.7

In exercises 1-9 square the given binomial.

1. $x - 6$	4. $2x - y$	7. $5a + 3b$
2. $3x + 1$	5. $3x + 4y$	8. $\tfrac{1}{2}x - 3$
3. $4y - 7$	6. $5 - x$	9. $\tfrac{1}{3}x - \tfrac{3}{4}$

In exercises 10-15 fill in the blank space to make each trinomial a perfect square.

10. $x^2 + 4x +$ _____   **13.** $x^2 +$ _____ $+ 81$

11. $x^2 - 3x +$ _____   **14.** $x^2 + 9x +$ _____

12. $x^2 +$ _____ $+ 25$ **15.** $x^2 - 32x +$ _____

In exercises 16-27 determine whether or not the given trinomial is a perfect square. If it is, write it as the square of a binomial.

16. $x^2 + 8x + 16$ **22.** $x^2 + 7x + \frac{49}{4}$

17. $x^2 - 26x + 169$ **23.** $x^2 + 5x + 25$

18. $x^2 + 32x + 64$ **24.** $x^2 - 16$

19. $x^2 - 14x + 49$ **25.** $x^2 - 9x + \frac{81}{2}$

20. $x^2 - 8x - 16$ **26.** $x^2 + \frac{3}{2}x + \frac{9}{16}$

21. $x^2 + 9$ **27.** $x^2 - \frac{5}{3}x + \frac{25}{36}$

In exercises 28-41 solve the given equation by completing the square.

28. $x^2 + 8x = 0$ **35.** $3x^2 - 12x + 7 = 0$

29. $x^2 + 18x = 19$ **36.** $6x^2 = -24x - 22$

30. $x^2 - 6x + 1 = 0$ **37.** $4x^2 = 24x - 27$

31. $x^2 + 10x + 13 = 0$ **38.** $12 = 7 - 4x^2$

32. $2x^2 - 3x - 2 = 0$ **39.** $x^2 + x = \frac{1}{2}$

33. $-x^2 - 20x - 64 = 0$ **40.** $9y^2 = 12y - 2$

34. $9x^2 - 18x - 7 = 0$ **41.** $4y^2 - 24y = -35$

8.8 THE QUADRATIC FORMULA

Let us now find the solution set of the general quadratic equation

$$ax^2 + bx + c = 0, \quad a \neq 0$$

by completing the square.

(1) Write the equation in the form

$$ax^2 + bx = -c$$

(2) We now multiply both sides of the equation by $\frac{1}{a}$ to obtain

$$\frac{1}{a}(ax^2 + bx) = \frac{1}{a}(-c)$$

or

$$x^2 + \frac{b}{a}x = -\frac{c}{a} \qquad \text{(Distributive law)}$$

(3) We now add $(\frac{1}{2} \cdot \frac{b}{a})^2 = (\frac{b}{2a})^2 = \frac{b^2}{4a^2}$ to *both sides* to make the left side a perfect square trinomial:

$$x^2 + \frac{b}{a}x + \frac{b^2}{4a^2} = -\frac{c}{a} + \frac{b^2}{4a^2}$$

or

$$(x + \frac{b}{2a})^2 = \frac{b^2 - 4ac}{4a^2} \qquad \text{(Adding fractions)}$$

(4) We now set $x + \frac{b}{2a}$ equal to the two square roots of $\frac{b^2 - 4ac}{4a^2}$.

$$x + \frac{b}{2a} = +\sqrt{\frac{b^2 - 4ac}{4a^2}} \qquad \Bigg| \qquad x + \frac{b}{2a} = -\sqrt{\frac{b^2 - 4ac}{4a^2}}$$

$$x + \frac{b}{2a} = \frac{\sqrt{b^2 - 4ac}}{\sqrt{4a^2}} \qquad \Bigg| \qquad x + \frac{b}{2a} = -\frac{\sqrt{b^2 - 4ac}}{\sqrt{4a^2}}$$

$$x + \frac{b}{2a} = \frac{\sqrt{b^2 - 4ac}}{2a} \qquad \Bigg| \qquad x + \frac{b}{2a} = -\frac{\sqrt{b^2 - 4ac}}{2a}$$

$$x = -\frac{b}{2a} + \frac{\sqrt{b^2 - 4ac}}{2a} \qquad \Bigg| \qquad x = -\frac{b}{2a} - \frac{\sqrt{b^2 - 4ac}}{2a}$$

$$x = \frac{-b + \sqrt{b^2 - 4ac}}{2a} \qquad \Bigg| \qquad x = \frac{-b - \sqrt{b^2 - 4ac}}{2a}$$

Therefore the solution set is

$$\left\{ \frac{-b + \sqrt{b^2 - 4ac}}{2a}, \frac{-b - \sqrt{b^2 - 4ac}}{2a} \right\}$$

Note

For the elements of the solution set to be real numbers the number under the radical, that is $b^2 - 4ac$, must be nonnegative. (0 or a positive number).

We have now developed a formula which can be used to find the solution set of any quadratic equation

$$ax^2 + bx + c = 0, \quad a \neq 0$$

That is,

$$x = \frac{-b \pm \sqrt{b^2 - 4ac}}{2a}, \text{ provided that}$$

$$b^2 - 4ac \geq 0$$

Example 1

Using the quadratic formula, find the solution set of the equation

$$x^2 - 7x + 5 = 0$$

Here $a = 1, b = -7, c = 5$,

$$x = \frac{-b \pm \sqrt{b^2 - 4ac}}{2a}$$

$$x = \frac{-(-7) \pm \sqrt{(-7)^2 - 4(1)(5)}}{2 \cdot 1}$$

$$x = \frac{7 \pm \sqrt{49 - 20}}{2}$$

$$x = \frac{7 \pm \sqrt{29}}{2}$$

Therefore the solution set is

$$\left\{ \frac{7 + \sqrt{29}}{2}, \frac{7 - \sqrt{29}}{2} \right\}$$

Example 2

Using the quadratic formula, find the solution set of the equation

$$3x^2 = 2(x + 3)$$

(1) To use the quadratic formula we must write the equation in the form of $ax^2 + bx + c = 0$

$$3x^2 = 2x + 6 \qquad\qquad \text{(Distributive law)}$$

or

$$3x^2 - 2x - 6 = 0$$

Thus $a = 3, b = -2$, and $c = -6$.

$$x = \frac{-(-2) \pm \sqrt{(-2)^2 - 4(3)(-6)}}{2 \cdot 3}$$

$$x = \frac{2 \pm \sqrt{4 + 72}}{6}$$

$$x = \frac{2 \pm \sqrt{76}}{6}$$

Since $\sqrt{76} = \sqrt{4 \cdot 19} = \sqrt{4}\sqrt{19} = 2\sqrt{19}$, we can write

$$x = \frac{2 \pm 2\sqrt{19}}{6} = \frac{2(1 \pm \sqrt{19})}{6} = \frac{1 \pm \sqrt{19}}{3}$$

Therefore the solution set is

$$\left\{ \frac{1 + \sqrt{19}}{3}, \frac{1 - \sqrt{19}}{3} \right\}$$

Example 3

Use the quadratic formula to find the solution set of the equation

$$x^2 + 6x + 9 = 0$$

$$x = \frac{-6 \pm \sqrt{6^2 - 4(1)(9)}}{2}$$

$$x = \frac{-6 \pm \sqrt{36 - 36}}{2}$$

$$x = \frac{-6 \pm 0}{2}$$

Therefor the solution set is $\{-3, -3\}$, or simply $\{-3\}$.

Exercise Set 8.8

In exercises 1-6 write the given equation in the form of $ax^2 + bx + c = 0$, and identify a, b, and c.

1. $2x^2 + 5x = 7$

2. $6x^2 = 7 - 15x$

3. $3x - 4 = x^2$

4. $-15 - 3x = 3x^2$

5. $(2x - 3)^2 + 4 = 0$

6. $(2x + 1)^2 - (x + 4)^2 + 4x + 14 = 0$

In exercises 7-26 use the quadratic formula to find the solution set of the given equation.

7. $x^2 + 3x - 40 = 0$

8. $x^2 - 3x - 3 = 0$

9. $5x^2 + 3x = 0$

10. $6x^2 + x - 12 = 0$

11. $3y^2 - 3y - 2 = 0$

12. $4y^2 - 1 = 0$

13. $2x^2 - 5x + 1 = 0$

14. $(2x - 1)^2 - 2 = 0$

15. $y^2 - 8y + 16 = 0$

16. $4y^2 - 6y = 0$

17. $2x^2 + 3x + 1 = 0$

18. $2x^2 + 7 = 10x$

19. $3x^2 - 7 = 0$

20. $4x^2 - 4x + 1 = 0$

21. $x^2 + \frac{1}{4}x - \frac{3}{8} = 0$

22. $\frac{1}{2}x^2 + 7x + 25 = 0$

23. $9y^2 - 12y + 4 = 0$

24. $9y^2 - 6y - 1 = 0$

25. $3 - 2x - 8x^2 = 0$

26. $7x - 2 - 6x^2 = 0$

REVIEW TEST FOR CHAPTER VIII

Note: This test should be completed in 75 minutes.

1. In each of the following factorizations enter the correct signs in the binomials.
   (a) $8x^2 + 22x - 63 = (4x \quad 7)(2x \quad 9)$
   (b) $6x^2 - 19x + 10 = (3x \quad 2)(2x \quad 5)$

2. Complete each of the following factorizations.
   (a) $25x^2 - 20x + 4 = (5x - 2)(\quad)$
   (b) $12x^2 + 8x - 15 = (\quad - 5)(\quad + 3)$

3. Compute each of the following products.
   (a) $(3x - 4)(4x + 5)$
   (b) $(2x - 7y)(5x - 2y)$

4. Square each of the following binomials.
   (a) $3x - 2$
   (b) $5a + 2b$

5. Determine whether or not each of the following is a perfect square. If it is, write it as the square of a binomial.
   (a) $x^2 - 25$
   (b) $x^2 + 4x + 16$
   (c) $x^2 - 40x + 400$
   (d) $x^2 + \frac{3}{4}x + \frac{9}{64}$
   (e) $36x^2 - 60x + 25$
   (f) $9x^2 + 12x + 16$

6. Factor each of the following expressions completely.
    (a) $4x^2 - 81y^2$
    (b) $x^2 - x - 30$
    (c) $14a^3b + 35ab^2 + 14a^2b^2$

7. Factor each of the following polynomials completely.
    (a) $x^3 - 25x$
    (b) $28x^3 - 62x^2 + 30x$
    (c) $3b^2x^6 - 243b^2x^2$

8. Find the solution set of each of the following equations by completing the square.
    (a) $y^2 + 4y - 21 = 0$
    (b) $3x^2 + 2x = 1$

9. Find the solution set of each of the following equations.
    (a) $5x^2 - 9x = 0$ (e) $16x^2 + 24x + 9 = 0$
    (b) $2x^2 - 14 = 0$ (f) $7x^2 - 10x - 1 = 0$
    (c) $2x^2 - 8x + 1 = 0$ (g) $6x^2 + 5x - 56 = 0$
    (d) $6x^2 + x = 35$ (h) $2x^2 + 8x + 3 = 0$

IX INTRODUCTION TO LOGIC

9.1 INTRODUCTION

Logic is concerned with the general principles of reasoning. Thus it has its value everywhere that reasoning must be applied. Today it has great application in advanced mathematics, in the design of computers and in many other areas of applied science. In this chapter we will introduce some basic ideas, terminology and notation of logic.

9.2 STATEMENTS

A STATEMENT

A *statement* is any sentence to which it is *meaningful* to assign *one and only one* of the truth values "true" and "false" at any given time. Thus a statement is either true or false at a given time, but *never both* simultaneously. Let us now consider the following examples of statements.

Examples of Statements

1. $7 + 1 = 8$
2. $6 + 3 < 4$

3. It is raining.
4. $x + 1 = 3$
5. I will travel to France by the year 2000.

In examples 1 and 2 we can easily determine a truth value upon reading the statement. Statement 3 may be either true or false depending upon the given time and place, but certainly never can it be both. The statement in example 4 is neither true nor false as stated. However it becomes true or false once we replace the variable by a given value. We can see that when $x = 5$, for example, the statement is false, and when $x = 2$ the statement is true. The truth value of statement 5 cannot be determined (until possibly the year 2000). However, it may still be *meaningful to assign a truth value* to this statement for the purposes of discussion.

The following sentences can never be true or false and it would be meaningless to assign a truth value to them:

Examples of Sentences Which Are Not *Statements*

6. How do you feel today?
7. Take care of yourself.
8. Leave immediately!
9. I believe it was raining.

A SIMPLE STATEMENT

Statements which contain only one assertion are called *simple statements*.

Example 10

The statement "It is a ball" would be a simple statement, whereas the statement "It is a red ball" would *not* be a simple statement, for it makes the two assertions "It is red" and "It is a ball."

A COMPOUND STATEMENT

A sentence which consists of two or more simple statements is called a *compound statement*. The simple statements of which a compound statement is comprised are called its *components*.

Example 11

The statement "John and Mary went to school" is a compound statement, for it consists of the two simple statements "John went to school" and "Mary went to school."

Example 12

The statement "If I study, then I will pass this course and graduate" is a compound statement, for it consists of the three simple statements "I study," "I will pass this course," and "I will graduate."

Notation

We will use small letters *a, b, c, . . .* to represent *simple* statements. Thus when we write "*r*: It is raining," this is read "*r* represents the statement: It is raining."

Exercise Set 9.2

In exercises 1-17 determine whether or not the given sentence is a statement. If the sentence is a statement, determine whether it is simple or compound.

1. Do exercise set 9.2 for homework.

2. 19 is an odd integer.

3. Wait for the mailman.

4. He is wealthy and handsome.

5. Bring on the Mets and the Yankees.

6. $2 - 4 = 2$.

7. It was a warm humid day.

8. I believe John was at the party.

9. Is $2 + 5 > 6$?

10. All rational numbers are integers.

11. If x is an element of set A, then x is an element of the set B.

12. Give me that old-time religion.

13. All squares are rectangles and all rectangles are squares.

14. What a beautiful work of art!

15. When will you complete your homework?

16. $6 - 9 > -1$ or $6 + 9 < -1$.

17. Come back immediately or I will not let you go out tomorrow.

9.3 CONJUNCTION, DISJUNCTION, AND NEGATION

CONJUNCTION

A compound statement consisting of two statements joined by one of the connectives "and," "but," or a compound statement which has the same meaning as two statements joined by one of the connectives "and" or "but" is called a *conjunction* of the two statements.

Examples of Conjunctions

1. "John is tall and handsome" is a conjunction of the two statements "John is tall" and "John is handsome."
2. "John went to school but Mary stayed home."
3. "It was a big red house" is a conjunction of the two statements "The house was big" and "The house was red."

Suppose we let p and q represent the following simple statements:

$$p: \text{ It is raining.}$$

$$q: \text{ I will take the car.}$$

The symbol "$\wedge$" will be used to represent the connective "and." Thus we can now symbolize the conjunction "It is raining and I will take the car" by $p \wedge q$.

Notation

In general if a and b represent any two simple statements, we can symbolize the conjunction of these two statements by writing

$$a \wedge b, \text{ which is read "} a \text{ and } b \text{"}$$

If j: John went to the store, and m: Mary went to the store, then $j \wedge m$ would symbolize the statement "John went to the store and Mary went to the store" or, more simply, "John and Mary went to the store." The question to be asked now is, when is this conjunction true and when is it false? This conjunction can be assigned the truth value "true" (T) only when *both component statements are true*, that is only when both John and Mary did go to the store. If either component statement is false or if both are false, then the conjunction is false.

In general a conjunction $a \wedge b$ is true only when *both* statements a and b are true; and otherwise it is false. This can be summarized in a table, known as a truth table for conjunction, which lists all possible truth values of the statement $a \wedge b$.

Truth Table for Conjunction

a	b	$a \wedge b$
T	T	T
T	F	F
F	T	F
F	F	F

TRUTH TABLE

In general any such table which lists *all possible truth values* for a given statement is known as a *truth table* for that statement.

Note 1

To construct the truth table for conjunction above we first list all possible combinations of true (T) and false (F) for the component statements a and b, and then, for each combination, the truth value of the conjunction is determined. As we will see in future examples any truth table which involves *two simple statements* will have *four rows*. That is, there are four possible combinations of true (T) and false (F) for the two simple statements.

Note 2

The word "but" acts exactly the same way as the word "and" in a conjunction.

Note 3

The *conjunction* of two statements in logic has as its parallel the *intersection* of two sets in set theory. This can be seen if we let:

$$a: x \in A$$

$$b: x \in B, \quad \text{where } A \text{ and } B \text{ are sets.}$$

Then $a \land b$ represents the statement $x \in A$ and $x \in B$, or more simply $x \in (A \cap B)$, which is true only when x belongs to both set A and set B, that is, only when statement a is true and statement b is true.

DISJUNCTION

A compound statement consisting of two statements joined by the connective "or," or a compound statement which has the same meaning as two statements joined by the connective "or" is called a *disjunction* of the two statements.

Examples of Disjunctions

4. "John is tall or handsome" is a disjunction of the two simple statements "John is tall" and "John is handsome."
5. John or Charlotte will go to the store" is a disjunction of the two simple statements "John will go to the store" and "Charlotte will go to the store."

Note

In logic the connective "or" is used in the *inclusive* sense, meaning "one or the other *or both*." Thus in example 4, when it is stated that "John is tall or handsome" it is meant that he is either tall or handsome *or both* tall and handsome.

Notation

The symbol "V" will be used to represent the connective "or." Thus if a and b represent any two simple statements, we can symbolize the *disjunction* of these two statements by writing

$$a \lor b, \text{ which is read "a or b"}$$

Let

$$a: \text{ He is an athlete.}$$

$$i: \text{ He is intelligent.}$$

Then $a \lor i$ would symbolize the statement "He is an athlete or he is intelligent." The question is now, when is this disjunction true and when is it false? This disjunction can be assigned the truth value "true" (T) if either one or the other component is true or if both are true, that is, if he is indeed an athlete or if he is intelligent or if he is both an athlete and intelligent. The disjunction is false only if he is neither an athlete nor intelligent, that is, if both components are false.

In general a disjunction $a \lor b$ is *false* only when both statements a and b are false; otherwise it is true. This can be summarized in a truth table for "$a \lor b$."

Truth Table for Disjunction

a	b	$a \lor b$
T	T	T
T	F	T
F	T	T
F	F	F

Note

The *disjunction* of two statements in logic has as its parallel the *union* of two sets in set theory. This can be seen if we let:

$$a: x \in A$$

$$b: x \in B, \qquad \text{where } A \text{ and } B \text{ are sets.}$$

Then $a \lor b$ represents the statement $x \in A$ or $x \in B$, or more simply $x \in (A \cup B)$, which is true when x belongs to the set A or to the set B or to both, that is, when statement a is true or b is true or both are true.

NEGATION

The *negation* or *denial* of a statement (no matter how complex) is the statement obtained by preceding the original statement with the words "*It is false that*" or "*It is not true that.*" That is, *to negate a statement is to say that the statement is false.*

Examples of Negations

6. The negation of the statement "John is rich" is the statement "It is false that John is rich" or, more simply, "John is not rich."

7. The negation of the statement "Steve studied and passed the course" is the statement "It is false that Steve studied and passed the course."

Notation

The negation of a statement a will be symbolized by

$\sim a$, where this is read "It is false that a"
or simply "not a"

Let r: It is raining. Then $\sim r$ would represent the statement "It is not raining." We can easily see that if r is true, then $\sim r$ must be false, and if r is false, then $\sim r$ must be true.

In general if a is any statement, then if a is true, $\sim a$ is false and if a is false, $\sim a$ is true. This can be summarized in a truth table for negation.

Truth Table for Negation

a	$\sim a$
T	F
F	T

Example 8

Using the letters s and p, symbolize the statement "It is false that Steve studied and passed the course."

Let s: Steve studied.

p: Steve passed the course.

The statement "Steve studied and passed the course" is symbolized by $s \wedge p$. The statement that we wish to symbolize is the negation of $s \wedge p$. Thus we must precede the entire statement $s \wedge p$ by the negation symbol. To do this we must make use of parentheses as follows:

$$\sim(s \wedge p)$$

If we had omitted the parentheses and written $\sim s \wedge p$, we would have been negating *only the* statement s and this would read "Steve did not study but he passed the course," which is not the statement that we wished to symbolize.

Example 9

What is the truth value of the statement $\sim(s \wedge p)$, given that s is true and p is false?

(1) Since s is true and p is false, $s \wedge p$ is false. (See truth table for conjunction.)
(2) Therefore $\sim(s \wedge p)$ *must be true*, for the negation of a false statement is true. (See truth table for negation.)

As we can see from example 8, the use of parentheses to indicate a grouping enables us to symbolize more complex statements.

Example 10

Let d: He is a democrat.

 o: He is over 30 years of age.

 s: He supports our foreign policy.

Symbolize the statement "He is over 30 years of age or a democrat, but he does not support our foreign policy," and determine the truth value of this statement given that d is false, o is true, and s is false.

The symbolization is $(o \vee d) \wedge \sim s$.

(Recall "but" acts the same as "and.")

In reading the above statement, we can see that "He is over 30 years of age or a democrat" is a complete grouping and therefore we enclose the statement $o \vee d$ in parentheses, thus avoiding ambiguity. If we had omitted the parentheses and written simply $o \vee d \wedge \sim s$, we could have interpreted this statement as $o \vee (d \wedge \sim s)$ which would read, "He is over 30 years of age, or he is a democrat and does not support our foreign policy," which is not the same statement as the original.

To determine the truth value of the statement $(o \vee d) \wedge \sim s$ under the conditions given above:

(1) o is true, d is true implies $o \vee d$ is true. (See disjunction truth table.)
(2) s is false; therefore $\sim s$ *is true*. (See negation truth table.)
(3) Therefore $(o \vee d) \wedge \sim s$ *is true*. (Conjunction of two true statements is true.)

Note

The negation of a statement in logic has as its parallel in set theory the *complement of a set.* This can be seen if we consider a universal set U and let

$$a: \ x \in A \qquad \text{where } A \text{ is a set.}$$

Then $\sim a$ would represent the statement $x \notin A$ or $x \in A'$ (the complement of A), which is true when x does not belong to the set A, that is, when the statement a is false.

Exercise Set 9.3

In exercises 1-6, write a conjunction of the two given statements and determine whether the conjunction is true or false.

1. $3(-2) = 1$
   $3 + 1 = 4$

2. $-3 > -5$
   $6(\frac{1}{2} + \frac{1}{6}) = 4$

3. $3 + (-4) = -12$
   $3 - (-5) = -2$

4. Paris is in France.
   $-2 - 5 = 10$

5. $6 \div 3 = 5 \div \frac{5}{2}$
   $(-2)(-5) = 10$

6. All integers are rational numbers.
   All nonterminating decimals are irrational numbers.

In exercises 7-10 write a disjunction of the two given statements and determine whether the disjunction is true or false.

7. $4 \div 0 = 4$
   $0 \div 0 = 1$

8. $\frac{2 + 7}{2} = 8$
   0 is an even integer.

9. $(-4)(-3) = 12$
   $-8 < -3$

10. Chicago is in California.
    $\{a, b, c\}$ is equivalent to $\{2, 4, 6\}$

11. Let t: He is a teacher.
        i: He is intelligent.
        w: He is wealthy.
    Symbolize the following statements:

    (a) He is a teacher and intelligent.
    (b) He is a teacher or he is not wealthy.

(c) He is wealthy but not intelligent.
(d) It is false that he is wealthy and intelligent.
(e) He is a teacher and intelligent, but he is not wealthy.
(f) He is wealthy, or he is intelligent and a teacher.
(g) He is wealthy or not intelligent, and he is not a teacher.
(h) It is false that he is wealthy and not intelligent, but he is a teacher.
(i) He is intelligent and wealthy, or he is intelligent and a teacher.

12. Let *f*: He is a football player.
    s: He has great physical strength.
    c: He has courage.

Write a verbal statement which describes each of the following statements given in symbolic form.

(a) $\sim f$
(b) $f \wedge s$
(c) $s \vee c$
(d) $s \wedge \sim c$
(e) $\sim f \wedge \sim c$
(f) $\sim(f \vee c)$
(g) $(f \wedge s) \wedge \sim c$
(h) $s \wedge (f \vee c)$
(i) $(c \vee \sim s) \wedge \sim f$
(j) $(f \wedge s) \vee (\sim f \wedge c)$
(k) $(f \vee s) \wedge (f \vee \sim c)$

In exercises 13-26 assume *a* and *b* are true and *c* is false. Determine the truth value of the given statement.

13. $\sim a$
14. $\sim a \vee c$
15. $a \vee \sim b$
16. $b \wedge c$
17. $\sim(a \wedge c)$
18. $\sim b \vee \sim c$
19. $a \wedge \sim c$
20. $\sim(\sim a \vee \sim b)$
21. $(a \wedge c) \vee b$
22. $(a \wedge b) \wedge c$
23. $(a \wedge c) \vee \sim b$
24. $\sim b \wedge (\sim a \vee \sim c)$
25. $(a \wedge b) \vee (a \wedge c)$
26. $(a \wedge \sim b) \vee (b \wedge \sim c)$

27. (a) What is the truth value of $a \wedge b$ if *b* is false?
    (b) What is the truth value of $a \vee b$ if *b* is true?

28. (a) What is the truth value of $(b \vee \sim a) \wedge \sim b$ if *b* is true?
    (b) What is the truth value of $(a \vee b) \vee c$ if *a* is true?

29. (a) If $a \wedge b$ is false, what is the truth value of $\sim a \vee \sim b$?
    (b) If $a \wedge b$ is true, what is the truth value of $\sim a \vee \sim b$?

30. If $(a \wedge \sim b) \vee (b \wedge \sim c)$ has truth value "true" and *a* has truth value "false," then the truth value of *b*: (a) is "true" (b) is "false" (c) cannot be determined.

9.4 THE CONDITIONAL AND BICONDITIONAL

CONDITIONAL STATEMENT

Suppose we let

> *a*: Bev studies.

> *b*: She will pass the course.

and consider the statement formed by joining these two statements using the words "if" and "then." That is, consider the statement, "If Bev studies, then she will pass the course." Such a statement is called a *conditional statement* or an *implication*, for in this statement studying implies or conditions passing.

A statement of the form "if *a* then *b*" or any statement which has the same meaning as such a statement is called a *conditional statement* or an *implication*. The statement "*a*" is called the *antecedent* of the implication and "*b*" is called the *consequent*.

Notation

The symbol "→" is used to represent the connective "if . . . then." Thus

$$a \to b \text{ is read "if } a \text{ then } b\text{"}$$

The conditional $a \to b$ can also be read:

(1) *a* implies *b*.
(2) *a* is sufficient for *b*.
(3) *b* is necessary for *a*.

Example 1

Let *r*: It rains.
   c: I will take the car.

Symbolize the statement, "If it rains, then I will not take the car."

Here the antecedent is the statement "It rains" and the consequent is the statement "I will not take the car," which is the negation of the statement *c*. Thus the symbolization would be

$$s \to \sim c$$

Example 2

Let *w*: John will win $100.

    t: The number 3 horse wins the race.

Symbolize the statement, "John will win $100 if the number 3 horse wins the race."

    Here the number 3 horse winning the race is implying John will win $100. That is, the given statement has the same meaning as the statement, "If the number 3 horse wins the race, then John will win $100." Therefore the statement *t* is the antecedent and *w* is the consequent. Thus the symbolization is:

$$t \rightarrow w$$

Example 3

Let *r*: He is rich.

    b: He has a beautiful wife.

Symbolize the statement, "It is necessary to be rich to have a beautiful wife."

    This statement can also be read, "If he has a beautiful wife, then he is rich." Thus the symbolization would be

$$b \rightarrow r$$

Example 4

Let *e*: You have eighteen dollars.

    b: You can bet on all nine races.

Symbolize the statement, "Having eighteen dollars is sufficient for betting on all nine races."

    This statement can also be read "If you have eighteen dollars, then you can bet on all nine races." Thus the symbolization would be

$$e \rightarrow b$$

Let us now determine when a conditional statement is true and when it is false. To this end suppose Martin Smith made the conditional statement, "If I come to the picnic, then I will arrange to have the soda there." Now let us consider the following situations:

(1) If Martin came to the picnic and did arrange to have the soda there, then he kept his promise, and thus his conditional statement was *true*.
(2) If Martin came to the picnic, but did not arrange to have the soda there, then he did not keep his promise, and thus his conditional statement was *false*.
(3) If Martin *did not come* to the picnic he is not required to arrange for the soda being there, for *he only specified that this would be done IF HE CAME*. Thus in this case, *whether or not* he arranged for the soda to be there we *cannot say that his conditional statement was false*. Since any statement must be either true or false at a given time we will assign the truth value "true" (T) to his conditional statement in both cases where he did not come.

Thus the conditional statement, "If I come to the picnic, then I will arrange to have the soda there" is false only when the antecedent "I come to the picnic" is true and the consequent "I will arrange to have the soda there" is false.

In general *any conditional statement a → b is false only when the antecedent, a, is true and the consequent, b, is false. Otherwise, the conditional is true.* This can be summarized in the following truth table for the conditional.

Truth Table for the Conditional

a	b	a → b
T	T	T
T	F	F
F	T	T
F	F	T

Example 5

Consider the conditional statement, "If 1 + 1 = 3, then New York City is in California." As ridiculous as this statement may sound, it is nevertheless a true statement, for the antecedent "1 + 1 = 3" is false. (See line 4 of the truth table for the conditional.)

Example 6

Consider the conditional statement, "If 1 + 1 = 2, then New York City is in California." Here the antecedent "1 + 1 = 2" is true but the consequent "New York City is in California" is false. Thus the conditional is false. (See line 2 of the truth table for the conditional.)

Example 7

Let e: The final exam is easy.

   p: I will pass this course.

Symbolize the statement, "I will not pass this course if the final exam is not easy," and determine its truth value given that e is true and p is false.

   Here the exam not being easy implies not passing the course. Thus the antecedent is "The final exam is not easy," symbolized $\sim e$, and the consequent is, "I will not pass the course," symbolize $\sim p$. The symbolization is then:

$$\sim e \rightarrow \sim p$$

   To determine the truth value:

(1) Since e is true, $\sim e$ *is false.*
(2) Since p is false, $\sim p$ *is true.*
(3) $\sim e \rightarrow \sim p$ is therefore *true*. (See row 3 of the truth table for the conditional.)

Note

In the above example, it was not necessary to determine the truth value of $\sim p$, for once we establish that the antecedent, $\sim e$, is false, we know that no matter what truth value the consequent has, the conditional statement is true.

Example 8

Let s: He studies.

   p: He passes.

    e: He will go to Europe.

    g: He will go to summer school.

Symbolize the statement, "If he studies and passes, then he will go to Europe and not go to summer school."

    Here the antecedent is the conjunction "He studies and passes" and the consequent is the conjunction, "He will go to Europe and not go to summer school."

    Thus the symbolization is

$$(s \land p) \rightarrow (e \land \mathord{\sim} g)$$

Note again the use of parentheses to indicate correct groupings.

Example 9

Let *r*: I will run the mile in under 5 minutes.

    t: I can make the track team.

Symbolize the statement, "I will run the mile in under 5 minutes, or if I don't run the mile in under 5 minutes then I cannot make the track team."

    This statement is a disjunction of the simple statement *r* and the implication $\mathord{\sim} r \rightarrow \mathord{\sim} t$, and so the symbolization is

$$r \lor (\mathord{\sim} r \rightarrow \mathord{\sim} t)$$

Example 10

Assume *p* and *q* are true and *r* and *s* are false. Determine the truth value of the statement

$$(p \lor \mathord{\sim} r) \rightarrow \mathord{\sim}(q \land \mathord{\sim} s)$$

(1)   Since *r* is false, $\mathord{\sim} r$ is true.
(2)   Thus, since *p* is also true, the antecedent of the conditional, $p \lor \mathord{\sim} r$, is *true*.
(3)   Since *s* is false, $\mathord{\sim} s$ is true.
(4)   Therefore, since *q* is true, $q \land \mathord{\sim} s$ is true.
(5)   But the consequent of the conditional is the negation of $q \land \mathord{\sim} s$, which is therefore *false*.

(6) Since we have a *true antecedent* and a *false consequent*, the entire conditional statement has truth value *"false."*

This problem can be summarized by the following table:

p	q	r	s	$\sim r$	Ante-cedent $p \vee \sim r$	$\sim s$	$q \wedge \sim s$	Consequent $\sim(q \wedge \sim s)$	$(p \vee \sim r) \rightarrow \sim(q \wedge \sim s)$
T	T	F	F	T	T	T	T	F	Ⓕ

BICONDITIONAL STATEMENT

A statement obtained by joining two statements with the words "if and only if" is called a *biconditional* statement.

Examples of Biconditionals

11. x is a positive real number if and only if it is greater than zero.
12. Set A is a subset of set B if and only if every element of A is also an element of B.
13. John will go to the party if and only if Mary goes.

Notation

The symbol "$\longleftrightarrow$" is used to represent the connective "if and only if." Thus

$$a \longleftrightarrow b \text{ is read "} a \text{ if and only if } b\text{"}$$

A biconditional is actually composed of *two* conditional statements. For example, the statement of example 11 is actually composed of the two conditionals:

If x is a positive real number, then it is greater than zero.

and

If x is greater than zero, then x is a positive real number.

In general by any biconditional of the form $a \longleftrightarrow b$ is meant:

$$(a \rightarrow b) \wedge (b \rightarrow a)$$

That is, a biconditional, $a \longleftrightarrow b$, is a conjunction of the two conditional statements $a \rightarrow b$ and $b \rightarrow a$.

We can determine the truth values of $a \longleftrightarrow b$ for each possible combination of truth values for a and b by determining the truth values of the above conjunctions.

(1) If *a is true and b is true*, then $a \rightarrow b$ is true, $b \rightarrow a$ is true, and thus the conjunction $(a \rightarrow b) \land (b \rightarrow a)$ is *true*.

(2) If *a is true and b is false*, then $a \rightarrow b$ is false, and thus the conjunction $(a \rightarrow b) \land (b \rightarrow a)$ is *false* (why?).

(3) If *a is false and b is true*, then $b \rightarrow a$ is false (why?), and thus the conjunction $(a \rightarrow b) \land (b \rightarrow a)$ is *false* (why?).

(4) If *a is false and b is false*, then both $a \rightarrow b$ and $b \rightarrow a$ are true (why?), and thus the conjunction $(a \rightarrow b) \land (b \rightarrow a)$ is true (why?).

This can be summarized in a truth table as follows:

Truth Table for the Biconditional

a	b	$a \longleftrightarrow b$
T	T	T
T	F	F
F	T	F
F	F	T

Note

As we can see, the biconditional $a \longleftrightarrow b$ is true only when both components have the same truth value (either both are true or both are false).

Example 14

Let p: John will secure a good position.
   h: John will be happy.
   g: He goes to college.
   w: He is born wealthy.

Symbolize the statement, "John will secure a good position and be happy if and only if he goes to college or is born wealthy."

This is a biconditional statement composed of the conjunction $(p \land h)$ and the disjunction $(g \lor w)$. The symbolization therefore is:

$$(p \land h) \longleftrightarrow (g \lor w)$$

Example 15

Determine the truth value of $\sim(r \lor q) \longleftrightarrow (\sim s \to p)$ given that p and q are true, r and s are false.

p	q	r	s	$r \lor q$	$\sim(r \lor q)$	$\sim s$	$\sim s \to p$	$\sim(r \lor q) \longleftrightarrow (\sim s \to p)$
T	T	F	F	T	F	T	T	(F)

SUMMARY

For future reference let us combine into one table all of our previous truth tables.

a	b	$\sim a$	$\sim b$	$a \land b$	$a \lor b$	$a \to b$	$a \longleftrightarrow b$
T	T	F	F	T	T	T	T
T	F	F	T	F	T	F	F
F	T	T	F	F	T	T	F
F	F	T	T	F	F	T	T

Exercise Set 9.4

1. State the antecedent and the consequent for each of the following conditional statements:
   (a) If John does a good job, then he will be reelected.
   (b) He is wealthy if he earns over $100,000 a year.
   (c) If $3x + 1 = 7$, then $x = 2$.
   (d) It is necessary to have courage in order to be a football player.
   (e) For x to be less than 7 it is sufficient for x to be less than 5.
   (f) $x > 0$ if x is positive.
   (g) To become President of the United States, it is necessary to be wealthy.

   In exercises 2-11 symbolize the given statement using the circled letters.

   Example: If he is (r) ich then he is not (h) appy.

   Here r: he is rich
       h: he is happy

The symbolization is $r \to \sim h$

2. If stock prices (f) all, then unemployment (r) ises.

3. He is my (f) ather if I am his (s) on.

4. He will be (h) appy if and only if he is (r) ich.

5. It is false that, he is a football (p) layer if and only if he is not (i) ntelligent.

6. He is not a (t) eacher if he is not (i) ntelligent but is (p) oor.

7. Ken will (w) in the race if and only if he (p) ractices every day or is (J) ucky.

8. If he enjoys (c) heckers or (s) crabble, then he doesn't enjoy (f) ootball.

9. He is a (b) achelor and (s) pends a lot of money, or if he is not a bachelor then he doesn't spend a lot of money.

10. If he (b) rushes his teeth he will have no (c) avities, and if he has no cavities his parents will (s) ave money.

11. In order to (d) o these problems, it is necessary that you (r) ead this chapter and (a) ttend class.

12. Let *w*: He works hard.
    e: He earns a lot of money.
    s: He is a smart investor.
    t: He will travel around the world.
    b: He is a bachelor.

Write a verbal statement which describes each of the following statements given in symbolic form:

(a) $w \rightarrow e$

(b) $e \leftrightarrow s$

(c) $(w \wedge e) \rightarrow t$

(d) $t \rightarrow (e \vee b)$

(e) $w \rightarrow \sim b$

(f) $(\sim w \wedge \sim e) \leftrightarrow (\sim b \vee \sim s)$

(g) $(s \wedge e) \vee (w \wedge \sim b)$

(h) $\sim(e \leftrightarrow w)$

(i) $(b \rightarrow t) \wedge [\sim b \rightarrow (w \wedge \sim t)]$

(j) $s \vee (\sim s \rightarrow \sim e)$

In exercises 13-25 assume that *a* and *b* are true and *c* and *d* are false. Determine the truth value of the given statement.

13. $a \rightarrow c$

14. $\sim d \leftrightarrow b$

15. $a \rightarrow (b \wedge d)$

16. $\sim c \leftrightarrow (\sim d \wedge a)$.

17. $\sim a \rightarrow (\sim b \vee c)$

18. $(\sim c \vee b) \rightarrow (\sim b \vee c)$

19. $a \rightarrow (\sim c \rightarrow \sim b)$

20. $\sim(a \vee c) \rightarrow \sim(c \wedge b)$

21. $\sim a \lor (b \land \sim c)$

22. $\sim \{\sim [\sim a \land (b \lor \sim c)]\}$

23. $[\sim(b \lor c) \leftrightarrow (\sim d \to a)] \land (a \land \sim b)$

24. $[a \to (c \to \sim d)] \to [(a \to \sim c) \to d]$

25. $(\sim a \to \sim b) \leftrightarrow (b \leftrightarrow a)$

26. (a) What is the truth value of $a \to b$ if b is true?
    (b) What is the truth value of $\sim a \to \sim b$ if a is true?

27. (a) If $a \to b$ is true, what is the truth value of $a \land \sim b$?
    (b) If $a \to b$ is true, what is the truth value of $\sim a \lor b$?
    (c) If $a \to b$ is false, what is the truth value of $\sim a \to \sim b$?
    (d) If $a \to b$ is false, what is the truth value of $\sim b \to \sim a$?

28. What is the truth value of $(a \land b) \to (a \lor b)$ if b is false?

29. What is the truth value of $(a \lor \sim b) \leftrightarrow (b \to a)$ if b is false?

9.5 TRUTH TABLES

As we've seen, by using the connectives $\land, \lor, \sim, \to, \leftrightarrow$ we can construct compound statements of varying complexity. A truth table can be constructed for any compound statement, no matter how complex. For example, let us consider the statement $a \lor (\sim a \to \sim b)$. The truth table for this compound statement would be constructed as follows:

a	b	$\sim a$	$\sim b$	$\sim a \to \sim b$	$a \lor (\sim a \to \sim b)$
T	T	F	F	T	T
T	F	F	T	T	T
F	T	T	F	F	F
F	F	T	T	T	T

To construct the above table we must:

(1) First note that there are two simple statements, a, b (components). This is determined simply by the number of letters involved. The first columns of the table are reserved for these letters.

(2) We then put in all possible combinations of truth values for these two simple statements, thus producing four rows for the truth table.

(3) We then include a column for each statement that is needed to *build up* the compound statement $a \lor ({\sim}a \rightarrow {\sim}b)$. For example, a column for ${\sim}a$ and a column for ${\sim}b$ are needed to determine the truth values of ${\sim}a \rightarrow {\sim}b$. In turn, a column for ${\sim}a \rightarrow {\sim}b$ is needed to determine the truth values of the disjunction $a \lor ({\sim}a \rightarrow {\sim}b)$. The only restriction in this procedure is that *each column is derived from previous columns*.

(4) Finally in the last column, we find the truth values of the desired compound statement.

Note

As we've seen, when *two simple statements* are involved in a compound statement, its truth table will have *four rows*. When *three simple statements* are involved in a compound statement, there are eight possible combinations of truth values for these three simple statements (try to determine these eight combinations) and thus its truth table will have *eight rows*. With four simple statements involved, the truth table will contain 16 rows, and in general with n *simple statements* involved, the truth table will contain 2^n *rows*.

Example 1

Construct the truth table for the statement ${\sim}(a \land b) \longleftrightarrow ({\sim}a \lor {\sim}b)$.

Note that there are two component statements a, b and thus the truth table will contain $2^2 = 4$ rows.

| 1 | 2 | (1,2) 3 $a \land b$ | (3) 4 ${\sim}(a \land b)$ | (1) 5 ${\sim}a$ | (2) 6 ${\sim}b$ | (5,6) 7 ${\sim}a \lor {\sim}b$ | (4,7) 8 ${\sim}(a \land b) \longleftrightarrow ({\sim}a \lor {\sim}b)$ |
a	b						
T	T	T	F	F	F	F	T
T	F	F	T	F	T	T	T
F	T	F	T	T	F	T	T
F	F	F	T	T	T	T	T

Note

The columns in the above table have been numbered and above the number of the column is the number(s) of the column(s) from which that column has been derived. For example, column 3 has been derived from columns 1 and 2; column 4 has been derived from column 3, etc.

Example 2

Construct a truth table for the statement $(a \wedge {\sim}b) \rightarrow {\sim}c$.

Note that there are three component statements, a, b, and c, and thus the truth table will contain $2^3 = 8$ rows.

1	2	3	(2) 4	(1,4) 5	(3) 6	(5,6) 7
a	b	c	${\sim}b$	$a \wedge {\sim}b$	${\sim}c$	$(a \wedge {\sim}b) \rightarrow {\sim}c$
T	T	T	F	F	F	T
T	T	F	F	F	T	T
T	F	T	T	T	F	F
T	F	F	T	T	T	T
F	T	T	F	F	F	T
F	T	F	F	F	T	T
F	F	T	T	F	F	T
F	F	F	T	F	T	T

Example 3

Construct a truth table for the statement $[(p \rightarrow q) \wedge (q \rightarrow r)] \wedge {\sim}(p \rightarrow r)$.

Here there are three component statements, p, q, and r, and thus the truth table will again have eight rows.

1	2	3	(1,2) 4	(2,3) 5	(4,5) 6	(1,3) 7	(7) 8	(6,8) 9
p	q	r	$p \rightarrow q$	$q \rightarrow r$	$(p \rightarrow q) \wedge (q \rightarrow r)$	$(p \rightarrow r)$	${\sim}(p \rightarrow r)$	$[(p \rightarrow q) \wedge (q \rightarrow r)] \wedge {\sim}(p \rightarrow r)$
T	T	T	T	T	T	T	F	F
T	T	F	T	F	F	F	T	F
T	F	T	F	T	F	T	F	F
T	F	F	F	T	F	F	T	F
F	T	T	T	T	T	T	F	F
F	T	F	T	F	F	T	F	F
F	F	T	T	T	T	T	F	F
F	F	F	T	T	T	T	F	F

In example 1 the given compound statement was *always true*, no matter what the truth values of the simple statements a and b were. In example 3, the given compound statement was *always false*, no matter what the truth values of the simple statements a, b, and c were.

TAUTOLOGY

Any statement which is *always true*, no matter what the truth values of its component statements are, is called a *tautology*.

Example 4

The most basic tautology is $a \lor \sim a$, where a represents any statement.

This statement actually says "*a* happens or it does not happen," which we know must always be true.

a	$\sim a$	$a \lor \sim a$
T	F	T
F	T	T

CONTRADICTION

Any statement which is *always false*, no matter what the truth values of its component statements are, is called a *contradiction*.

Example 5

The most basic contradiction is $a \land \sim a$, where a represents any statement.

This statement actually says "*a* happens but it does not happen," which we know is impossible.

a	$\sim a$	$a \land \sim a$
T	F	F
F	T	F

Example 6

Determine whether the following statement is a tautology, a contradiction, or neither.

$$[(a \to b) \land \sim b] \to \sim a$$

a	b	$a \to b$	$\sim b$	$(a \to b) \wedge \sim b$	$\sim a$	$[(a \to b) \wedge \sim b] \to \sim a$
T	T	T	F	F	F	T
T	F	F	T	F	F	T
F	T	T	F	F	T	T
F	F	T	T	T	T	T

This statement is a tautology.

Note

If a given statement is a tautology, the negation of that statement would be a contradiction. If a given statement is a contradiction, its negation would be a tautology.

LOGICAL EQUIVALENCE

Two statements are said to be *logically equivalent* if they have the same truth tables. That is, two statements are logically equivalent if whenever one is true, the other is true *and* whenever one is false, the other is false.

Example 7

Show that the statements $p \to q$ and $\sim p \vee q$ are logically equivalent.

p	q	$p \to q$	$\sim p$	$\sim p \vee q$
T	T	T	F	T
T	F	F	F	F
F	T	T	T	T
F	F	T	T	T

Both statements have
identical truth tables.

In the above example, if we were to consider the biconditional $(p \to q) \longleftrightarrow (\sim p \vee q)$, this statement would be a tautology. (Why?) This leads us to restate the definition of logically equivalent statements in terms of the biconditional.

LOGICALLY EQUIVALENT STATEMENTS

Two statements are logically equivalent if and only if the biconditional composed of these two statements is a tautology.

In example 1 of this section we can see that the statement $\sim(a \wedge b) \longleftrightarrow (\sim a \vee \sim b)$ is a tautology. Therefore, by our definition of logically equivalent statements we can say that $\sim(a \wedge b)$ is equivalent to $\sim a \vee \sim b$.

Example 8

Determine whether or not the two statements (1) "If I study then I'll pass the course" and (2) "If I don't study then I won't pass the course" are logically equivalent.

Let s: I study.
    p: I will pass the course.

Then statements (1) and (2) can be symbolized as follows:

(1) $s \rightarrow p$
(2) $\sim s \rightarrow \sim p$

Constructing the truth tables for these statements we obtain:

s	p	$s \rightarrow p$	$\sim s$	$\sim p$	$\sim s \rightarrow \sim p$
T	T	T	F	F	T
T	F	F	F	T	T
F	T	T	T	F	F
F	F	T	T	T	T

Since these statements *do not* have the same truth tables, they are *not* equivalent.

Note

Essentially logically equivalent statements are statements which have the *same meaning.*

Example 9

Determine whether or not the following statements have the same meaning:

(1) "If he has the money, then he will buy a car."
(2) "If he doesn't buy a car, then he doesn't have the money."

Let m: He has the money.
    b: He will buy a car.

Then statements (1) and (2) are symbolized as follows:

(1) $m \rightarrow b$
(2) $\sim b \rightarrow \sim m$

Constructing truth tables for these statements we obtain:

m	b	$m \rightarrow b$	$\sim b$	$\sim m$	$\sim b \rightarrow \sim m$
T	T	T	F	F	T
T	F	F	T	F	F
F	T	T	F	T	T
F	F	T	T	T	T

Since these statements have the same truth tables, they are logically equivalent and thus have the same meaning.

Exercise Set 9.5

1. Construct a truth table for each of the following statements. Determine whether the given statement is a tautology, contradiction, or neither.

   (a) $(a \rightarrow b) \wedge (a \wedge \sim b)$
   (b) $[a \wedge (a \rightarrow b)] \rightarrow b$
   (c) $(a \rightarrow b) \longleftrightarrow (\sim b \rightarrow \sim a)$
   (d) $[(q \longleftrightarrow p) \rightarrow (q \rightarrow p)] \vee \sim q$
   (e) $(a \rightarrow b) \rightarrow (a \wedge b)$
   (f) $(a \rightarrow b) \longleftrightarrow (\sim a \rightarrow \sim b)$
   (g) $[(a \rightarrow b) \vee (a \rightarrow c)] \longleftrightarrow [a \rightarrow (b \wedge c)]$
   (h) $[a \rightarrow (b \vee c)] \longleftrightarrow [\sim c \rightarrow (a \rightarrow b)]$
   (i) $[a \rightarrow (b \wedge c)] \longleftrightarrow [a \wedge (\sim b \vee \sim c)]$

2. Which of the following statements corresponds to the given truth table?

a	b	
T	T	T
T	F	T
F	T	F
F	F	T

   (a) $a \rightarrow b$
   (b) $a \wedge \sim b$
   (c) $b \rightarrow \sim a$
   (d) $b \rightarrow a$
   (e) $\sim a \vee b$

3. Which of the following statements corresponds to the given truth table?

a	b	
T	T	T
T	F	T
F	T	T
F	F	F

(a) $a \wedge b$
(b) $a \vee \sim b$
(c) $\sim a \wedge \sim b$
(d) $a \rightarrow \sim b$
(e) $\sim(\sim a \wedge \sim b)$

4. Let p: $x \in P$

  q: $x \in Q$,   where P and Q are sets

Which of the following sets would be described by the given truth table?

p	q	
T	T	T
T	F	T
F	T	F
F	F	T

(a) $P \cup Q$
(b) $P \cap Q$
(c) $P \cup Q'$
(d) $P' \cap Q$
(e) $(P \cup Q)'$

In exercises 5-10 choose the *letter or letters* corresponding to each statement which is equivalent to the given statement.

5. $a \rightarrow b$:

(a) $b \rightarrow a$
(b) $\sim b \rightarrow \sim a$
(c) $\sim a \rightarrow \sim b$
(d) $\sim a \vee b$
(e) $a \wedge \sim b$

6. $(a \wedge \sim a) \vee b$:

(a) a
(b) $a \wedge \sim b$
(c) $a \vee \sim a$
(d) b
(e) none of these

7. $\sim a \vee b$:

(a) $a \wedge \sim b$
(b) $\sim a \rightarrow b$
(c) $\sim(a \wedge \sim b)$
(d) $a \vee \sim b$
(e) none of these

8. $a \vee (b \wedge \sim a)$:

(a) $a \wedge \sim a$
(b) $a \vee \sim a$
(c) $a \vee b$
(d) $a \wedge b$
(e) $(a \vee b) \wedge (a \vee \sim a)$

9. $a \rightarrow (b \wedge c)$:   (a) $(a \rightarrow b) \wedge (b \rightarrow c)$
                                (b) $(a \rightarrow b) \wedge (a \rightarrow c)$
                                (c) $(a \rightarrow b) \vee (a \rightarrow c)$
                                (d) $\sim a \vee (b \wedge c)$
                                (e) $(\sim a \vee b) \wedge (\sim a \vee c)$

10. $a \rightarrow (b \rightarrow c)$:   (a) $a \rightarrow (b \wedge c)$
                                (b) $(a \rightarrow b) \wedge (b \rightarrow c)$
                                (c) $(a \wedge b) \rightarrow c$
                                (d) $(a \vee b) \rightarrow c$
                                (e) $(a \rightarrow b) \rightarrow c$

11. Determine whether or not the following statements are equivalent.
    (a) If I don't have the money, then I can't buy the car.
    (b) If I have the money, then I can buy the car.

12. Determine whether or not the following statements are equivalent.
    (a) If I don't get permission, I will go anyway.
    (b) I will get permission or I will go anyway.

13. Which of the following statements is equivalent to the statement, "If a team has good pitching, it will win the pennant"?
    (a) If a team doesn't have good pitching, it will not win the pennant.
    (b) If a team wins the pennant, it has good pitching.
    (c) A team has good pitching or it will not win the pennant.
    (d) If a team doesn't win the pennant, then it doesn't have good pitching.

9.6 MORE ON NEGATION

As we have seen in Section 9.3, to negate a statement is to say that the statement is false. To form the negation of a statement, we precede that statement with the words "It is false that." Symbolically, this is accomplished by preceding the entire statement (using parentheses where necessary) by the symbol "$\sim$."

Suppose, for example, we consider the negation of the statement, "John and Mary went to the store." Letting j: John went to the store, and m: Mary went to the store, then $j \wedge m$ would represent "John and Mary went to the store." To negate the statement $j \wedge m$, we simply write $\sim(j \wedge m)$, which is read, "It is false that John and Mary went to the store."

However, we would like to express the statement, "It is false that John and Mary went to the store" in another way. That is, we would like to find another statement which is *logically equivalent* to this statement. Since this statement is the negation of a conjunction, to find a logically equivalent statement, we need only look at the truth table for conjunction.

j	m	$j \wedge m$
T	T	T
T	F	F
F	T	F
F	F	F

Here we see that $j \wedge m$ is false when either j is false or m is false or both are false, that is, when either John didn't go to the store or Mary didn't go to the store or both didn't go to the store (rows 2, 3, and 4). This can all be expressed by the statement "John or Mary didn't go to the store." Symbolically this would be:

$$\sim j \ \vee \ \sim m$$

NEGATION OF A CONJUNCTION

In general, the negation of any conjunction, $\sim(a \wedge b)$, is logically equivalent to the disjunction $\sim a \ \vee \ \sim b$.

$\sim(a \wedge b)$ is logically equivalent to $\sim a \ \vee \ \sim b$

This can be proven by showing that both statements have the same truth table.

a	b	$a \wedge b$	$\sim(a \wedge b)$	$\sim a$	$\sim b$	$\sim a \ \vee \ \sim b$
T	T	T	F	F	F	F
T	F	F	T	F	T	T
F	T	F	T	T	F	T
F	F	F	T	T	T	T

Note

The *negation of a conjunction of two statements* (no matter how complex the two statements are) is logically equivalent to the *disjunction* of the *negations of EACH statement.*

Example 1

Write a statement logically equivalent to $\sim[a \wedge (b \rightarrow c)]$.

This is the negation of a conjunction which is logically equivalent to the disjunction:

$\sim a \lor \sim(b \to c)$ (Recall, both statements are negated.)

Let us now consider a similar procedure to arrive at a logically equivalent statement to the *negation of a disjunction,* $\sim(a \lor b)$. If we refer to the truth table for disjunction below, we see that $a \lor b$ is *false* only when *both* a and b are false (row 4). This can be expressed by the statement $\sim a \land \sim b$. That is, the negation of any disjunction, $\sim(a \lor b)$, is logically equivalent to the *conjunction* $\sim a \land \sim b$.

a	b	$a \lor b$
T	T	T
T	F	T
F	T	T
F	F	F

Let us now prove that $\sim(a \lor b)$ is logically equivalent to $\sim a \land \sim b$ by once again showing that both statements have the same truth table.

a	b	$a \lor b$	$\sim(a \lor b)$	$\sim a$	$\sim b$	$\sim a \land \sim b$
T	T	T	F	F	F	F
T	F	T	F	F	T	F
F	T	T	F	T	F	F
F	F	F	T	T	T	T

NEGATION OF A DISJUNCTION

$\sim(a \lor b)$ is logically equivalent to $\sim a \land \sim b$

Note

The *negation of a disjunction of two statements* (no matter how complex the two statements are) is logically equivalent to the *conjunction* of the *negations of EACH statement.*

Example 2

Write a statement logically equivalent to $\sim[(a \rightarrow b) \lor (b \rightarrow c)]$.

This is the negation of a disjunction, which is logically equivalent to the conjunction:

$\sim(a \rightarrow b) \land \sim(b \rightarrow c)$ (Recall, both statements are negated.)

Example 3

Write a statement logically equivalent to $\sim[a \lor (b \land c)]$.

A logically equivalent statement would be:

$$\sim a \land \sim(b \land c) \quad \text{(Why?)}$$

The negation procedure can be carried one step further by writing $\sim(b \land c)$ equivalently as $\sim b \lor \sim c$, thus obtaining the statement:

$$\sim a \land (\sim b \lor \sim c)$$

(Note that the parentheses are still kept to indicate correct groupings.)

Suppose we now consider the statement "John is not handsome." If we let h: John is handsome, then the given statement is symbolized $\sim h$. The negation of the statement "John is not handsome" would be "It is false that John is not handsome," symbolized $\sim(\sim h)$. This obviously says that John is handsome. That is, $\sim(\sim h)$ is logically equivalent to h.

DOUBLE NEGATION

In general, the negation of the negation of any statement is logically equivalent to that statement.

$$\sim(\sim a) \text{ is logically equivalent to } a.$$

Example 4

$$\sim[\sim(a \land b)] \text{ is logically equivalent to } a \land b.$$

Example 5

Write a statement logically equivalent to $\sim(a \lor \sim b)$.

$\sim(a \lor \sim b)$ is equivalent to $\sim a \land \sim(\sim b)$ (Negation of a
                                              disjunction)

Going one step further, since $\sim(\sim b)$ is equivalent to b (double negation), we have that:

$$\sim(a \ \vee \ \sim b) \text{ is logically equivalent to } \sim a \ \wedge \ b$$

Example 6

Negate the following statement, and write the negation in an equivalent form, carrying out the negation procedures as far as possible:

$$(a \ \vee \ \sim b) \ \wedge \ \sim c$$

The negation of the given statement is:

$$\sim[(a \ \vee \ \sim b) \ \wedge \ \sim c]$$

which is equivalent to:

$$\sim(a \ \vee \ \sim b) \ \vee \ \sim(\sim c) \qquad \text{(Negation of a conjunction)}$$

which is equivalent to:

$$\sim(a \ \vee \ \sim b) \ \vee \ c \qquad \text{(double negation)}$$

which is equivalent to:

$$[\sim a \ \wedge \ \sim(\sim b)] \ \vee \ c \qquad \text{(Negation of a disjunction)}$$

which is equivalent to:

$$(\sim a \ \wedge \ b) \ \vee \ c \qquad \text{(Double negation)}$$

We would now like to arrive at a logically equivalent statement to the negation of a conditional statement, $\sim(a \ \rightarrow \ b)$. If we refer to the truth table for the conditional below, we see that $a \ \rightarrow \ b$ is false only when the antecedent a is true *and* the consequent b is false. This can be expressed by the statement $a \ \wedge \ \sim b$. That is, the negation of a conditional statement, $\sim(a \ \rightarrow \ b)$, is logically equivalent to the *conjunction $a \ \wedge \ \sim b$.*

a	b	$a \rightarrow b$
T	T	T
T	F	F
F	T	T
F	F	T

To prove this, let us compare the truth tables for the statements $\sim(a \ \rightarrow \ b)$ and $a \ \wedge \ \sim b$.

a	b	$a \to b$	$\sim(a \to b)$	$\sim b$	$a \land \sim b$
T	T	T	F	F	F
T	F	F	T	T	T
F	T	T	F	F	F
F	F	T	F	T	F

NEGATION OF A CONDITIONAL

$\sim(a \to b)$ is logically equivalent to $a \land \sim b$

Note

The *negation of any conditional statement* is logically equivalent to the *conjunction* of the *antecedent* of that conditional statement and the *negation of the consequent.*

Example 7

Negate the statement $p \to \sim q$ and write the negation in an equivalent form.

The negation of $p \to \sim q$ is $\sim(p \to \sim q)$, which is equivalent to the conjunction of the antecedent p and the negation of the consequent, $\sim(\sim q)$. That is,

$\sim(p \to \sim q)$ is logically equivalent to $p \land \sim(\sim q)$

which is equivalent to:

$p \land q$ (Double negation)

Example 8

Negate the statement $\sim r \to s$ and write the negation in an equivalent form.

The negation of $\sim r \to s$ is $\sim(\sim r \to s)$, which is equivalent to the conjunction

$\sim r \land \sim s$ (Recall that the consequent is negated but the antecedent is not negated.)

Example 9

Write a statement logically equivalent to $\sim[(\sim a \lor b) \to (c \land d)]$

$\sim[(\sim a \ \lor \ b) \ \to \ (c \ \land \ d)]$ is logically equivalent to

$(\sim a \ \lor \ b) \ \land \ \sim(c \ \land \ d)$ (Negation of a conditional)

Recall once again that the antecedent $(\sim a \ \lor \ b)$ is not negated, but the consequent $(c \ \land \ d)$ is negated.

This statement above is in turn equivalent to:

$(\sim a \ \lor \ b) \ \land \ (\sim c \ \lor \ \sim d)$ (Negation of a conjunction.)

Example 10

What is meant by the statement, "It is false that if he studies, then he will pass the course"?

The meaning can easily be arrived at if we symbolize the above statements:

Letting s: He studies.
         p: He will pass the course.

then the symbolization of the above statement is $\sim(s \ \to \ p)$, which is logically equivalent to $s \ \land \ \sim p$ (negation of a conditional), which reads "He studies but will not pass the course."

Example 11

Given that the statement, "If it rains, then I will not take the car" has truth value "true" (T), what statement will have truth value "false" (F)?

We know that the negation of a statement has the opposite truth value. Thus we are looking for the negation of the above statement.

Let r: It rains.
    c: I will take the car.

Then the given statement is $r \ \to \ \sim c$ and its negation would be $\sim(r \ \to \ \sim c)$, which is logically equivalent to $r \ \land \ c$.

Thus the desired statement is, "It is raining and I will take the car."

Exercise Set 9.6

In exercises 1-10 negate the given statement, and write the negation in an equivalent form, carrying out the negation procedures as far as possible.

1. $\sim a \lor \sim b$ 6. $\sim k \lor (1 \to m)$

2. $a \land \sim b$ 7. $(\sim c \to d) \lor (c \to \sim d)$

3. $\sim a \to \sim b$ 8. $(p \land \sim q) \to (r \land s)$

4. $p \land (q \lor \sim r)$ 9. $\sim(\sim a \to b)$

5. $(r \land s) \to w$ 10. $u \to \sim(\sim p \leftrightarrow \sim s)$

11. Which of the following statements is the negation of the statement, "Martin will attend medical school and not be drafted."
    (a) Martin will attend medical school and be drafted.
    (b) Martin will not attend medical school or not be drafted.
    (c) Martin will not be drafted or will attend medical school.
    (d) Martin will not be drafted and will not attend medical school.
    (e) Martin will be drafted or not attend medical school.

12. The negation of the statement, "Tomorrow will be cloudy or it will rain" is:
    (a) Tomorrow will not be cloudy but it will rain.
    (b) If tomorrow is cloudy, then it won't rain.
    (c) Tomorrow will be cloudy and it will not rain.
    (d) Tomorrow will not be cloudy and it will not rain.
    (e) None of these.

13. If the statement, "If Mr. Jones was a good businessman, he would not have gone bankrupt" has truth value false (F), which of the following statements has truth value true (T)?
    (a) Mr. Jones was not a good businessman or he would not have gone bankrupt.
    (b) If Mr. Jones went bankrupt, then he was not a good businessman.
    (c) Mr. Jones was a good businessman but he went bankrupt.
    (d) Mr. Jones was not a good businessman and he did not go bankrupt.
    (e) Mr. Jones was not a good businessman and he went bankrupt.

REVIEW TEST FOR CHAPTER IX

Note: This test should be completed in 1 hour.

Choose the letter corresponding to the correct answer:

1. If a compound statement has five component statements, how many rows would there be in the truth table for this statement?
    (a) 4   (b) 10   (c) 25   (d) 32   (e) 16

2. A correct symbolization for the statement, "It is necessary to have good (r)eflexes to be a good basketball (p)layer" is:

   (a) $r \rightarrow p$ (b) $r \lor p$ (c) $p \rightarrow r$ (d) $p \land r$ (e) none of these

3. A correct symbolization for the statement, "Jim will grow (t)aller if he doesn't stay up (l)ate" is:

   (a) $t \rightarrow l$ (d) $\sim l \rightarrow t$
   (b) $t \rightarrow \sim l$ (e) $l \rightarrow t$
   (c) $t \leftrightarrow \sim l$

4. Which one of the following combinations of truth values can be used to show that the statement $a \lor (b \rightarrow c)$ is not a tautology?

   (a) a is true, b is true, c is true.
   (b) a is true, b is true, c is false.
   (c) a is false, b is false, c is false.
   (d) a is false, b is false, c is true.
   (e) a is false, b is true, c is false.

5. The truth table below corresponds to which of the following statements:

a	b	
T	T	F
T	F	T
F	T	T
F	F	T

   (a) $a \lor b$
   (b) $\sim b \rightarrow a$
   (c) $a \lor \sim b$
   (d) $a \rightarrow \sim b$
   (e) $a \land \sim b$

6. The truth table below corresponds to which of the following statements:

a	b	
T	T	F
T	F	T
F	T	T
F	F	F

   (a) $a \leftrightarrow b$
   (b) $\sim a \leftrightarrow \sim b$
   (c) $a \rightarrow \sim b$
   (d) $\sim a \land \sim b$
   (e) $a \leftrightarrow \sim b$

7. If $\sim a \lor b$ is a true statement, then which one of the following statements must also be true?

   (a) $b \rightarrow a$ (b) $\sim a \rightarrow b$ (c) $b \leftrightarrow a$ (d) $\sim b \rightarrow a$ (e) $\sim b \rightarrow \sim a$

8. Which one of the following statements is a tautology?

   (a) a (b) $a \land \sim a$ (c) $\sim a$ (d) $a \lor \sim a$ (e) none of these

   For questions 9, 10, and 11, assume that p and q are true and r is false.

9. The truth value of $\sim(p \lor \sim r)$ is: (a) true   (b) false.

10. The truth value of $(p \wedge \sim r) \leftrightarrow \sim q$ is: (a) true   (b) false.

11. The truth value of $(\sim r \rightarrow \sim p) \rightarrow [(\sim p \wedge \sim q) \rightarrow \sim r]$ is: (a) true   (b) false.

12. The negation of $\sim a \wedge (b \vee \sim c)$ is:
    (a) $a \wedge (\sim b \vee c)$ (d) $a \vee (\sim b \wedge c)$
    (b) $a \wedge (b \vee \sim c)$ (e) none of these
    (c) $\sim a \vee (b \wedge \sim c)$

13. The negation of $\sim a \rightarrow (b \wedge c)$ is:
    (a) $a \rightarrow (\sim b \vee \sim c)$ (d) $(b \wedge c) \rightarrow \sim a$
    (b) $a \wedge (\sim b \vee \sim c)$ (e) none of these
    (c) $\sim a \rightarrow \sim (b \wedge c)$

14. The statement $(a \wedge b) \rightarrow \sim a$ is a:
    (a) tautology   (b) contradiction   (c) neither

15. Given that a is true, then the truth value of $(a \vee b) \rightarrow (a \wedge b)$:
    (a) is true   (b) is false   (c) cannot be determined

16. If the statement $\sim p \rightarrow (q \wedge r)$ has truth value "true" and p has truth value "false" then the truth value of q:
    (a) is true   (b) is false   (c) cannot be determined

17. $\sim [\sim (p \wedge q)]$ is logically equivalent to:
    (a) $p \vee q$ (d) $\sim p \wedge \sim q$
    (b) $p \wedge q$ (e) none of
    (c) $\sim p \vee \sim q$ these

18. The negation of the statement, "John and Mary went to the store" is:
    (a) John and Mary didn't go to the store.
    (b) John or Mary didn't go to the store.
    (c) John went to the store but Mary didn't go to the store.
    (d) If John went to the store, then Mary did go.
    (e) None of these.

19. Assume the following two statements are true:
    "Smoking leads to lung cancer" and "Mr. Jones had lung cancer." Based upon these true statements, which statement below must be true?
    (a) Mr. Jones smoked.
    (b) Mr. Jones didn't smoke.
    (c) It cannot be determined whether Mr. Jones smoked or not.
    (d) Lung cancer occurs mostly in men.
    (e) Mr. Jones had a disease in his lungs when he was a boy.

20. Assume the following statement is true: "The game will not be played if it rains." Suppose the game was played. Which statement below must be true?
    (a) It rained.
    (b) It didn't rain.
    (c) It was sunny.
    (d) The players wanted to play.
    (e) None of these.

X PROBABILITY

10.1 INTRODUCTION

Throughout our lives we find ourselves trying to predict the outcome of future events. For example, we may ask such questions as, "What are the chances that the Yankees will win the pennant?"; "What are the chances that I'll get an A in this course?"; "What are the chances of drawing an ace in a card game?"; "What are the chances that I'll live to be 100?". This idea of chance in making predictions has application in many different fields. For example, predictions are constantly being made in gambling, in business, in medicine, and in psychology. Having application in so many different areas, it becomes necessary to define mathematically what is meant by chance or "probability," and how to measure it. In this chapter we will show how the probability of an event occurring is in some cases determined.

10.2 SAMPLE SPACE

Let us consider the experiment consisting of tossing a single coin. It is easy to see that there are two possible outcomes of this experiment, that of the coin turning up heads, and that of the coin turning up tails.

SAMPLE SPACE

The set whose elements are all the possible outcomes of an experiment is called a *sample space* for that experiment, and will be denoted by S.

Notation

We will let $n(S)$ denote the number of elements in S, that is the number of possible outcomes.

In the example given above the sample space would be

$$S = \{H, T\} \quad \text{and} \quad n(S) = 2$$

Example 1

Write a sample space for the experiment consisting of tossing a single die, having six faces marked by dots indicating the numbers 1 through 6 inclusive?

$$S = \{1, 2, 3, 4, 5, 6\}$$

Example 2

Write a sample space for the experiment consisting of tossing a coin three times in succession?

One possible outcome of this experiment would be a head on the first toss, a head on the second toss, and a head on the third toss. Another outcome would be a head on the first toss, a head on the second toss, and a tail on the third toss. Thus we can see that the sample space would consist of ordered triples such as (H, H, H) and (H, H, T). The entire sample space would be

$$S = \{(H, H, H), (H, H, T), (H, T, H), (H, T, T), (T, H, H), (T, H, T), (T, T, H), (T, T, T)\}$$

Here $n(S = 8$.

Example 3

Write a sample space for the experiment consisting of tossing a pair of dice?

One possible outcome would be a 1 on the first die and a 3 on the second die. This outcome would be different from the outcome consisting of a 3 on the first die and a 1 on the second die. (Think of this as if one die were red and the other green.) The sample space then would consist of 36 ordered pairs.

$$S = \{(1, 1), (1, 2), (1, 3), (1, 4), (1, 5), (1, 6)$$
$$(2, 1), (2, 2), (2, 3), (2, 4), (2, 5), (2, 6)$$
$$(3, 1), (3, 2), (3, 3), (3, 4), (3, 5), (3, 6)$$
$$(4, 1), (4, 2), (4, 3), (4, 4), (4, 5), (4, 6)$$
$$(5, 1), (5, 2), (5, 3), (5, 4), (5, 5), (5, 6)$$
$$(6, 1), (6, 2), (6, 3), (6, 4), (6, 5), (6, 6)\}$$

Here $n(S) = 36$.

AN EVENT

An *event* is a subset of the sample space of an experiment.

Example 4

Consider the experiment of example 1 above whose sample space was $S = \{1, 2, 3, 4, 5, 6\}$. Consider the event consisting of all outcomes in which the die turns up a number less than 3. Thus if we denote this event by E, we have

$$E = \{1, 2\}$$

Notation

$n(E)$ will denote the number of elements in the set E. Thus in example 4, $n(E) = 2$.

Example 5

Consider the experiment of example 2, whose sample space was

$$S = \{(H, H, H), (H, H, T), (H, T, H), (H, T, T), (T, H, H), (T, H, T),$$
$$(T, T, H), (T, T, T)\}$$

An event might be the set of all outcomes in which exactly two heads were obtained. Then

$$E = \{(H, H, T), (H, T, H), (T, H, H)\}$$

Here $n(E) = 3$.

Example 6

Consider the experiment of example 3, where $n(S) = 36$. An event here would be that of tossing a total of 7 on the pair of dice. Then

$$E = \{(1, 6), (2, 5), (3, 4), (4, 3), (5, 2), (6, 1)\}$$

Here $n(E) = 6$.

Exercise Set 10.2

In exercises 1-7 write a sample space for the given experiment.

1. A coin is tossed twice in succession.

2. A coin is tossed, then a die is tossed.

3. A bag contains three balls: one red, one white and one blue. One ball is chosen, replaced, and then a second ball is chosen.

4. Repeat the experiment of exercise 3 without replacing the first ball after it is chosen.

5. Two digits are to be drawn in succession from the numbers 1, 2, 3, 4 (without replacing a digit after it is drawn) to form a two-digit number.

6. From a group of four people, A, B, C, and D, a committee of two people is to be chosen by random selection.

7. A coin is tossed four times in succession.

8. For the sample space of exercise 3:
   (a) Let E be the event consisting of all outcomes in which both balls chosen are of the same color. Find $n(E)$.
   (b) Let F be the event consisting of all outcomes in which exactly one ball chosen is blue. Find $n(F)$.

9. Repeat exercise 8 using the sample space of exercise 4.

10. For the sample space of exercise 5:
    (a) List all outcomes in which both digits are odd.
    (b) List all outcomes in which one digit is even and the other odd.
    (c) List all outcomes in which the number formed is greater than 31.

11. For the sample space of exercise 6:
    (a) Let E be that event in which A is selected for the committee. Find $n(E)$.
    (b) Let F be that event in which either B or C is on the committee. Find $n(F)$.

12. For the sample space of exercise 7:
   (a) List all outcomes in which at least two heads turn up.
   (b) List all outcomes in which exactly two tails turn up.

10.3 PROBABILITY OF AN EVENT

Before we proceed with the definition of the probability of an event, we will assume throughout this chapter that *each outcome of an experiment can occur with equal likelihood.* For example, if we toss a die, we will assume the die is not "loaded," that is, each number is equally likely to turn up.

PROBABILITY OF AN EVENT

If a sample space S consists of $n(S)$ equally likely outcomes, then the probability of an event E, where $E \subseteq S$, denoted by $P(E)$, is defined as

$$P(E) = \frac{n(E)}{n(S)}$$

Example 1

What is the probability of obtaining exactly two heads upon three successive tosses of a coin?

If you recall from example 2 of the preceding section (10.2) $n(S) = 8$. In example 5 of that section we found $n(E) = 3$. Thus

$$P(E) = \frac{n(E)}{n(S)} = \frac{3}{8}$$

Example 2

What is the probability of tossing a total of 7 on a pair of dice?

If you recall from example 3 of the preceding section (10.2) $n(S) = 36$. Also in example 6 of that section we found $n(E) = 6$. Thus

$$P(E) = \frac{n(E)}{n(S)} = \frac{6}{36} = \frac{1}{6}$$

Example 3

Suppose a bag contains five red balls and three white balls. If one ball is to be chosen from the bag, what is the probability that it is red?

Here there are eight possible outcomes, that is, any one of eight different balls can be selected. We can think of these balls as being labeled in the following manner:

$$S = \{r_1, r_2, r_3, r_4, r_5, w_1, w_2, w_3\}$$

Thus $n(S) = 8$.

The event E consists of all outcomes in which a red ball is selected. That is, $E = \{r_1, r_2, r_3, r_4, r_5\}$ and $n(E) = 5$.

Thus

$$P(E) = \frac{n(E)}{n(S)} = \frac{5}{8}$$

Exercise Set 10.3

1. From an ordinary deck of 52 cards one card is to be drawn. What is the probability that
   (a) the card drawn is an ace?
   (b) the card drawn is the 7 of clubs?
   (c) the card drawn is a picture card?
   (d) the card drawn is a spade?

2. On a single toss of a pair of dice what is the probability of obtaining
   (a) a total of six?
   (b) a total greater than 4?
   (c) a total less than 4?
   (d) an even number on each die?
   (e) any total but 5?

3. There are four entrances to a building. If two men are to enter the building at random, what is the probability that they will use the same door?

4. One ball is to be chosen at random from a bag containing six red balls and ten green balls. What is the probability that the ball chosen is
   (a) red?   (b) green?   (c) blue?

5. A bag contains three balls: one white, one red, and one blue. One ball is chosen, replaced, and then a second ball is chosen. What is the probability that
   (a) both balls chosen are of the same color?
   (b) the two balls chosen are of different colors?
   (c) at least one ball chosen is blue?

6. Two digits are to be drawn in succession from the numbers 1, 2, 3, 4 (without replacing a digit after it is drawn) to form a two-digit number.

What is the probability that
(a) the number is odd?
(b) the number formed is greater than 31?
(c) the sum of the two digits is divisible by 5?

7. From a group of four people, A, B, C, D, a committee of two people is to be chosen by random selection. What is the probability that
(a) A is selected for the committee?
(b) A is not selected for the committee?
(c) B is selected but C is not selected?

8. A coin is tossed four times in succession. What is the probability of obtaining
(a) at least two heads?
(b) four tails?
(c) two heads and two tails?
(d) three heads and one tail?

9. If John, Mary, and Charlotte buy three tickets together for a basketball game, what is the probability that John and Mary sit next to one another if they all select their seats at random?

10. Suppose a bag contains four balls numbered 1, 2, 3, and 4. If two balls are chosen at random from the bag, what is the probability that their difference is 1?

10.4 $P(E \cup F)$: MUTUALLY EXCLUSIVE EVENTS

What is the probability of tossing a total of 7 or 11 on a pair of dice? The event E in this case would be the set

$$E = \{(1, 6), (2, 5), (3, 4), (4, 3), (5, 2), (6, 1), (5, 6), (6, 5)\}$$

Since we know that $n(S) = 36$, we would obtain

$$P(E) = \tfrac{8}{36} = \tfrac{2}{9}$$

This result could have been obtained by considering the event given as the union of two events, that of tossing a total of 7 and that of tossing a total of 11. The probability of tossing a total of 7 is $\tfrac{6}{36}$ and the probability of tossing an 11 is $\tfrac{2}{36}$. Adding these two results, we obtain $\tfrac{6}{36} + \tfrac{2}{36} = \tfrac{8}{36} = \tfrac{2}{9}$. The fact that enables us to simply add the probability of tossing a 7 to the probability of tossing an 11 to obtain the probability of tossing a 7 or an 11 is that on any *single* toss of the dice it is possible for a total of 7 to turn up or a total of 11 to turn up but never can both a 7 and an 11 turn up.

MUTUALLY EXCLUSIVE EVENTS

If two events E and F have no outcome in common, that is, if $E \cap F = \emptyset$, then these events are said to be *mutually exclusive*.

In the example above if we let E be the event consisting of all outcomes in which a total of 7 turns up, and F be the event consisting of all outcomes in which a total of 11 turns up, then

$$E = \{(1, 6), (2, 5), (3, 4), (4, 3), (5, 2), (6, 1)\}$$

$$F = \{(5, 6), (6, 5)\}$$

$$E \cap F = \emptyset,$$

that is, E and F are *mutually exclusive*.

$$P(E \cup F) = P(E) + P(F) = \tfrac{6}{36} + \tfrac{2}{36} = \tfrac{8}{36} = \tfrac{2}{9}$$

We can now state the following general result

If E and F are mutually exclusive events, then

$$P(E \cup F) = P(E) + P(F)$$

Example 1

Suppose a bag contains 5 red balls, 10 green balls, 15 orange balls, and 15 yellow balls. If one ball is to be chosen from the bag, what is the probability that it will be red or green?

Here $n(S) = 45$. If R is the event consisting of all outcomes in which a red ball is selected and G, that of selecting a green ball, then since we cannot select both a red and a green ball, R and G are *mutually exclusive events*.

Now $n(R) = 5, n(G) = 10$ and thus

$$P(R \cup G) = P(R) + P(G)$$

$$= \tfrac{5}{45} + \tfrac{10}{45}$$

$$= \tfrac{15}{45}$$

$$= \tfrac{1}{3}$$

In example 2 of Section 10.3 we calculated the probability of tossing a total of 7 on a pair of dice to be $\tfrac{1}{6}$. Suppose we ask the question, "What is the probability that a total of 7 does not turn up?", or stated another way, "What is the probability of obtaining any total but 7?" We could consider this event as the union of *10 mutually exclusive events,*

$$2 \cup 3 \cup 4 \cup 5 \cup 6 \cup 8 \cup 9 \cup 10 \cup 11 \cup 12$$

and add the probabilities of these 10 events.

$$P(2) = \tfrac{1}{36}, \quad P(8) = \tfrac{5}{36}$$

$$P(3) = \tfrac{2}{36}, \quad P(9) = \tfrac{4}{36}$$

$$P(4) = \tfrac{3}{36}, \quad P(10) = \tfrac{3}{36}$$

$$P(5) = \tfrac{4}{36}, \quad P(11) = \tfrac{2}{36}$$

$$P(6) = \tfrac{5}{36}, \quad P(12) = \tfrac{1}{36}$$

Adding these results, we obtain the desired probability to be

$$\tfrac{30}{36} = \tfrac{5}{6}$$

This problem can be approached in another way if we observe the following facts:

(1) If we take the sample space S to be the universal set for this discussion, and let E be the set of all outcomes in which a total of 7 turns up, then the event that we are considering here, that of any total but 7 turning up would be E', *the complement of E.*
(2) $E \cup E' = S = U$
$E \cap E' = \emptyset$, implying that E and E' are mutually exclusive events.
(3) Then

$$\left.\begin{array}{c} P(E \cup E') \\ \text{or} \\ P(S) \end{array}\right\} = P(E) + P(E')$$

(4) $P(S) = \frac{n(S)}{n(S)} = 1$. That is, the probability of obtaining an outcome in the sample space is 1. In this problem this means that the probability of *some total* from 2 to 12 turning up is 1.
(5) Thus $P(E) + P(E') = 1$, but we know $P(E) = \tfrac{1}{6}$.

(6) Therefore

$$\tfrac{1}{6} + P(E') = 1$$
$$P(E') = 1 - \tfrac{1}{6} = \tfrac{5}{6}$$

We can summarize the results of the above problem with the following general statements:

A. The probability of an event that is certain to occur is 1.
B. If E' is the complement of an event E in a sample space S, then $P(E) + P(E') = 1$.

Example 2

If a single card is to be chosen from an ordinary deck of 52 cards, what is the probability that it will be an ace or a king? What is the probability that it will not be an ace or a king?

(a) $N(S) = 52$
Letting A be the set of aces and K, the set of kings we have $n(A) = 4$, $n(K) = 4$ and $A \cap K = \emptyset$. Thus $P(A \cup K) = P(A) + P(K) = \tfrac{4}{52} + \tfrac{4}{52} = \tfrac{8}{52} = \tfrac{2}{13}$

(b) The set consisting of those outcomes in which an ace or a king is not chosen would be the complement of $A \cup K$, that is, $(A \cup K)'$. Thus the probability that the card is not an ace or a king is

$$1 - P(A \cup K) = 1 - \tfrac{2}{13} = \tfrac{11}{13}$$

Example 3

What is the probability of tossing a total of 13 on a pair of dice?

Again $n(S) = 36$. However $E = \emptyset$, for there are no outcomes consisting of a total of 13. Thus

$$P(E) = \frac{n(E)}{n(S)} = \tfrac{0}{36} = 0$$

We can now make two more general statements.

C. The probability of an impossible event is 0.
D. The probability of any event E is always greater than or equal to 0 and less than or equal to 1. That is, $0 \leqslant P(E) \leqslant 1$.

10.5 $P(E \cup F)$: NONMUTUALLY EXCLUSIVE EVENTS

NONMUTUALLY EXCLUSIVE EVENTS

We may want to know the probability that E or F will occur where E and F are *not mutually exclusive*, that is, they have at least one outcome in common. For example, we may ask, "What is the probability that at least one die shows a 3 upon tossing a pair of dice?" Again there are 36 outcomes in the sample space. If E is the set of outcomes in which the first die turns up 3, then $n(E) = 6$, and if F is the set of outcomes in which the second die turns up 3, then $n(F) = 6$ (see Figure 10.1).

(1, 1), (1, 2),	(1, 3),	(1, 4), (1, 5), (1, 6),
(2, 1), (2, 2),	(2, 3),	(2, 4), (2, 5), (2, 6),
(3, 1), (3, 2),	(3, 3),	(3, 4), (3, 5), (3, 6),
(4, 1), (4, 2),	(4, 3),	(4, 4), (4, 5), (4, 6),
(5, 1), (5, 2),	(5, 3),	(5, 4), (5, 5), (5, 6),
(6, 1), (6, 2),	(6, 3),	(6, 4), (6, 5), (6, 6)

FIGURE 10.1

We can see that the intersection of these two events, $E \cap F$, is the set $\{(3, 3)\}$ and thus if we were to simply add the probability that the first die turns up 3 to the probability that the second die turns up 3, then we will have counted the probability of both dice turning up 3, that is $P(E \cap F)$, twice. Therefore to correct for this we must subtract the probability of $E \cap F$ (once). Thus in this case

$$P(E \cup F) = P(E) + P(F) - P(E \cap F)$$

$$= \frac{6}{36} + \frac{6}{36} - \frac{1}{36}$$

$$= \frac{11}{36}$$

We can summarize the above with the following general result:

If events E and F are not mutually exclusive, then

$$P(E \cup F) = P(E) + P(F) - P(E \cap F)$$

Example 1

If one card is to be chosen from an ordinary deck of 52 cards, what is the probability that it will be red or a king?

Here $n(S) = 52$.

There are 26 red cards in the deck (13 diamonds and 13 hearts). Thus if R is that event of choosing a red card, we have $n(R) = 26$. There are four kings in the deck so that if K is that event of choosing a king, $n(K) = 4$. The sets R and K are not mutually exclusive for there are two red kings (king of diamonds and king of hearts). Thus

$$P(R \cup K) = P(R) + P(K) - P(E \cap K)$$
$$= \tfrac{26}{52} + \tfrac{4}{52} - \tfrac{2}{52}$$
$$= \tfrac{28}{52} = \tfrac{7}{13}$$

Exercise Set 10.5

1. Upon a single toss of a pair of dice, what is the probability
   (a) of obtaining a total of 5 or 8?
   (b) of not obtaining a total of 5 or 8?

2. If the probability that John will throw a strike on any given pitch of a base-ball is $\tfrac{5}{7}$, what is the probability of his throwing a ball?

3. Upon drawing one card from an ordinary deck of 52 cards, what is the probability that this card will be
   (a) a queen or a king?
   (b) a diamond or a picture card?
   (c) a red card or not a picture card?

4. Suppose there are 1000 students in a certain school. On a given Saturday there was a football game in the afternoon and a basketball game at night. 800 of the students attended the football game, 400 attended the basketball game, and 300 attended both games. If one student from the school is selected at random on the following Monday morning, what is the proba-bility that
   (a) he or she attended the basketball game?
   (b) he or she attended at least one of the games?
   (c) he or she attended neither of the games?

5. Suppose a bag contains five white balls, seven green balls, eight red balls and ten blue balls. If one ball is to be chosen at random, what is the probability that it will be
   (a) red or green?
   (b) white or blue?

6. Upon surveying a class of 30 students it was found that 10 students were taking history, 12 were taking mathematics and 10 were taking English.

Three students were taking both history and mathematics and four students were taking both mathematics and English. If one student were chosen at random, what is the probability that he or she is taking
(a) mathematics?
(b) English?
(c) history or mathematics?
(d) mathematics or English?

7. If a letter of the alphabet is chosen at random, what is the probability that it will be
(a) a vowel?
(b) a letter in the word committee?
(c) a vowel or a letter from a to g?

8. Of 150 people that ate dinner in a certain restaurant on a given evening, 70 people had meat, 60 had salad, and 20 of those people that had meat also had salad. If one person from the people that had dinner were chosen at random, what is the probability that he or she
(a) had meat or salad?
(b) had neither meat nor salad?

10.6 $P(E \cap F)$: INDEPENDENT EVENTS

INDEPENDENT EVENTS

Two events are said to be *independent* if the happening of one in no way affects the happening of the other.

Suppose we have two bags, each containing three balls, one white, one red, and one blue. If one ball is selected from each bag what is the probability that the first ball selected is red and the second ball white? The sample space would be

$$S = \{(w, w), (w, r), (w, b), (r, w), (r, r), (r, b), (b, w), (b, r), (b, b)\}$$

and we can see that the probability that the first ball selected is red and the second white, $E = \{(r, w)\}$, is $\frac{1}{9}$.

This problem could have been approached by letting R be the event of selecting a red ball from the first bag and W, the event of selecting a white ball from the second bag. We should note that R and W are independent events, for selecting a red ball from the first bag no way affects the selection of a white ball from the second bag. $P(R) = \frac{1}{3}$, $P(W) = \frac{1}{3}$ and upon multiplying these results we would obtain the probability of R *and* W (or $P(R \cap W)$) to be $(\frac{1}{3})(\frac{1}{3}) = \frac{1}{9}$.

The above problem is an illustration of the following general statement:

If two events E and F are independent, then
$P(E \cap F) = P(E)P(F)$.

Example 1

If a pair of dice are tossed twice, what is the probability of a total of 7 turning up both times?

The probability of obtaining a total of 7 on the first toss is $\frac{1}{6}$ (example 2, Section 10.3). The probability of obtaining a total of 7 on the second toss is also $\frac{1}{6}$ (the first toss no way affects the second toss). The two events being independent, the probability that both tosses result in a total of 7 is $(\frac{1}{6})(\frac{1}{6}) = \frac{1}{36}$.

We can extend the general result of this section to include *any number* of independent events. For example,

If E, F, G are independent events, then
$P(E \cap F \cap G) = P(E)P(F)P(G)$

Example 2

What is the probability of tossing a head each time on four successive tosses of a coin?

The probability of the coin turning up heads on any given toss is $\frac{1}{2}$ (the outcome on any given toss of the coin does not affect the outcome on any other toss). Thus the probability of obtaining four heads is

$$(\tfrac{1}{2})(\tfrac{1}{2})(\tfrac{1}{2})(\tfrac{1}{2}) = \tfrac{1}{16}$$

Example 3

Suppose it is determined that the probability of Tom throwing a strike whenever he pitches a baseball is $\frac{3}{8}$. If Tom throws two pitches, what is the probability that one will be a strike and the other a ball?

(1) By what we know about complementary events, the probability of throwing a ball on any given pitch is $1 - \frac{3}{8} = \frac{5}{8}$.
(2) Tom can throw a strike and a ball by

(a) throwing a strike on the first pitch and a ball on the second; or

(b) throwing a ball on the first pitch and a strike on the second.

(3) Since the outcome on the first pitch no way affects the outcome on the second pitch, the probability of (a) occurring is $(\frac{3}{8})(\frac{5}{8})$ = $\frac{15}{64}$, and the probability of (b) occurring is $(\frac{5}{8})(\frac{3}{8})$ = $\frac{15}{64}$.

(4) Now since on any *two* pitches both (a) and (b) cannot occur, that is, since (a) and (b) are mutually exclusive events, the probability of throwing a strike and a ball is $\frac{15}{64}$ + $\frac{15}{64}$ = $\frac{30}{64}$ = $\frac{15}{32}$.

Exercise Set 10.6

1. If the probability of John winning a certain game is $\frac{1}{4}$ and the probability of Ken winning another game is $\frac{2}{5}$, what is the probability that
   (a) both John and Ken will win?
   (b) John will win and Ken will lose?
   (c) both John and Ken will lose?

2. If a pair of dice is tossed three times, what is the probability that a total of 9 will turn up on each toss?

3. If a coin is tossed three times, what is the probability of obtaining a head on each of the first two tosses and a tail on the third toss?

4. Suppose a bag contains five white, seven green and eight red balls. If one ball is selected at random, replaced, and a second one chosen, what is the probability that
   (a) both are white?
   (b) both are red or both are white?
   (c) both are the same color?

5. If a pair of dice is tossed twice, what is the probability of obtaining a 7 or an 11 on both tosses?

6. A box contains five cards: the two of spades, the two of clubs, the four of hearts, the four of diamonds, and the seven of spades. If two cards are to be drawn from the box, the first one replaced before the second one is chosen, what is the probability that
   (a) both cards will be red?
   (b) the first card will be a two and the second a four?
   (c) both cards will be the same color?
   (d) one will be a spade and the other a club?

7. If the probability of Martin passing an exam is $\frac{4}{5}$, that of Mary passing the same exam $\frac{1}{5}$ and that of Christine passing this exam $\frac{3}{5}$, what is the probability that of these three students exactly two will pass the exam?

8. One bag contains five red balls and ten green balls and a second bag contains six red balls and nine green balls. If one ball is drawn from each bag, what is the probability that
    (a) both are red?
    (b) both are of the same color?
    (c) one is red and the other green?

9. Suppose it is determined that the probability of Lew making a foul shot any time he shoots one in a basketball game is $\frac{3}{4}$. The next time Lew takes two foul shots, what is the probability that
    (a) he makes both shots?
    (b) he misses both shots?
    (c) he makes one and misses the other?

10. Tom and Bill practice shooting at a moving target. If the probability that Tom hits the target is $\frac{7}{10}$ and the probability that Bill hits the target is $\frac{4}{10}$, what is the probability, when both shoot simultaneously, that at least one of them hits the target?

11. From an ordinary deck of 52 cards, three cards are drawn in succession, replacing each one before the next is drawn. What is the probability that
    (a) all are diamonds?
    (b) all are jacks or aces?
    (c) all are one suit?

REVIEW TEST FOR CHAPTER X

Note: This test should be completed in 75 minutes.

1. If a coin is tossed eight times in succession, what is the probability of tossing a head on the seventh toss?

2. If three coins are tossed, what is the probability that the three will land heads or the three will land tails?

3. If one card is drawn from an ordinary deck of 52 cards, replaced, and a second card drawn, what is the probability of drawing two aces?

4. Suppose an exam has two multiple choice questions, with four possible answers to each question. If you guess the answer to each question, what is the probability that you guess
    (a) the first answer correctly?
    (b) the first answer incorrectly?
    (c) both answers correctly?
    (d) the first or the second answer correctly?

5. One thousand raffle tickets have been sold. You have bought 10 tickets. If two prizes are to be awarded and the first ticket drawn is not replaced, what is the probability
   (a) of your winning the first prize?
   (b) that if you don't win the first prize, you win the second prize?

6. If in problem 5 above the first ticket drawn *is replaced*, what is the probability that
   (a) you will win both prizes?
   (b) you will win the first or the second prize?

7. Suppose it is known that 1 out of every 100 cars produced in a certain plant has a defect in its braking system. What is the probability that two successive cars produced in this plant will have a defect in their braking systems?

8. A man owns a house in the city and a cabin in the mountains. In any one year the probability of the house being burglarized is $\frac{1}{100}$ and the probability of the cabin being burglarized is $\frac{2}{100}$. For any one year, what is the probability that
   (a) both will be burglarized?
   (b) one or the other will be burglarized?
   (c) neither will be burglarized?

9. An insurance company made a survey and found that for every 1000 cars insured in a given year, 100 will be involved in an accident, 50 will be stolen, and 30 of those stolen will be involved in an accident. What is the probability that an insured car is
   (a) stolen?
   (b) involved in an accident?
   (c) stolen or involved in an accident?
   (d) neither stolen nor involved in an accident?

ANSWERS

Chapter I

Exercise Set 1.2

1. (a) Saturday, Sunday
   (b) 13, 23, 33, 43
   (c) January, June, July
   (d) a, e, i, o, u
   (f) i, n, t, e, r, s, c, o
   (g) 10, 15, 20, 25, 30, 35
2. (a) The set of the first four letters of the English alphabet.
   (b) The set of days of the week beginning with the letter T.
   (c) The set of whole numbers between 1 and 43 that end in 2.
   (d) The set of months of the year that begin with the letter A.
   (e) The set of playing positions on a men's basketball team.

Exercise Set 1.3

1. (c) $\{1, 2, 3, 4\}$ (d) $\{4, 5, 6, 7, \ldots\}$ (e) $\{5, 10, 15, 20, \ldots\}$
2. (a) $\{x \mid x$ is a whole number between 0 and 6$\}$
   (b) $\{x \mid x$ is a positive whole number greater than 10$\}$
   (c) $\{x \mid x$ is a state in the U.S.A. beginning with the letter K$\}$
   (d) $\{x \mid x$ is a number between 10 and 100 that is divisible by 11$\}$
   (e) $\{x \mid x$ is a positive number divisible by 10$\}$
3. (a) $\{x \mid x$ is the first President of the United States$\}$
   (b) $\{$South Carolina, South Dakota$\}$
   (c) $\{x \mid x$ is a positive even number$\}$
   (d) $\{$pitcher, catcher, 1st base, 2nd base, 3rd base, shortstop, left field, right field, center field$\}$
   (e) $\{x \mid x$ is a suit in an ordinary deck of playing cards$\}$
4. (a) true   (b) true   (c) false   (d) true   (e) false

Exercise Set 1.4

| 1. false | 3. true | 5. false | 7. true | 9. true |
| 2. false | 4. true | 6. true | 8. true | 10. false |

345

11. {10, 12, 14, 16, 18}
12. {x | x is an odd integer between 6 and 14 }
13. {x | x is an integer between 0 and −6}
14. {0, 1, 2, 3, 4, . . .}
15. {x | x is an odd integer between 1 and 40 that is divisible by 3 }
16. {0, +2, −2, +4, −4, +6, −6, . . .}   20. false
17. $\frac{103}{9}$ 21. true
18. $\frac{23}{99}$ 22. false
19. true   23. false

Exercise Set 1.5

1. finite	9. infinite	17. true
2. infinite	10. finite	18. false
3. finite	11. no	19. true
4. finite	12. yes	20. true
5. finite	13. no	21. false
6. infinite	14. no	22. true
7. finite	15. no	23. false
8. finite	16. false	

Exercise Set 1.6

1. false	5. true	9. false
2. false	6. false	10. true
3. false	7. true	
4. true	8. true	

*11. $U = \{x$ | x is a letter of the English alphabet}
*12. $U = \{-7, -5, -3, -1, 0, 2, 4, 6, 8\}$
*13. $U = \{x$ | x is a make of General Motors' cars}
14. $\emptyset$, {1}, {3}, {1, 3}; $\emptyset$, {1}, {3}
15. $\emptyset$, {a}, {b}, {c}, {d}, {a, b}, {a, c}, {a, d}, {b, c}, {b, d}, {c, d}, {a, b, c}, {a, b, d}, {a, c, d}, {b, c, d}, {a, b, c, d}; all but {a, b, c, d}
16. $A \subset U, B \subset U, C \subset U, D \subset U, D \subset A, D \subset B, D \subset C$

Exercise Set 1.7

1. 2, 4	9. 6, 8, 10	17. A
2. 1, 3, 4, 5, 6, 7, 9	10. 2	18. U
3. 1, 3, 5, 7, 9	11. {2, 3, 5, 6}	19. A
4. $\emptyset$	12. U	20. $\emptyset$
5. 1, 3, 5, 6, 7, 8, 9, 10	13. U	21. A
6. 2, 4, 6, 7, 8, 9, 10	14. $\emptyset$	22. A'
7. 2, 4, 6	15. U	
8. 2, 8, 10	16. U	

*Many choices are possible.

23. The set of all automobiles which are not Volkswagens.
24. The set of all Volkswagens with an exterior color of white (set of all white Volkswagens).
25. The set of all automobiles which are Volkswagens or have automatic transmissions.
26. The set of all Volkswagens which do not have an exterior color of white.
27. The set of all automobiles which do not have automatic transmission and a white exterior color.
28. The set of all Volkswagens with automatic transmission.
29. (e)   30. (b)   31. (a)   32. (c)

Exercise Set 1.8

1.
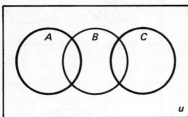

2.
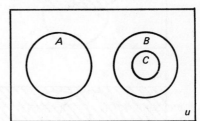

3.
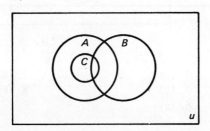

4. (a)   6. (e)
5. (d)   7. (a)

8.
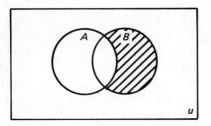

9.
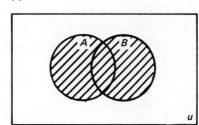

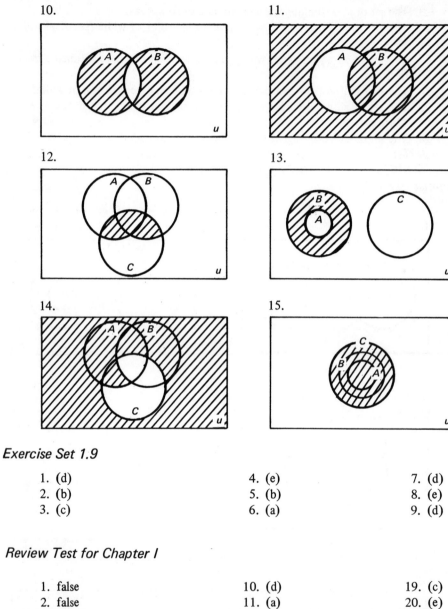

10.   11.

12.   13.

14.   15.

Exercise Set 1.9

1. (d)	4. (e)	7. (d)
2. (b)	5. (b)	8. (e)
3. (c)	6. (a)	9. (d)

Review Test for Chapter I

1. false	10. (d)	19. (c)
2. false	11. (a)	20. (e)
3. false	12. (a)	21. (b)
4. false	13. (d)	22. (c)
5. false	14. (c)	23. (e)
6. false	15. (b)	24. (b)
7. false	16. (e)	25. (b)
8. true	17. (a)	
9. (b)	18. (b)	

Chapter II

Exercise Set 2.1

10. $\frac{9}{24}, \frac{10}{24}$ (Many other answers are possible.)

Exercise Set 2.2

1. >	5. >	9. <
2. <	6. >	10. >
3. <	7. =	
4. =	8. =	

11.

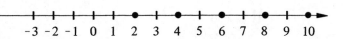

12.

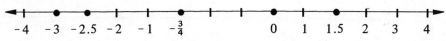

13.

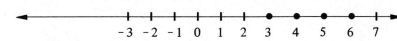

14. ∅

15.

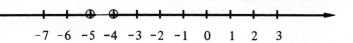

16.

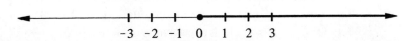

17.

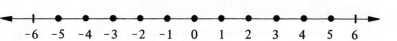

18.

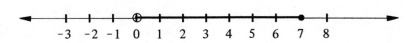

19. ∅

20.

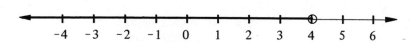

21.

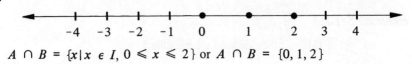

$A \cap B = \{x | x \in I, 0 \leqslant x \leqslant 2\}$ or $A \cap B = \{0, 1, 2\}$

22.

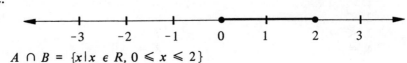

$A \cap B = \{x | x \in R, 0 \leqslant x \leqslant 2\}$

23. $A \cap B = \emptyset$

24.

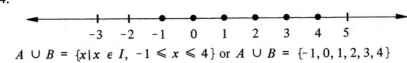

$A \cup B = \{x | x \in I, -1 \leqslant x \leqslant 4\}$ or $A \cup B = \{-1, 0, 1, 2, 3, 4\}$

25.

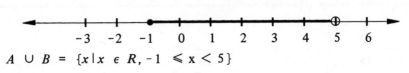

$A \cup B = \{x | x \in R, -1 \leqslant x < 5\}$

26.

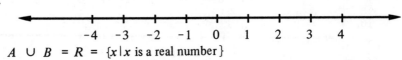

$A \cup B = R = \{x | x$ is a real number$\}$

27. (a)

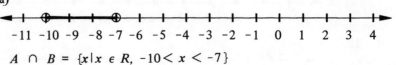

$A \cap B = \{x | x \in R, -10 < x < -7\}$

(b)

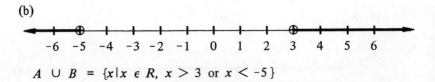

$A \cup B = \{x | x \in R, x > 3$ or $x < -5\}$

28. (a) $A \cap B = \emptyset$ (b) $A \cup B = \{x | x \in R, -4 < x < 2\}$
29. $\{x | x \in R, x < 0 \text{ or } x \geq 1\}$
30. $\{x | x \in I, -4 \leq x \leq 2\}$ or $\{-4, -3, -2, -1, 0, 1, 2\}$
31. $\{x | x \in R, -3 < x \leq 4\}$ 32. $\{x | x \in R, x < -2\}$
33. $\{x | x \in I, -1 \leq x \leq 1 \text{ or } x \in R, x \geq 3\}$

Exercise Set 2.3

1. yes
2. yes
3. no
4. yes
5. no
6. yes
7. -91
8. 37
9. -11
10. $\frac{1}{2}$
11. $5\frac{3}{8}$
12. -6
13. -3.715
14. $-\sqrt{2}$
15. $-(3 + 9)$ or -12
16. $\frac{1}{7}$
17. $\frac{1}{-7}$
18. $\frac{1}{\sqrt{3}}$
19. $\frac{1}{\frac{3}{5}}$ (or $\frac{5}{3}$)
20. $\frac{1}{.4}$
21. No inverse exists.
22. $\frac{3}{4}$
23. 1
24. $\frac{1}{-1}$ (or -1)

25. 7
26. -7
27. $\frac{1}{3\frac{1}{2}}$ (or $\frac{2}{7}$)
28. closure
29. additive identity
30. commutative law of addition
31. associative law of addition
32. additive inverse
33. multiplicative identity
34. distributive law
35. distributive law
36. commutative law of multiplication
37. multiplicative identity
38. multiplicative inverse
39. commutative law of multiplication
40. additive inverse
41. associative law of addition
42. distributive law
43. false
44. false
45. true
46. false
47. true

Exercise Set 2.4

1. 8
2. 0
3. 2
4. 3
5. -2
6. -5
7. -4
8. -5
9. -5
10. -1
11. 3
12. -8
13. -1
14. -3
15. 2

Exercise Set 2.5

1. 8
2. $\frac{3}{2}$
3. 0
4. 5
5. 0.37
6. 0.25

7. (a) commutative law   (c) Rule II(a)
   (b) associative law   (d) Rule IV(a)
8. (a) definition of subtraction (c) Rule II(a)
   (b) associative law   (d) Rule III(a)
9. (a) commutative law   (c) Rule II(a)
   (b) associative law   (d) Rule IV(a)
10. (a) definition of subtraction (d) Rule II(a)
    (b) commutative law   (e) Rule IV(a)
    (c) associative law
11. (a) definition of absolute value (e) associative law
    (b) associative law   (f) Rule IV(a)
    (c) definition of subtraction   (g) Rule II(a)
    (d) Rule IV(a)

12. 19	19. −2	26. −1	33. −6	40. 0
13. 6	20. 2	27. 0	34. 9	41. −19
14. −3	21. 2	28. −22	35. −3	42. 13
15. −15	22. 25	29. 12	36. 31	
16. −12	23. 5	30. 5	37. 2	
17. 0	24. 40	31. 6	38. 22	
18. 8	25. 12	32. −7	39. 6	

Exercise Set 2.6A

1. 25	6. −45	11. 1	16. 54	21. −30
2. −6	7. 12	12. 0	17. 3	22. 22
3. 0	8. 81	13. 20	18. 9	
4. 65	9. 240	14. 15	19. 20	
5. 24	10. 30	15. −45	20. 17	

Exercise Set 2.6B

1. $15 \cdot \frac{1}{4}$	5. $\frac{1}{7} \cdot 0$	9. $\frac{1}{9}$	13. $-\frac{7}{5}$
2. $\frac{5}{8}$	6. $\frac{7}{6}$	10. $\frac{3}{8}$	14. −196
3. $\frac{1}{13} \cdot 18$	7. $\frac{4}{11}$	11. 0	15. 1
4. $\frac{-12}{5}$	8. $-\frac{1}{2}$	12. 1	16. 3

Exercise Set 2.6C

1. 8	5. 3	9. $-\frac{5}{4}$	13. 0
2. −4	6. $\frac{3}{2}$	10. $\frac{10}{3}$	14. $-\frac{25}{3}$
3. $\frac{2}{9}$	7. $\frac{1}{2}$	11. $-\frac{25}{12}$	15. $\frac{1}{36}$
4. $\frac{1}{4}$	8. $\frac{2}{5}$	12. $\frac{8}{3}$	16. $\frac{9}{25}$

Exercise Set 2.6D

1. -30
2. 2
3. $\frac{13}{2}$
4. $-\frac{1}{2}$
5. -510
6. $\frac{3}{4}$
7. 3
8. 24

9. -3
10. -3
11. 0
12. $\frac{5}{12}$
13. 24
14. 6
15. 30
16. 11

17. $-\frac{22}{3}$
18. $-\frac{7}{27}$
19. -24
20. 10
21. $-\frac{5}{21}$
22. $\frac{64}{3}$
23. 6
24. $-\frac{1}{6}$

25. $\frac{6}{5}$
26. -1
27. 100
28. -27
29. undefined
30. $-\frac{3}{2}$

Exercise Set 2.7

1. yes
2. no
3. yes
4. no
5. no
6. no
7. no
8. yes
9. yes
10. no

11. $\frac{19}{6}$
12. $\frac{9}{4}$
13. $\frac{14}{15}$
14. $-\frac{11}{8}$
15. $-\frac{7}{12}$
16. $\frac{11}{6}$
17. $-\frac{19}{24}$

18. $\frac{97}{36}$
19. $\frac{267}{40}$
20. $\frac{25}{6}$
21. $-\frac{1}{8}$
22. $\frac{17}{60}$
23. 1
24. $-\frac{1}{9}$

25. -11
26. $\frac{29}{15}$
27. $-\frac{5}{3}$
28. $-\frac{69}{2}$
29. $-\frac{17}{12}$
30. $\frac{5}{16}$

Review Test for Chapter II

1. 0
2. negative
3. -11
4. 1
5. $\frac{8}{3}$
6. $+$
7. distributive law
8. closure

9. -16
10. $\frac{2}{9}$
11. false
12. false
13. true
14. false
15. $\frac{13}{84}$

16. $\frac{1}{6}, \frac{1}{5}, \frac{1}{3}, \frac{1}{2}, \frac{5}{6}$

17.
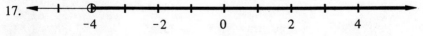

18. (a) $\{x \mid x \in R, x \geqslant -2\}$ (b) $\{x \mid x \in R, 3 < x \leqslant 5\}$
19. $\{-5, -4, 1, 2, 3\}$
20. $\emptyset$
21. -3
22. $\frac{21}{8}$

23. $\frac{4}{5}$
24. -4
25. 9

Chapter III

Exercise Set 3.2

1. 8
2. 9
3. -32
4. 9
5. $\frac{27}{64}$
6. $-\frac{1}{32}$
7. -125
8. 256
9. -162
10. 9
11. -5
12. -2
13. 64
14. 20,736
15. $-2^4 = -16; (-2)^4 = +16$

16. $\left(\frac{2}{3}\right)^3 = \frac{8}{27}; \frac{2^3}{3} = \frac{8}{3}$
17. $5x^3 = (5)x^3; (5x)^3 = (125)x^3$
18. $-6a^2 = (-6)a^2; (-6a)^2 = 36a^2$
19. $27x^3$
20. $-27y^3$
21. $16x^4$
22. $-72x^2$
23. $2000y^3$
24. $1024y^3$
25. $x^4 y^6$
26. $a^7 b^2$
27. $a^2 b^2 c^2$
28. $-8a^3 b^6$
29. when x is a negative number
30. when n is an even number

Exercise Set 3.3

1. 256
2. 729
3. -27
4. 4
5. 27
6. 1
7. $\frac{9}{16}$
8. $\frac{1}{27}$
9. .5
10. $\frac{1}{-2}$
11. $\frac{1}{328}$
12. -5
13. -.3
14. 36
15. $-\frac{1}{7}$

16. $\frac{2}{3}$
17. true
18. false
19. false
20. false
21. false
22. true
23. true
24. false
25. true
26. true
27. true
28. false
29. false
30. true
31. x^{10}
32. x^8

33. a^{10}
34. c^6
35. $b^4 x^4$
36. $x^3 y^6$
37. $\frac{1}{x^5}$
38. b^3
39. $\frac{a^3}{27}$
40. $\frac{x^5}{y^5}$
41. $81a^4$
42. $25y^6$
43. $-x^3 y^6$
44. $4a^4 x^2$
45. x^{ab}
46. $x^{2d} y^{3d}$
47. $9x^3 y^3$

48. $-6a^5 b^4$
49. $2x^5 y^{10}$
50. x^{a+b+c}
51. $-3a^8 b^7$
52. $\frac{x^{12}}{a^8}$
53. $x^2 y^4$
54. $\frac{-2d}{c^2}$
55. $2y$
56. $2a^3 bc$
57. $\frac{10x}{y^3}$
58. $16x^4 y^8$
59. $6x^3$
60. $-4x^{13} y^8$
61. $\frac{c^4}{b}$

Exercise Set 3.4

1. $\frac{1}{16}$
2. 1
3. $\frac{-27}{64}$
4. 1
5. $\frac{1}{25}$
6. $\frac{1}{81}$
7. 64
8. $\frac{1}{2}$
9. $\frac{11}{24}$
10. 2
11. 110,000
12. 100

13. 324
14. $\frac{1}{2}$
15. x^{-2}
16. $x^{-1}y^{-3}$
17. $a^2 b^{-4}$
18. $6xy^2 a^{-2}b^{-5}$
19. $ax^2 b^2 y^{-4}$
20. $3a^5 b^6 cd^2 e^3$
21. $\frac{1}{x^3}$
22. 1296
23. $\frac{1}{x^2}$
24. y
25. 1

26. $\frac{1}{x^8}$
27. a^3
28. $\frac{a^{10}}{y^{10}}$
29. $\frac{2}{x^3 y}$
30. $x^4 y^2$
31. $\frac{-6}{a^3 c^5}$
32. 12
33. $\frac{5x^3}{2y^3}$
34. $\frac{3x^2 y^2}{z^6}$
35. $\frac{1}{a^2 b^{10}}$
36. $\frac{4x^{12}}{9y^{10}z^6}$

Exercise Set 3.5

1. 4
2. 3
3. 0
4. 9
5. -12
6. 28
7. 2
8. 5
9. -1
10. 1

11. 0
12. 0
13. 0
14. -6
15. 3
16. 125
17. 27
18. 0
19. 14
20. 1

21. 0
22. 20
23. 0
24. 5
25. 13
26. (a) $a + 4$
    (b) $a - 3$
    (c) $3a$
    (d) $2a + 3$
    (e) $3a - 2$

27. (a) $x + 3$
    (b) $x - 4$
    (c) $3x$
    (d) $x + 6$
    (e) $2x + 3$
28. (a) 23
    (b) 16
    (c) 60
    (d) 26
    (e) 43

Exercise Set 3.6

1. monomial
2. monomial
3. monomial
4. polynomial
5. polynomial
6. polynomial
7. monomial
8. polynomial
9. neither
10. neither
11. neither
12. polynomial

13. polynomial
14. polynomial
15. polynomial
16. monomial
17. 3; -4
18. $\frac{2}{3}$; -4; 7; -1
19. -4
20. 2, -5
21. yes, for $\frac{2}{3}$ can be written as $\frac{2}{3}x^0$
22. $(7 \cdot 10^2) + (2 \cdot 10) + (7 \cdot 10^0)$
23. yes

Exercise Set 3.7

1. $3x^3$; yes
2. $6x^2y^3$; yes
3. $6x^2y^{-1}$; no
4. 6; yes
5. $-36x^3y^4z$; yes
6. $36x^4y^2$; yes
7. $4x^2$; yes
8. $-2x$; yes
9. $3x^{-1}y$; no
10. z^{-1}; no
11. $2x^4yz^2$; yes
12. $12a^2x^5y^2$; yes
13. $11x$
14. $2x^2$
15. $4xy$
16. $-4xy^2$
17. $8xy$
18. 0
19. $5x + 1$
20. $-4x$
21. $6x - 9z$
22. $-6x$
23. $-x - 11$
24. $x^2 - 3xy + 6y^2$
25. $4x + 6$
26. $4x - 6$
27. $8x^2 - 2y + 3$
28. $x^2 + 3xy - 3y^2$
29. $-x^2 + 9x - 19$
30. $6a^2$
31. $3x^3 - 5x^2 + 2x + 1$
32. $x^4 + x^3 - 7x + 5$
33. $x^2 + 7x$
34. $-x^4 + 4x^3 - 2x^2 - 1$

Exercise Set 3.8

1. $18x + 9y$
2. $-6a + 8b$
3. $3c - 5d$
4. $6x^2 - 14x$
5. $-ay + 3y^2$
6. $-3x^3 + 12x$
7. $x^3y + xy^3$
8. $2x^2y^3 + 2x^4y^2$
9. $3x^2y - 12xy^2 + 9x^2y^2$
10. $-2x^4y^3 - 4x^3y^4 + 6x^2y$
11. $-5z^4 + 20xz^3 + 15z$
12. $-x^4yz - x^2y^3z - x^2yz^3$
13. $x^2 + 3x - 10$
14. $x^2 + 10x + 21$
15. $6x^2 - 11x + 3$
16. $x^2 - 25$
17. $y^2 - a^2$
18. $x^2 - y^2$
19. $y^2 - 12y + 36$
20. $4x^2 + 20x + 25$
21. $x^2 - 2xy + y^2$
22. $9y^2 - 12xy + 4x^2$
23. $-2x^2 + 13xy - 20y^2$
24. $x^3 - x^2y - y^2x + y^3$
25. $s^4 - 4$
26. $r^6 - s^6$
27. $x^3 - 7x - 6$
28. $2y^3 + 6y^2 - 9y - 4$
29. $x^3 + x^2y - 6xy^2 + 5x - 10y$
30. $a^3 - b^3$
31. $1 - x^3$
32. $x^3 + x^2 - 14x - 24$
33. $15 - 26x + 3x^2 + 2x^3$
34. $x^4 + x^3y + xy^3 - y^4$
35. $10x + 30$
36. $20x + 70$ miles; $4x^2 + 20x + 21$ miles
37. $4x + 2y$
38. $-6a + 2b$
39. $x + 9$
40. $-2y + 6$
41. $3s^2 + 2r$
42. $-3y^2 + 2xy$
43. $a + 4b$
44. $3xy - 4y^2$
45. $2x^2 + 3x - 1$
46. $6x^2 + 5x - 3$
47. $-2x + x^4y^5 - \frac{1}{7}x^5y^4$
48. $s^3 - rs + r^2s^2 - r^3$
49. $-2a^2b^2 + 4ab + 6$
50. $-4x^2 + 2x - 3$

Exercise Set 3.9

1. 8
2. −6
3. 20
4. −11
5. not a real number
6. $\frac{1}{9}$
7. $-\frac{3}{7}$
8. 37

9. $-\frac{7}{16}$
10. −9
11. −3
12. 3
13. −1
14. 4
15. −1
16. $-\frac{2}{3}$

17. −7
18. not a real number (r is negative, n is even)
19. −3
20. $\frac{2}{3}$
21. 1.2
22. −0.09
23. 0.2
24. −0.4

Exercise Set 3.10A

1. $\sqrt{x}$
2. $\sqrt[7]{x^5}$
3. $\sqrt[5]{xy}$
4. $\sqrt{(3xy)^3}$
5. $3\sqrt[3]{x^5}$
6. $\sqrt[4]{x+y}$
7. $-2\sqrt{x}$
8. $\sqrt[5]{(2x^3)^3}$
9. $x^{1/2}$
10. $x^{1/8}$
11. $x^{8/5}$
12. $x^{5/8}$

13. $x^{5/8}$
14. $(xy)^{1/4}$
15. $(x+y)^{2/3}$
16. $(x^{12}y^7)^{1/7}$
17. 10
18. −6
19. $\frac{1}{3}$
20. $\frac{1}{2}$
21. −32
22. 8
23. $\frac{4}{9}$
24. 81
25. 0.001
26. 0.0081

27. $\frac{64}{125}$
28. 0.0004
29. $\frac{1}{2}$
30. $\frac{1}{8}$
31. $\frac{1}{8}$
32. $\frac{1}{9}$
33. −1
34. $\frac{1}{27}$
35. 3
36. $\frac{9}{4}$

Exercise Set 3.10B

1. $2\sqrt{2}$
2. $4\sqrt{2}$
3. $10\sqrt{3}$
4. $6\sqrt{3}$
5. $2\sqrt[3]{3}$
6. $3\sqrt[3]{4}$
7. $2\sqrt[4]{3}$
8. $0.2\sqrt[3]{3}$
9. $\frac{2\sqrt{2}}{7}$

10. $\frac{1}{5}$
11. $\frac{4\sqrt[3]{2}}{3}$
12. $\frac{3\sqrt[4]{2}}{2}$
13. $5\sqrt{2}$
14. $6\sqrt{2}$
15. 15
16. $4\sqrt{3}$
17. $3\sqrt[3]{4}$

18. −12
19. 6
20. 12
21. false
22. false
23. true
24. false
25. true
26. false
27. $6x$
28. x^2
29. x^2

30. x^2

31. $x^{3/4}$

32. x^3

33. $4x^{3/2}$

34. $18x$

35. $81x$

36. $5x^2y^{4/3}$

37. $x^{7/6}y^{11/6}$

38. $12xy^3$

39. $xy^{1/3}$

40. $9x^4y^6$

41. $\dfrac{y^2}{x^4}$

42. $\dfrac{3x}{y^{2/3}}$

43. $\dfrac{7x^2y^2}{z}$

44. $\dfrac{3x^2y}{2}$

45. $\dfrac{x^9z^3}{y^3}$

46. $\dfrac{x^2}{y^2}$

47. $\dfrac{y^2}{x^4}$

48. $\dfrac{x^{15}}{y^{25}}$

Review Test for Chapter III

1. false

2. false

3. true

4. false

5. false

6. $\frac{125}{8}$

7. $\frac{4}{81}$

8. $\frac{1}{9}$

9. $-\frac{21}{8}$

10. -25

11. 41

12. $-2x^3y^2$

13. $\dfrac{36z^6}{x^2y^3}$

14. $\dfrac{1}{z^3}$

15. $\dfrac{x^4}{4y^4}$

16. $\dfrac{(x+y)^2}{x^3}$

17. $-x - 10y + 7z$

18. $14x^3 + 2xy + 13y^2$

19. $a^4 - b^4$

20. $1 - 3xy^2 + 4x^2y$

21. $-3s^4 + s^3 - 8s + 8$

22. $(1 \cdot 10^3) + (9 \cdot 10) + (2 \cdot 10^0)$

23. $2(x - 4)$

24. $4x - 9$ points

25. $\dfrac{-128y^{15}}{x^3z^4}$

26. $\frac{27}{8}$

27. $5\sqrt[4]{2}$

28. xy^2

29. $6x^{9/8}y^{1/3}z^{1/2}$

30. $\dfrac{1}{25x^{1/3}}$

31. $16y^{7/2}$

32. $\dfrac{x}{y^3}$

Chapter IV

Exercise Set 4.1

1. identity

2. conditional equation

3. identity

4. identity

5. conditional equation

6. conditional equation

7. identity

8. conditional equation

9. no

10. no

11. yes

12. no

13. yes

14. $\{1\}$

15. $\{6\}$

16. $\{8\}$

17. $\{-7\}$

18. $\emptyset$

19. $\{21\}$

20. $\{-3\}$

21. $\{-9\}$

Exercise Set 4.2

1. yes
2. yes
3. yes
4. no
5. yes
6. no
7. no
8. no

9. $\{4\}$
10. $\{\frac{22}{3}\}$
11. $\{10\}$
12. $\{-6\}$
13. $\{\frac{2}{3}\}$
14. $\{-3\}$
15. $\{0\}$
16. $\{2\}$

17. $\{\frac{12}{7}\}$
18. $\{1\}$
19. $\{\frac{1}{3}\}$
20. $\{21\}$
21. $\{6\}$
22. $\{2\}$
23. $\{\frac{31}{4}\}$
24. $\{9\}$

25. $\{24\}$
26. $\{-\frac{120}{19}\}$
27. $\{\frac{7}{3}\}$
28. $\{-\frac{7}{2}\}$
29. $\{6\}$
30. $\{1\}$

Exercise Set 4.3A

1. (a) $1, 2, 3, 6, 9, 18$
   (b) $1, 2, 3, 4, 6, 8, 12, 24$
   (c) $1, 2, 4, 8, 16, 32, 64, 128$
   (d) $1, 3, 5, 9, 15, 25, 45, 75, 225$
   (e) $1, 3, 9, 27, 81, 243$
2. $A \cap B = \{x \mid x$ is an integral multiple of 6$\}$
3. $A \cap B = \{x \mid x$ is an integral multiple of 6$\}$;
   $A \cup B = \{x \mid x$ is an integral multiple of 3$\}$
4. $A \cap B = \{x \mid x$ is an integral multiple of 35$\}$
5. (a) $2^3 \cdot 3$
   (b) 3^4
   (c) $2^2 \cdot 3^2 \cdot 5$
   (d) $2 \cdot 5 \circ 7^2$
   (e) $3^2 \cdot 7 \cdot 13$
6. 21
7. 168
8. 56
9. 36
10. 600

11. 2340
12. 5940
13. $\frac{13}{15}$
14. $-\frac{11}{8}$
15. $\frac{193}{60}$

16. $-\frac{7}{24}$
17. $\frac{46}{15}$
18. $\frac{103}{72}$
19. $-\frac{2}{5}$

20. $\frac{212}{21}$
21. $-\frac{173}{40}$
22. $-\frac{1}{24}$

Exercise Set 4.3B

1. $2^3 x^4$
2. $3(x - 3)$
3. $3x(x - 2)$
4. $2 \cdot 3(x - 4)$
5. $x^2(x - 1)$
6. $2 \cdot 3^2 x(x - 1)$
7. $18x^3$
8. $30x$
9. $4(x - 3)$(or $4x - 12$)
10. $6y(y - 2)$
11. $36x^2(x - 2)$
12. $6(x - 2)(x - 4)$
13. $6x^2(x - 2)^2$
14. $3y^2(y + 5)$

Exercise Set 4.4

1. $\{-5\}$
2. $\{3\}$
3. $\{4\}$
4. $\{9\}$

5. $\{\frac{3}{2}\}$
6. $\{7\}$
7. $\{0\}$
8. $\{3\}$

9. $\{-\frac{3}{2}\}$
10. $\{-3\}$
11. $\{5\}$
12. $\{-\frac{7}{6}\}$

13. $\{2\}$
14. $\{-4\}$
15. $\{3\}$

16. $\{x \mid x$ is a real number, $x \neq 0\}$

17. $\emptyset$ 20. $\emptyset$ 23. $\{-\frac{3}{2}\}$ 26. $\{-3\}$
18. $\{5\}$ 21. $\{-7\}$ 24. $\emptyset$
19. $\{\frac{4}{3}\}$ 22. $\{-10\}$ 25. $\emptyset$

Exercise Set 4.5

1. (a) $x + 7$ (c) $2x$ (e) $4x + 8$ (g) $6(x - 8)$
   (b) $x - 5$ (d) $2x - 3$ (f) $3(x + 4)$
2. (a) $y + 5$ (c) $3y$ (e) $2(y - 3)$
   (b) $y - 3$ (d) $4(y + 3)$ (f) $\frac{1}{2}(y - 3)$
3. $x + 7$
4. $s + 8$
5. $\frac{x}{10}$; $15(\frac{x}{10})$ or $\frac{3x}{2}$
6. $\frac{y}{x}$; $\frac{zy}{x}$
7. $3x + 6$
8. $5y + 2$
9. $4x - 4$
10. necktie, $4; shirt, $12
11. 22, 23, 24
12. Tom, $60; Sammy, $180; Mike, $70
13. 2, 8
14. 5 pounds at 40 cents and 2 pounds at 70 cents
15. Jim, 6; Perry, 12
16. 200
17. Charlotte, 11; Christine, 33
18. 14 years
19. 10 quarters, 34 dimes
20. 22, 24, 26

Exercise Set 4.6

1. $-12 < -1 < 4$
2. $-5 < -3 < -1$
3. $-1\frac{1}{2} < -1 < 0$
4. $-\frac{2}{3} < -\frac{1}{2} < -\frac{1}{3}$
5. $\frac{1}{3} < \frac{8}{15} < \frac{7}{12} < \frac{5}{6}$
6. $-2\frac{3}{4} < -2\frac{2}{3} < -2\frac{3}{7} < -2\frac{1}{5}$
7. (a), (d), (h), (i), (j)
8. $-2, -1, 0, 1, 2, 3, 4$
9. 4, 5, 6, 7, 8, 9
10. $-9, -6, -3, 0, 3, 6, 9, 12, 15, 18$
11. (a) $-1, 0$
    (b) $-4, -3, -2, -1, 0, 1, 2, 3, \ldots$
12. $A \cap B = \emptyset$
13. (a) $A \cap B = \{x \mid x \in R, -3 < x < -1\}$
    (b) $A \cup B = \{x \mid x \in R, x > 4 \text{ or } x < 0\}$

Exercise Set 4.7

1. $\{x \mid x \in R, x > -3\}$
2. $\{x \mid x \in R, x < 13\}$
3. $\{x \mid x \in R, x > 1\}$
4. $\{x \mid x \in R, x < -2\}$
5. $\{x \mid x \in R, x > -4\}$
6. $\{x \mid x \in R, x > 5\}$
7. $\{x \mid x \in R, x > -3\}$
8. $\emptyset$
9. $\{x \mid x \in R, x < 0\}$
10. $\{x \mid x \in R, x < -\frac{5}{2}\}$
11. $\{x \mid x \in R, x < 16\}$
12. $\{x \mid x \in R, x > 10\}$
13. $\{x \mid x \in R, x < -\frac{9}{2}\}$
14. $\{x \mid x \in R, x > -8\}$
15. $\{x \mid x \in R, x < -\frac{120}{19}\}$
16. $\{x \mid x \in R, x > 6\}$

17. $\emptyset$
18. $\{x \mid x \in R, x < 3\}$
19. $\{x \mid x \in R, x > -\frac{8}{5}\}$
20. $\{y \mid y \in R\} = R$

21. $\{x \mid x \in R, -2 < x < 7\}$
22. $\{x \mid x \in R, 4 < x < 5\}$
23. $\emptyset$
24. $\{0, 1, 2, 3, 4, 5\}$

Review Test for Chapter IV

1. (a) 72
   (b) 120
2. (a) $\{-4, -3, -2, 3\}$
   (b) $\{x \mid x \text{ is an integer}\}$
3. (a) $-\frac{25}{42}$
   (b) $-\frac{63}{10}$
4. (a) $2^3(x - 4)$
   (b) $3x^2(-2x - 9)$
5. (a) $\emptyset$
   (b) $\{11, 13, 17, 19, 23, 24, 27,$
       $29, 30, 31, 33, 36\}$
6. (a) $x < -3$ or $x > 4$
   (b) $-7 < x < 4$

7. $36x^3(x + 2)^3$
8. (a) $\{x \mid x \in R, x > \frac{21}{8}\}$
   (b) $\{x \mid x \in R\}$
9. (a) $\{\frac{1}{3}\}$
   (b) $\{1\}$
10. $\{8\}$
11. $\emptyset$
12. $\{\frac{1}{2}\}$
13. (a) $\{x \mid x \in R, x < 12\}$
    (b) $\emptyset$
14. 8 and 32
15. 10, 12, 14

Chapter V

Exercise Set 5.1

1. false
2. false
3. true
4. true
5. false
6. (a) true
   (b) false
   (c) false
   (d) true
   (e) false

Exercise Set 5.2

1. $\{0\}$
2. $\{4, -4\}$
3. $\{7, -7\}$
4. $\emptyset$
5. $\{2, -1\}$
6. $\{2, -10\}$
7. $\{5, -2\}$
8. $\{\frac{1}{8}, \frac{5}{8}\}$
9. $\{15, -3\}$
10. $\{1, -\frac{19}{9}\}$
11. $\{5, -4\}$
12. $\{-4, \frac{4}{3}\}$
13. $\{-3, 0\}$
14. $\emptyset$
15. $\{3, -5\}$
16. $\emptyset$

Exercise Set 5.3

1. $\{x \mid x \in R, -1 < x < 4\}$
2. $\{x \mid x \in R, -10 < x < -5\}$
3. $\{x \mid x \in R, -6 < x < 6\}$
4. $\{x \mid x \in R, x \geqslant 3 \text{ or } x \leqslant -3\}$
5. $\emptyset$
6. $\{x \mid x \in R, -5 \leqslant x \leqslant 5\}$
7. $\{x \mid x \in R, 1 < x < 7\}$
8. $\{x \mid x \in R\}$
9. $\{x \mid x \in R, x \geqslant 4 \text{ or } x \leqslant -14\}$
10. $\{x \mid x \in R, -2 \leqslant x \leqslant 3\}$
11. $\emptyset$
12. $\{x \mid x \in R, -\frac{2}{3} < x < \frac{2}{3}\}$

13. $\{x \mid x \in R, -\frac{1}{8} < x < \frac{7}{8}\}$
14. $\{-2\}$
15. $\{x \mid x \in R, x > 2 \text{ or } x < -14\}$
16. $\{x \mid x \in R, x \geqslant 5 \text{ or } x \leqslant 1\}$
17. $\emptyset$
18. $\{x \mid x \in R, x \leqslant -2 \text{ or } x \geqslant \frac{10}{3}\}$
19. $\{x \mid x \in R, -1 < x < 2\}$
20. $\{x \mid x \in R, x \neq 2\}$
21. $\{x \mid x \in R, -8 < x \leqslant 6\}$
22. $\{x \mid x \in R, -5 < x < -2$
     $\text{or } 3 < x < 9\}$

Review Test for Chapter V

1. $\{x \mid x \in R, x \geqslant 3 \text{ or } x \leqslant -9\}$
2. $\{-1, -7\}$
3. $\emptyset$
4. $\{x \mid x \in R, -\frac{7}{3} < x < 3\}$
5. $\{\frac{1}{4}, -\frac{1}{4}\}$
6. $\{-\frac{5}{3}, 3\}$
7. $\{y \mid y \in R, y \geqslant \frac{13}{2} \text{ or } y \leqslant -\frac{11}{2}\}$

8. $\{y \mid y \in R\}$
9. $\{x \mid x \in R, -3 < x < 3\}$
10. $\{1, -1\}$
11. $\{-1, -3\}$
12. $\{x \mid x \in R, -3 < x < 1\}$
13. $\{x \mid x \in R, x \neq 2\}$
14. $\{x \mid x \in R, -\frac{1}{2} < x < \frac{7}{6}\}$

Chapter VI

Exercise Set 6.1

1. $\{(1, 1), (1, 2)\}$
2. $\{(-2, 3), (-1, 3), (0, 3)\}$
3. $\{(c, b), (c, e), (d, b), (d, e)\}$
4. $\{(-1, 1), (-1, 2), (-1, 3), (1, 1), (1, 2), (1, 3)\}$
5. $\{(0, 0)\}$
6. $\{(x_1, y_1), (x_1, y_2), (x_2, y_1), (x_2, y_2), (x_3, y_1), (x_3, y_2), (x_4, y_1), (x_4, y_2)\}$
7. $\{(-5, -5), (-5, -1), (-5, 0), (-5, 3), (-1, -5), (-1, -1), (-1, 0), (-1, 3),$
    $(0, -5), (0, -1), (0, 0), (0, 3), (3, -5), (3, -1), (3, 0), (3, 3)\}$
8. $\{(0, -2), (0, -1), (0, 0), (0, 1), (0, 2), (1, -2), (1, -1), (1, 0), (1, 1), (1, 2)\}$
9. 100; 100
10. 25
11. 72

Exercise Set 6.2

1.

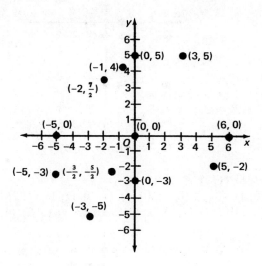

2.

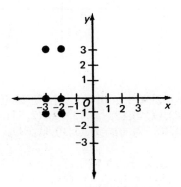

(−2, 3), (−2, 0), (−2, −1)
(−3, 3), (−3, 0), (−3, −1)

3.

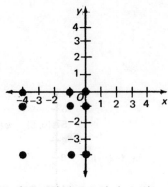

(−4, −4), (−4, −1), (−4, 0),
(−1, −4), (−1, −1), (−1, 0),
(0, −4), (0, −1), (0, 0)

4. (a) (1, 1), (1, 2), (2, 1), (2, 2)
   (b) (0, 1), (0, 2), (0, 3), (0, 4), (1, 0), (1, 1), (1, 2), (1, 3), (1, 4), (2, 0),
       (2, 1), (2, 2), (2, 3), (2, 4), (3, 0), (3, 1), (3, 2), (4, 0), (4, 1), (4, 2)

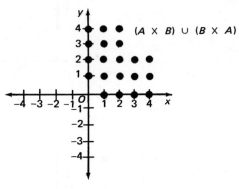

$(A \times B) \cup (B \times A)$

5. (−1, −3), (−1, −2), (−1, −1), (−1, 0), (0, −3), (0, −2), (0, −1), (0, 0), (1, −3),
   (1, −2), (1, −1), (1, 0), (2, −3), (2, −2), (2, −1), (2, 0)
6. (0, 0), (0, −1), (0, −2), (0, −3), (1, 0), (1, −1), (1, −2), (1, −3)

Exercise Set 6.3

1. (a) $\frac{7}{2}$ 3. (a) 0   7. yes
   (b) $-\frac{7}{3}$ (b) $-\frac{6}{5}$ 8. no
                                                    9. $c = 4$
   (c) −1   (c) $\frac{8}{15}$ 10. $c = -1$
   (d) −5   (d) $\frac{5}{7}$ 11. $c = -4$
2. (a) 4   4. no   12. $c = \frac{21}{5}$
   (b) 4   5. no
   (c) 4   6. yes
   (d) any real number

13.

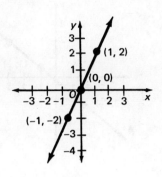

14.

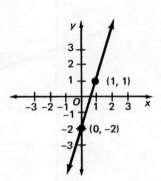

15.

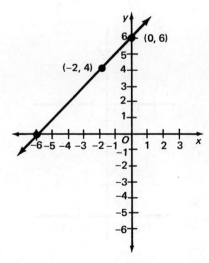

16.

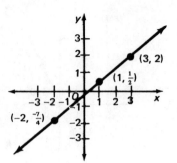

17.

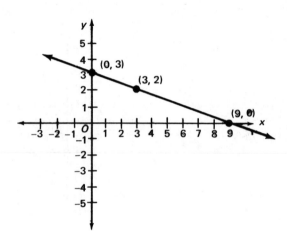

18.

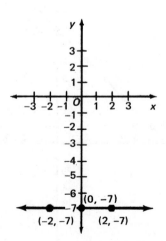

19.

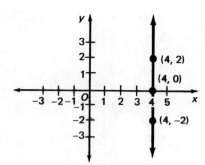

20.

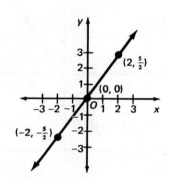

21.

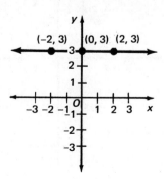

22.

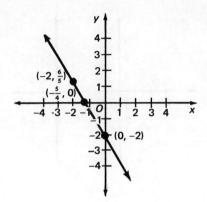

23.

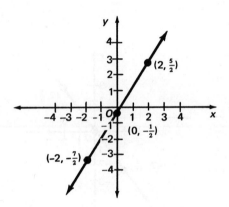

24.

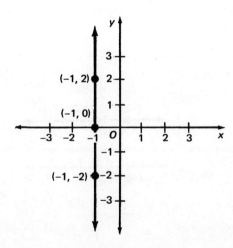

25.

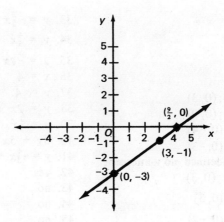

26.

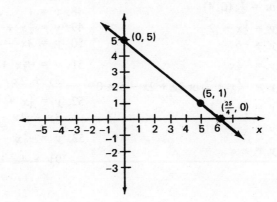

Exercise Set 6.4

1. $-\frac{1}{3}$

2. $-\frac{4}{3}$

3. 0

4. undefined

5. $\frac{2}{3}$

6. $\frac{8}{7}$

7. $\frac{1}{11}$

8. $\frac{18}{7}$

*Many possible answers.

*9. (a) $(2, 5)$
   (b) $(4, -3)$
   (c) $(1, 5)$
   (d) $(1, -2)$
   (e) $(1, 0)$
   (f) $(5, -2)$

*10. (a) $(6, 5)$
   (b) $(4, 8)$
   (c) $(4, 4)$
   (d) $(4, 1)$
   (e) $(10, 2)$
   (f) $(4, 3)$

11. yes

12. no

13. no

14. yes

15. yes

16. $m = -4; (0, 3)$

17. $m = -\frac{1}{2}; (0, 0)$

18. $m = 0; (0, -4)$

19. $m = \frac{3}{2}; (0, -3)$

20. slope undefined; no y-intercept

21. $m = -\frac{3}{8}; (0, 3)$

22. $m = \frac{2}{5}; (0, 3)$

23. $m = \frac{1}{3}; (0, -2)$

24. $m = -3; (0, 20)$

25. $m = \frac{9}{2}; (0, 4)$

26. $y = \frac{1}{2}x - 2$

27. $y = -6$

28. $y = -\frac{2}{3}x$

29. $y = -\frac{2}{3}x + \frac{5}{3}$ or $3y + 2x - 5 = 0$

30. $y = \frac{3}{2}x - 1$

31. $y = \frac{5}{2}x - 10$

32. $y = x$

33. $y = -\frac{3}{2}x - 7$

34. $y = \frac{4}{5}x$

35. $y = -2x + 4$

36. $x = 4$

37. $y = 4$

38. $y = 2x + 1$

39. $y = \frac{1}{2}x - 3$

40. $3y + 5x - 23 = 0$

41. $y = -\frac{4}{3}x + 2$ or $3y + 4x - 6 = 0$

42. yes

43. no

44. no

45. no

46. yes

47. no

48. $y = 1$

49. $y = \frac{5}{2}x + 3$

50. $y = 3x - 1$

51. $y = -\frac{2}{3}x + 5$ or
$3y + 2x - 15 = 0$

52. $y = \frac{7}{3}x + \frac{28}{3}$ or
$3y - 7x - 28 = 0$

53. $y = -\frac{4}{9}x - \frac{26}{9}$ or
$9y + 4x + 26 = 0$

Exercise Set 6.5

1.

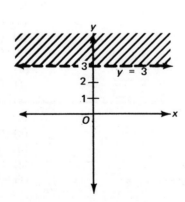

2.

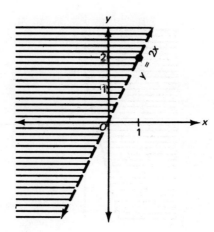

3.

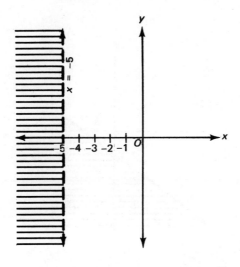

4.

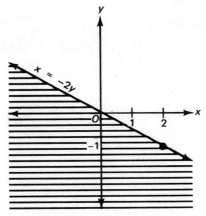

11.

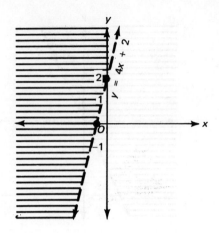

12.

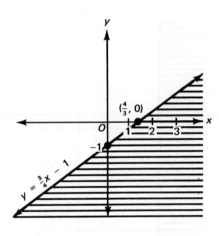

Review Test for Chapter VI

1. $(-1,-1), (-1,1), (-1,3), (1,-1), (1,1), (1,3), (3,-1), (3,1), (3,3)$
2. $\{(-1,-1)\,(-1,0)\,(0,-1)\,(0,0)\}$
3. (a) undefined
   (b) 1
4. (a) $m = -\frac{3}{2}; (0, \frac{7}{2})$ (b) $m = 0; (0,-3)$ (c) $m = -\frac{4}{9}; (0,0)$
5. (a) 36   (b) 18
6. (a) $(4,0)$ (b) $(\frac{5}{2},0)$ (c) no x-intercept
7. $k = 7$
8. $A = 3$

9. (a) $m = \frac{3}{4}$; $(0, 2)$

(b)

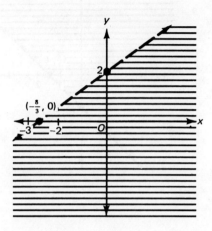

10. yes; slope of segment $AB = -\frac{1}{2}$ = slope of segment BC

11. (a)

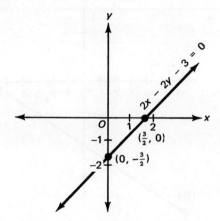

(b)

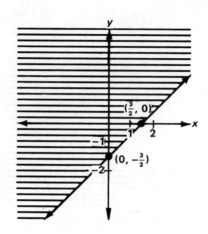

12.

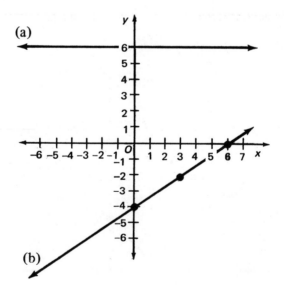

13. (a)

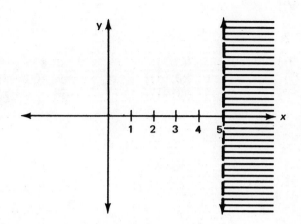

(b)

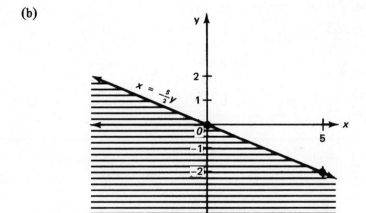

14. (a) $y = x + 1$ (b) $y = -3x - 9$

15. $y = -\frac{1}{2}x - \frac{5}{2}$ or $2y + x + 5 = 0$

Chapter VII

Exercise Set 7.2

1. $\{(-4, 3)\}$
2. $\{(8, 7)\}$
3. $\{(-1, -2)\}$
4. $\emptyset$
5. $\{(2, 3)\}$
6. $\{(0, -1)\}$
7. $\{(1, 4)\}$
8. $\emptyset$
9. $\{(-2, -3)\}$
10. $\{(-3, -\frac{3}{2})\}$

Exercise Set 7.3

1. $\{(2, 5)\}$
2. $\{(2, 8)\}$
3. $\{(2, 5)\}$
4. $\{(0, 2)\}$
5. $\emptyset$
6. $\{(2, 6)\}$
7. $\{(\frac{2}{5}, -\frac{14}{5})\}$
8. $\{(-5, -3)\}$
9. $\{(\frac{1}{3}, 3)\}$
10. $\{(3, 6)\}$
11. $\{(\frac{12}{11}, \frac{9}{11})\}$
12. $\{(-3, 2)\}$
13. $\{(2, -\frac{7}{3})\}$
14. $\{(-2, 3)\}$

Exercise Set 7.4

1. $\{(5, 2)\}$
2. $\{(-\frac{1}{2}, 4)\}$
3. $\{(\frac{1}{2}, \frac{1}{2})\}$
4. $\{(3, \frac{4}{3})\}$
5. $\{(-3, 2)\}$
6. $\emptyset$
7. $\{(-1, -2)\}$
8. $\{(7, 4)\}$
9. $\{(12, -5)\}$
10. $\{(\frac{3}{4}, \frac{2}{3})\}$
11. $\{(6, 4)\}$
12. $\{(-2, 2)\}$
13. $\{(-\frac{1}{3}, -2)\}$
14. $\{(\frac{1}{2}, 4)\}$

Exercise Set 7.5

1. 5
2. -20
3. 0
4. -12
5. 17
6. 17
7. $\{(-5, 8)\}$
8. $\{(0, 1)\}$
9. $\{(2, 0)\}$
10. $\{(6, 4)\}$
11. $\emptyset$
12. $\{(0, 0)\}$
13. $\{(\frac{2}{3}, \frac{3}{4})\}$
14. $\emptyset$
15. $\{(\frac{9}{4}, -\frac{25}{4})\}$
16. $\{(\frac{2}{5}, \frac{5}{6})\}$
17. $\{(\frac{-30}{17}, \frac{-31}{17})\}$
18. $\{(-\frac{9}{2}, -7)\}$
19. $\{(-4, -1)\}$
20. $\emptyset$

Exercise Set 7.6

1. (a) $\begin{vmatrix} 4 & 0 \\ -2 & 7 \end{vmatrix}$

   (b) $\begin{vmatrix} -1 & 0 \\ 6 & 7 \end{vmatrix}$

   (c) $\begin{vmatrix} 3 & 2 \\ 6 & 7 \end{vmatrix}$

   (d) $\begin{vmatrix} 3 & -5 \\ 6 & -2 \end{vmatrix}$

   (e) $\begin{vmatrix} -5 & 2 \\ 4 & 0 \end{vmatrix}$

   (f) $\begin{vmatrix} 3 & 2 \\ -1 & 0 \end{vmatrix}$

2. (a) $\begin{vmatrix} 5 & 0 \\ -8 & -3 \end{vmatrix} = -15$

   (b) $\begin{vmatrix} -1 & 9 \\ -8 & -3 \end{vmatrix} = 75$

   (c) $\begin{vmatrix} 5 & 0 \\ -1 & 9 \end{vmatrix} = 45$

   (d) $\begin{vmatrix} -7 & 5 \\ 4 & -8 \end{vmatrix} = 36$

3.
$$-2\begin{vmatrix} 6 & 3 \\ 1 & -3 \end{vmatrix} + (-4)\begin{vmatrix} -1 & 4 \\ 1 & -3 \end{vmatrix} - 5\begin{vmatrix} -1 & 4 \\ 6 & 3 \end{vmatrix} = -2(-21) - 4(-1) - 5(-27)$$
$$= 181$$

4.
$$+(-4)\begin{vmatrix} 1 & 2 \\ -2 & -3 \end{vmatrix} - 5\begin{vmatrix} 4 & 2 \\ -1 & -3 \end{vmatrix} + 0\begin{vmatrix} 4 & 1 \\ -1 & -2 \end{vmatrix} = -4(1) - 5(-10) + 0(-7)$$
$$= 46$$

5.
$$3\begin{vmatrix} 4 & 6 \\ 7 & 1 \end{vmatrix} - 0 + 0 = -114$$

6.
$$+3\begin{vmatrix} 7 & -2 \\ 1 & 5 \end{vmatrix} - (-4)\begin{vmatrix} 1 & -2 \\ 2 & 5 \end{vmatrix} + 1\begin{vmatrix} 1 & 7 \\ 2 & 1 \end{vmatrix} = 134$$

7.
$$1\begin{vmatrix} -3 & 4 \\ -4 & 1 \end{vmatrix} - (-1)\begin{vmatrix} -5 & 4 \\ 2 & 1 \end{vmatrix} + 3\begin{vmatrix} -5 & -3 \\ 2 & -4 \end{vmatrix} = 78$$

8.
$$4\begin{vmatrix} -1 & 0 \\ -2 & 3 \end{vmatrix} - 8\begin{vmatrix} 0 & -5 \\ -2 & 3 \end{vmatrix} + 0 = 68$$

9.
$$-2\begin{vmatrix} 4 & 6 \\ 7 & 9 \end{vmatrix} + 5\begin{vmatrix} 1 & 3 \\ 7 & 9 \end{vmatrix} - 8\begin{vmatrix} 1 & 3 \\ 4 & 6 \end{vmatrix} = 0$$

10.
$$3\begin{vmatrix} 2 & 3 \\ 4 & 7 \end{vmatrix} - 1\begin{vmatrix} 1 & 3 \\ -1 & 7 \end{vmatrix} - 5\begin{vmatrix} 1 & 2 \\ -1 & 4 \end{vmatrix} = -34$$

11. -126 12. -140 13. 75 14. 183

Exercise Set 7.7

1. $x = \frac{73}{45},\ y = -\frac{1}{45},\ z = -\frac{4}{9}$

2. $x = \frac{7}{16},\ y = \frac{71}{32},\ z = -\frac{1}{4}$

3. $x = \frac{10}{11},\ y = \frac{27}{11},\ z = -\frac{35}{11}$

4. $x = \frac{15}{8},\ y = -\frac{5}{4},\ z = -\frac{47}{16}$

5. $x = \frac{5}{2},\ y = \frac{3}{2},\ z = \frac{5}{2}$

6. $x = 2,\ y = -3,\ z = 1$

7. $x = 6,\ y = 6,\ z = \frac{15}{2}$

8. $x = 2,\ y = 1,\ z = 1$

9. $x = 1,\ y = 2,\ z = 3$

10. $x = 1,\ y = -\frac{1}{3},\ z = \frac{4}{3}$

11. $x = 0,\ y = 1,\ z = 0$

12. $x = 2,\ y = 3,\ z = -2$

Review Test for Chapter VII

1. (a) $\{(-2, 3)\}$ (b) $\emptyset$

2. (a) $\{(2, 3)\}$ (b) $\{(-4, 0)\}$

3. (a) $\{(\frac{2}{3}, -2)\}$ (b) $\{(-\frac{5}{2}, \frac{3}{2})\}$

4. (a) 10 (c) 25

    (b) -1 (d) 1

5. (a) 67 (c) 30

    (b) 0

6. (a) 8
   (b) 0

(c) 8

7. (a) $\emptyset$

(b) $\{(0,-2)\}$

8. (a) $x = \frac{3}{13}$, $y = \frac{11}{13}$, $z = \frac{4}{13}$

(b) $x = \frac{1}{3}$, $y = -\frac{2}{5}$, $z = 1$

9. (a) $x = -1$, $y = \frac{2}{3}$, $z = 2$

(b) $x = \frac{2}{3}$, $y = \frac{1}{2}$, $z = -\frac{1}{5}$

10. $x = -3$, $y = 4$, $z = -2$

Chapter VIII

Exercise Set 8.1

1. $(x - 5)$
2. $(x^2 + 7)$
3. $(3x + 7)$
4. (7)
5. $(4x)$

6. $(x^2 + 3x + 6)$
7. $(4x^2)$
8. $(5x - y)$
9. $(3a^3 b)$
10. $(a + 2c + 5bc^2)$

11. $(x - 4)$
12. $(x + 9)(x - 9)$
13. $(x + 3)(x - 3)$
14. $(x - 3)$
15. $(x + 2)$

Exercise Set 8.2

1. $3(2x - 3y)$

2. $4(a + 2b)$

3. can't be factored ($3x + 7y$ is a prime polynomial.)

4. $4(x^2 + 1)$
5. $4a(x - 2y)$
6. $b(x^2 + 4)$
7. can't be factored
8. $7x(x + 3)$
9. $6x^2(x^2 - 3)$
10. $4y^2x^2(y - 3x)$
11. $7xy^2z(x - 2z)$
12. $5(x - 3y + 5w)$
13. $4y(6y^2 + 4y - 3)$

14. $a^5(6 - 8a^2 + 3a^4)$
15. can't be factored
16. $xy(4xz + 5yz + 6)$
17. $5a^2c(b^2c - 2 - 3bc)$
18. $3x^{125}(1 - 3x^3)$
19. $a(7a + 8b - 14b^2 - 3ab^2)$
20. $3xyz(x - 2y + 3z - 6)$
21. $-2(x - 1)$
22. $6(1 + 3x)(x - y)$
23. $(x + y)2x$

24. $5(x - 3)[1 + 2(x + 1)] = 5(x - 3)(2x + 3)$

25. $y(x + 2)^2(x + 4)$

26. $(x + y)(3x - y)$

Exercise Set 8.3

1. $x^2 - 25$
2. $4x^2 - 36$
3. $a^4 - 16$
4. $25y^2 - 4x^2$
5. $x^6 - 4$
6. $9 - x^4$
7. $a^4 - b^4$

8. $a^6 - b^6$
9. $(x + 9)(x - 9)$
10. $(10 + x)(10 - x)$
11. can't be factored
12. $2(x + 5)(x - 5)$
13. $(3x + 8y)(3x - 8y)$
14. $(5x + 2)(5x - 2)$

15. This can't be factored into polynomial factors with *integral* coefficients.

16. $(2a + 3b)(2a - 3b)$
17. $(b^2 + c)(b^2 - c)$
18. $(x^2 + 6)(x^2 - 6)$
19. $(x^2 + 4)(x + 2)(x - 2)$
20. $3(4x^2 + 9)(2x + 3)(2x - 3)$

21. $(xy + 3)(xy - 3)$
22. $(a^3 + 7)(a^3 - 7)$
23. can't be factored
24. $(x^3 + y^3)(x^3 - y^3)$
25. $(a^4 + b^3)(a^4 - b^3)$

26. $(x^4 + y^4)(x^2 + y^2)(x + y)(x - y)$
27. $2x^2(4x^2 + 3)(4x^2 - 3)$
28. $4(6 + x^4)(6 - x^4)$
29. $ab(ab + 1)(ab - 1)$
30. $x^3(x^3 - 9)$, can't be factored further

Exercise Set 8.4

1. $x^2 + 12x + 35$
2. $x^2 + 2x - 35$
3. $x^2 - 7x + 12$
4. $x^2 - x - 12$
5. $x^2 - 49$
6. $15 - 8x + x^2$
7. $8x^2 + 22x + 15$
8. $30x^2 - 7x - 2$
9. $18x^2 - 36x + 10$
10. $16x^2 - 9$
11. $-3x^2 + 8x + 35$
12. $x^2 + 3xy + 2y^2$
13. $6x^2 - 7xy - 3y^2$

14. $16x^2 - 25y^2$
15. $24x^2y^2 - 2axy - 2a^2$
16. $-42x^2y + 35xy + 18x - 15$
17. $(x + 2)$
18. $(x - 10)$
19. $(x - 10)(x - 1)$
20. $(x + 9)$
21. $(2y - 3)$
22. $(4x + 1)(2x - 7)$
23. $(2x - 3)(3x - 4)$
24. $(3x + y)$
25. $(x + 2)(x - 5)$
26. $(x - 5)(x - 2)$

27. This can't be factored as a product of two binomials with *integral* co-
    efficients.

28. $(x + 8)(x + 1)$
29. $(x - 4)(x + 2)$
30. $(x - 8)(x + 4)$
31. $(y + 9)(y - 6)$

32. $(y - 18)(y - 3)$
33. $(a - 6)(a + 5)$
34. $(b + 15)(b - 2)$
35. $(18 + y)(2 - y)$

36. $(3 - x)(12 - x)$ or $(x - 3)(x - 12)$
37. $(x + 12y)(x + 3y)$
38. $(x + 7y)(x - 4y)$
39. $(2x + 5)(x + 3)$
40. $(2x + 5)(x - 3)$
41. $(3x - 1)(x - 12)$
42. can't be factored
43. $(4x - 3)(2x + 1)$
44. $(5x - 1)(3x - 4)$
45. $(3x - 5)(2x + 7)$
46. $(8x + 3)(x + 1)$
47. $(3x - 1)(x - 3)$

48. $(6x - 1)(x + 7)$
49. $(7y + 2)(y - 6)$
50. $(11x - 3)(2x + 1)$
51. $(4x - 1)(3x - 2)$
52. can't be factored
53. can't be factored
54. $(10x + 9)(x - 1)$
55. $(3a - 5b)(2a - b)$
56. $(8x + 3y)(3x - y)$
57. $(3x + 7)(3x - 7)$
58. $8(x + 3)(x - 3)$

59. $x(2x + 1)(2x - 1)$

60. $3y(y - 3)(y - 1)$

61. $(x + 5)(x + 5)$

62. $4(5x + 2y)(5x - 2y)$

63. $x(1 + y)(1 - y)$

64. $x^2(x + 4)(x + 2)$

65. $2x^3(x - 3)(x - 3)$

66. $3x(x + 2y)(x - 2y)$

67. $4xy^2(x - 4)$

68. $3ab(2a + b)(a - b)$

69. $x(x + 2y)(x + 2y)$

70. $x(x^2 + 1)(x + 1)(x - 1)$

Exercise Set 8.6

1. $\{5, -5\}$

2. $\{2, -2\}$

3. $\{0, 7\}$

4. $\{0, -\frac{5}{4}\}$

5. $\{7, -3\}$

6. $\{2, \frac{5}{2}\}$

7. $\{\sqrt{7}, -\sqrt{7}\}$

8. $\{0, -8\}$

9. $\{-5, -3\}$

10. $\{8, -5\}$

11. $\{\frac{1}{2}, -4\}$

12. $\{1, -\frac{5}{3}\}$

13. $\{\frac{3}{4}, \frac{5}{2}\}$

14. $\{\frac{1}{2}, 4\}$

15. $\{0, -10\}$

16. $\{0, 4\}$

17. $\{0, 3\}$

18. $\{\frac{1}{9}, -\frac{2}{3}\}$

19. $\{2\}$

20. $\{\sqrt{6}, -\sqrt{6}\}$

21. $\{-2\}$

22. $\{2, -7\}$

23. $\{6, -4\}$

24. $\{\frac{1}{3}, -\frac{1}{4}\}$

25. $\{-5, -\frac{3}{2}\}$

26. $\{-2, -\frac{1}{3}\}$

27. $\{0, \frac{6}{7}\}$

28. $\{3, -3\}$

Exercise Set 8.7

1. $x^2 - 12x + 36$

2. $9x^2 + 6x + 1$

3. $16y^2 - 56y + 49$

4. $4x^2 - 4xy + y^2$

5. $9x^2 + 24xy + 16y^2$

6. $25 - 10x + x^2$

7. $25a^2 + 30ab + 9b^2$

8. $\frac{1}{4}x^2 - 3x + 9$

9. $\frac{1}{9}x^2 - \frac{1}{2}x + \frac{9}{16}$

10. 4

11. $\frac{9}{4}$

12. $+10x$ or $-10x$

13. $+18x$ or $-18x$

14. $\frac{81}{4}$

15. 256

16. yes; $(x + 4)^2$

17. yes; $(x - 13)^2$

18. no

19. yes; $(x - 7)^2$

20. no

21. no

22. yes; $(x + \frac{7}{2})^2$

23. no

24. no

25. no

26. yes; $(x + \frac{3}{4})^2$

27. yes; $(x - \frac{5}{6})^2$

28. $\{0, -8\}$

29. $\{1, -19\}$

30. $\{3 + \sqrt{8}, 3 - \sqrt{8}\}$ or $\{3 + 2\sqrt{2}, 3 - 2\sqrt{2}\}$

31. $\{-5 + 2\sqrt{3}, -5 - 2\sqrt{3}\}$

32. $\{2, -\frac{1}{2}\}$

33. $\{-4, -16\}$

34. $\{\frac{7}{3}, -\frac{1}{3}\}$

35. $\{\frac{6 + \sqrt{15}}{3}, \frac{6 - \sqrt{15}}{3}\}$

36. $\{\frac{-6 + \sqrt{3}}{3}, \frac{-6 - \sqrt{3}}{3}\}$

37. $\{\frac{9}{2}, \frac{3}{2}\}$

38. $\emptyset$

39. $\{\frac{-1 + \sqrt{3}}{2}, \frac{-1 - \sqrt{3}}{2}\}$

40. $\{\frac{2 + \sqrt{2}}{3}, \frac{2 - \sqrt{2}}{3}\}$

41. $\{\frac{7}{2}, \frac{5}{2}\}$

Exercise Set 8.8

1. $2x^2 + 5x - 7 = 0; a = 2, b = 5, c = -7$
2. $6x^2 + 15x - 7 = 0; a = 6, b = 15, c = -7$
3. $x^2 - 3x + 4 = 0; a = 1, b = -3, c = 4$
4. $3x^2 + 3x + 15 = 0; a = 3, b = 3, c = 15$
5. $4x^2 - 12x + 13 = 0; a = 4, b = -12, c = 13$
6. $3x^2 - 1 = 0; a = 3, b = 0, c = -1$
7. $\{5, -8\}$
8. $\{\frac{3 + \sqrt{21}}{2}, \frac{3 - \sqrt{21}}{2}\}$
9. $\{0, -\frac{3}{5}\}$
10. $\{\frac{4}{3}, -\frac{3}{2}\}$
11. $\{\frac{3 + \sqrt{33}}{6}, \frac{3 - \sqrt{33}}{6}\}$
12. $\{\frac{1}{2}, -\frac{1}{2}\}$
13. $\{\frac{5 + \sqrt{17}}{4}, \frac{5 - \sqrt{17}}{4}\}$
14. $\{\frac{1 + \sqrt{2}}{2}, \frac{1 - \sqrt{2}}{2}\}$
15. $\{4\}$
16. $\{0, \frac{3}{2}\}$

17. $\{-1, -\frac{1}{2}\}$
18. $\{\frac{5 + \sqrt{11}}{2}, \frac{5 - \sqrt{11}}{2}\}$
19. $\{\sqrt{\frac{7}{3}}, -\sqrt{\frac{7}{3}}\}$
20. $\{\frac{1}{2}\}$
21. $\{\frac{1}{2}, -\frac{3}{4}\}$
22. $\emptyset$
23. $\{\frac{2}{3}\}$
24. $\{\frac{1 + \sqrt{2}}{3}, \frac{1 - \sqrt{2}}{3}\}$
25. $\{\frac{1}{2}, -\frac{3}{4}\}$
26. $\{\frac{2}{3}, \frac{1}{2}\}$

Review Test for Chapter VIII

1. (a) $(4x - 7)(2x + 9)$ (b) $(3x - 2)(2x - 5)$
2. (a) $(5x - 2)$ (b) $(6x - 5)(2x + 3)$
3. (a) $12x^2 - x - 20$ (b) $10x^2 - 39xy + 14y^2$
4. (a) $9x^2 - 12x + 4$ (b) $25a^2 + 20ab + 4b^2$
5. (a) no   (c) yes; $(x - 20)^2$ (e) yes; $(6x - 5)^2$
   (b) no   (d) yes; $(x + \frac{3}{8})^2$ (f) no
6. (a) $(2x + 9y)(2x - 9y)$ (c) $7ab(2a^2 + 5b + 2ab)$
   (b) $(x - 6)(x + 5)$
7. (a) $x(x + 5)(x - 5)$ (c) $3b^2x^2(x^2 + 9)(x + 3)(x - 3)$
   (b) $2x(7x - 5)(2x - 3)$
8. (a) $\{3, -7\}$ (b) $\{\frac{1}{3}, -1\}$
9. (a) $\{0, \frac{9}{5}\}$ (e) $\{-\frac{3}{4}\}$
   (b) $\{\sqrt{7}, -\sqrt{7}\}$ (f) $\{\frac{5 + 4\sqrt{2}}{7}, \frac{5 - 4\sqrt{2}}{7}\}$
   (c) $\{\frac{4 + \sqrt{14}}{2}, \frac{4 - \sqrt{14}}{2}\}$ (g) $\{\frac{8}{3}, -\frac{7}{2}\}$
   (d) $\{\frac{7}{3}, -\frac{5}{2}\}$ (h) $\{\frac{-4 + \sqrt{10}}{2}, \frac{-4 - \sqrt{10}}{2}\}$

Chapter IX

Exercise Set 9.2

1. no	7. yes; compound	13. yes; compound
2. yes; simple	8. no	14. no
3. no	9. no	15. no
4. yes; compound	10. yes; simple	16. yes; compound
5. no	11. yes; compound	17. no
6. yes; simple	12. no	

Exercise Set 9.3

1. $3(-2) = 1$ and $3 + 1 = 4$; false
2. $-3 > -5$ and $6(\frac{1}{2} + \frac{1}{6}) = 4$; true
3. $3 + (-4) = -12$ and $3 - (-5) = -2$; false
4. Paris is in France and $-2 - 5 = 10$; false
5. $6 \div 3 = 5 \div \frac{5}{2}$ and $(-2)(-5) = 10$; true
6. All integers are rational numbers, and all nonterminating decimals are irrational numbers; false
7. $4 \div 0 = 4$, or $0 \div 0 = 1$; false
8. $\frac{2 + 7}{2} = 8$, or 0 is an even integer; true
9. $(-4)(-3) = 12$, or $-8 < -3$; true
10. Chicago is in California, or $\{a, b, c\}$ is equivalent to $\{2, 4, 6\}$; true
11. (a) $t \wedge i$
    (b) $t \vee \sim w$
    (c) $w \wedge \sim i$
    (d) $\sim(w \wedge i)$
    (e) $(t \wedge i) \wedge \sim w$
    (f) $w \vee (i \wedge t)$
    (g) $(w \vee \sim i) \wedge \sim t$
    (h) $\sim(w \wedge \sim i) \wedge t$
    (i) $(i \wedge w) \vee (i \wedge t)$
12. (a) He is not a football player.
    (b) He is a football player and has great physical strength.
    (c) He has great physical strength or courage.
    (d) He has great physical strength but does not have courage.
    (e) He is not a football player and does not have courage.
    (f) It is false that he is a football player or has courage.
    (g) He is a football player and has great physical strength, but he has no courage.
    (h) He has great physical strength, and he is a football player or has courage.
    (i) He has courage or does not have great physical strength, and he is not a football player.
    (j) He is a football player and has great physical strength, or he is not a football player but has courage.
    (k) He is a football player or has great physical strength, and he is a football player or does not have courage.

13. false	18. true	23. false
14. false	19. true	24. false
15. true	20. true	25. true
16. false	21. true	26. true
17. true	22. false	

27. (a) false   (b) true
28. (a) false   (b) true
29. (a) true   (b) false
30. (a)

Exercise Set 9.4

1. (a) Antecedent: John does a good job.
      Consequent: He will be reelected.
   (b) Antecedent: He earns over $100,000 a year.
      Consequent: He is wealthy.
   (c) Antecedent: $3x + 1 = 7$
      Consequent: $x = 2$
   (d) Antecedent: You are a football player.
      Consequent: You have courage.
   (e) Antecedent: x is less than 5.
      Consequent: x is less than 7.
   (f) Antecedent: x is positive.
      Consequent: $x > 0$
   (g) Antecedent: You become President of the United States.
      Consequent: You are wealthy.

2. $f \rightarrow r$ 7. $w \leftrightarrow (p \lor 1)$
3. $s \rightarrow f$ 8. $(c \lor s) \rightarrow \sim f$
4. $h \leftrightarrow r$ 9. $(b \land s) \lor (\sim b \rightarrow \sim s)$
5. $\sim(p \leftrightarrow \sim i)$ 10. $(b \rightarrow \sim c) \land (\sim c \rightarrow s)$
6. $(\sim i \land p) \rightarrow \sim t$ 11. $d \rightarrow (r \land a)$

12. (a) If he works hard, then he earns a lot of money.
    (b) He earns a lot of money if and only if he is a smart investor.
    (c) If he works hard and earns a lot of money, then he will travel around the world.
    (d) If he travels around the world, then he earns a lot of money or is a bachelor.
    (e) If he works hard, then he is not a bachelor.
    (f) He doesn't work hard and doesn't earn a lot of money if and only if he is not a bachelor or is not a smart investor.
    (g) He is a smart investor and earns a lot of money, or he works hard and is not a bachelor.
    (h) It is false that, he earns a lot of money if and only if he works hard.
    (i) If he is a bachelor, then he will travel around the world, but if he is not a bachelor, then he works hard and will not travel around the world.

(j) He is a smart investor, or if he is not a smart investor, then he will not earn a lot of money.

13. false	16. true	19. false	22. false
14. true	17. true	20. true	23. false
15. false	18. false	21. true	24. false

25. true

26. (a) true   (b) true

27. (a) false   (c) true

    (b) true   (d) false

28. true   29. true

Exercise Set 9.5

1. (a) contradiction   (d) tautology   (g) neither
   (b) tautology   (e) neither   (h) tautology
   (c) tautology   (f) neither   (i) contradiction

2. (d)	6. (d)	10. (c)
3. (e)	7. (c)	11. no
4. (c)	8. (c), (e)	12. yes
5. (b), (d)	9. (b), (d), (e)	13. (d)

Exercise Set 9.6

1. $a \wedge b$ 8. $(p \wedge \sim q) \wedge (\sim r \vee \sim s)$
2. $\sim a \vee b$ 9. $\sim a \rightarrow b$
3. $\sim a \wedge b$ 10. $u \wedge (\sim p \leftrightarrow \sim s)$
4. $\sim p \vee (\sim q \wedge r)$ 11. (e)
5. $(r \wedge s) \wedge \sim w$ 12. (d)
6. $k \wedge (1 \wedge \sim m)$ 13. (c)
7. $(\sim c \wedge \sim d) \wedge (c \wedge d)$

Review Test for Chapter IX

1. (d)	6. (e)	11. (a)	16. (a)
2. (c)	7. (e)	12. (d)	17. (b)
3. (d)	8. (d)	13. (e)	18. (b)
4. (e)	9. (b)	14. (c)	19. (c)
5. (d)	10. (b)	15. (c)	20. (b)

Chapter X

Exercise Set 10.2

1. $S = \{(H, H), (H, T), (T, H), (T, T)\}$
2. $S = \{(H, 1), (H, 2), (H, 3), (H, 4), (H, 5), (H, 6), (T, 1), (T, 2), (T, 3),$
   $(T, 4), (T, 5), (T, 6)\}$
3. $S = \{(r, r), (r, w), (r, b), (w, r), (w, w), (w, b), (b, r), (b, w), (b, b)\}$
4. $S = \{(r, w), (r, b), (w, r), (w, b), (b, r), (b, w)\}$
5. $S = \{12, 13, 14, 21, 23, 24, 31, 32, 34, 41, 42, 43\}$
6. $S = \{AB, AC, AD, BC, BD, CD\}$
7. $S = \{(H, H, H, H), (H, H, H, T), (H, H, T, H), (H, H, T, T), (H, T, H, H),$
   $(H, T, H, T), (H, T, T, H), (H, T, T, T), (T, H, H, H), (T, H, H, T),$
   $(T, H, T, H), (T, H, T, T), (T, T, H, H), (T, T, H, T), (T, T, T, H),$
   $(T, T, T, T)\}$
8. (a) $n(E) = 3$ (b) $n(F) = 4$
9. (a) $n(E) = 0$ (b) $n(F) = 4$
10. (a) 13, 31   (c) 32, 34, 41, 42, 43
    (b) 12, 14, 21, 23, 32, 34, 41, 43
11. (a) $n(E) = 3$ (b) $n(F) = 5$
12. (a) $(H, H, H, H), (H, H, H, T), (H, H, T, H), (H, H, T, T), (H, T, H, H),$
    $(H, T, H, T), (H, T, T, H), (T, H, H, H), (T, H, H, T), (T, H, T, H),$
    (T, T, H, H)
    (b) $(H, H, T, T), (H, T, H, T), (H, T, T, H), (T, H, H, T), (T, H, T, H),$
    (T, T, H, H)

Exercise Set 10.3

1. (a) $\frac{1}{13}$ (b) $\frac{1}{52}$ (c) $\frac{3}{13}$ (d) $\frac{1}{4}$
2. (a) $\frac{5}{36}$ (c) $\frac{1}{12}$ (d) $\frac{1}{4}$ (e) $\frac{8}{9}$
   (b) $\frac{5}{6}$
3. $\frac{1}{4}$
4. (a) $\frac{3}{8}$ (b) $\frac{5}{8}$ (c) 0
5. (a) $\frac{1}{3}$ (b) $\frac{2}{3}$ (c) $\frac{5}{9}$
6. (a) $\frac{1}{2}$ (b) $\frac{5}{12}$ (c) $\frac{1}{3}$
7. (a) $\frac{1}{2}$ (b) $\frac{1}{2}$ (c) $\frac{1}{3}$
8. (a) $\frac{11}{16}$ (b) $\frac{3}{8}$ (c) $\frac{1}{4}$
9. $\frac{2}{3}$
10. $\frac{1}{2}$

Exercise Set 10.5

1. (a) $\frac{1}{4}$ (b) $\frac{3}{4}$
2. $\frac{2}{7}$
3. (a) $\frac{2}{13}$ (b) $\frac{11}{26}$ (c) $\frac{23}{26}$
4. (a) $\frac{2}{5}$ (b) $\frac{9}{10}$ (c) $\frac{1}{10}$
5. (a) $\frac{1}{2}$ (b) $\frac{1}{2}$
6. (a) $\frac{2}{5}$ (b) $\frac{1}{3}$ (c) $\frac{19}{30}$ (d) $\frac{3}{5}$
7. (a) $\frac{5}{26}$ (b) $\frac{3}{13}$ (c) $\frac{5}{13}$
8. (a) $\frac{11}{15}$ (b) $\frac{4}{15}$

Exercise Set 10.6

1. (a) $\frac{1}{10}$ (b) $\frac{3}{20}$ (c) $\frac{9}{20}$
2. $\frac{1}{729}$
3. $\frac{1}{8}$
4. (a) $\frac{1}{16}$ (b) $\frac{89}{400}$ (c) $\frac{69}{200}$
5. $\frac{4}{81}$
6. (a) $\frac{4}{25}$ (b) $\frac{4}{25}$ (c) $\frac{13}{25}$ (d) $\frac{4}{25}$
7. $\frac{59}{125}$
8. (a) $\frac{2}{15}$ (b) $\frac{8}{15}$ (c) $\frac{7}{15}$
9. (a) $\frac{9}{16}$ (b) $\frac{1}{16}$ (c) $\frac{6}{16}$
10. $\frac{41}{50}$
11. (a) $\frac{1}{64}$ (b) $\frac{8}{2197}$ (c) $\frac{1}{16}$

Review Test for Chapter X

1. $\frac{1}{2}$
2. $\frac{1}{4}$
3. $\frac{1}{169}$
4. (a) $\frac{1}{4}$ (b) $\frac{3}{4}$ (c) $\frac{1}{16}$ (d) $\frac{7}{16}$
5. (a) $\frac{1}{100}$ (b) $\frac{10}{999}$
6. (a) $\frac{1}{10,000}$ (b) $\frac{199}{10,000}$
7. $\frac{1}{10,000}$
8. (a) $\frac{1}{5000}$ (b) $\frac{37}{2500}$ (c) $\frac{4851}{5000}$
9. (a) $\frac{1}{20}$ (b) $\frac{1}{10}$ (c) $\frac{3}{25}$ (d) $\frac{22}{25}$

INDEX